MENTAL ARCHITECTURE
Building The Mind One Moment At A Time

Howard Blumenfeld

Printed in the United States of America

ISBN 978-0-578-55646-8

First Edition

14 13 12 11 10 / 10 9 8 7 6 5 4 3 2 1

"When you grow up you tend to get told the world is the way it is and your life is just to live your life inside the world. Try not to bash into the walls too much. Try to have a nice family, have fun, save a little money. That's a very limited life.

Life can be much broader once you discover one simple fact: Everything around you that you call life was made up by people that were no smarter than you and you can change it, you can influence it, you can build your own things that other people can use.

Once you learn that, you'll never be the same again."

— Steve Jobs

Dedicated to Victoria F. Blumenfeld
Forever and always my Torie Bear

Table of Contents

Foreword ix

Chapter 1 – No Space 1

Object Recognition 1

Anthropomorphism 4

The Sound of Silence 13

Chapter 2 – No Point in Time 23

The Mind's Clock 23

Past, Present, and Future 27

Memories 38

The Effects of Drugs on Time Perception 42

The Effects of Mental Illness on Time Perception 46

Unconscious Time 50

The Role of the Imagination in Time Perception 57

Does Consciousness = Time Perception? 63

Chapter 3 – No Infinity 67

Counting 67

The Challenge of Infinity 71

What is the size of the Universe? 75

Chapter 4 – No Perspective 79

Mathematics is a Human Invention 79

The Problems with Logic 83

Object Representation and Identification 86

The Link Between Distractibility and Creativity 93

The Effects of Nicotine Administration
on Distractibility 95

The Psychology of Advertising 98

The Fallacy of Measurement 103

A Matter of Perspective 107

Chapter 5 – No Normal **115**

Discrimination 115

Meaningful Relationships 121

Discovering Beauty 131

Labels are Dangerous 139

Advancements in Mental Health Awareness 143

The Link between Mental Illness and Creativity 147

Understanding Intelligence 150

Embrace your Individuality 163

Chapter 6 – No Decisions **165**

The Power of the Unconscious Mind 165

Genetic Memories 173

Déjà vu 174

Sleep, Dreaming, and Metacognition 176

The Problem of Indecisiveness 179

Mindfulness 181

Chapter 7 – No Identity **185**

Early Childhood Identity Development 185

Comprehensive Identity Development Theories 199

Identity as a Physiological and Psychological

Construct 216

The Hard Problem of Consciousness 226

Figures 233

Appendix 237

Notes 239

References 276

List of Abbreviations 315

Index ....
318

Foreword

Mental Architecture covers a range of personable and philosophical topics of interest to the casual reader. This book confronts several popular notions and assumptions about reality, including where the center of your self is located or how your brain categorizes information to allow you to perceive and sense objects in the world around you. There is also a message of self-improvement within this book, as many of the topics discussed are relatable and personally relevant.

Chapter 1 discusses the concept and importance of emptiness and space, including how they are involved in the way your brain perceives and distinguishes objects from one another, including the physiological processes involved. This chapter also covers the human tendency to recognize faces in otherwise inanimate objects, and the relevance of silence in music and oral communication.

Chapter 2 is about the way the human mind perceives time. Physiological time-keeping structures and processes are revealed. How individuals process temporal events is also explored, with particular attention given to the way the brain constructs the present and categorizes the past. We then explore the inner workings of human memory, including the subjective and measurable effects of pharmacological agents and mental illness on temporal perception. Following that, we discuss the blurred lines between consciousness and time perception and examine the role the imagination plays in temporality.

In Chapter 3, we look at the difference between the countable and uncountable, the finite and infinite, and whether or not specific mathematical ideas make sense in practice. A brief history of counting, including multicultural practices, is mentioned as we transition into the psychology behind this practice and its implications toward object recognition. We present some serious challenges with the utility of the infinite, including its place in discussing physical concepts such as the size of the Universe.

Chapter 4 looks at mathematics as a human invention and explores whether math develops from scientific discoveries or if it informs them instead. Classical problems inherent to logical systems, including Gödel's incompleteness theorem, are covered, as are the limitations of such systems. We also talk about how the brain filters out irrelevancies in your environment to present you with a cohesive and sensible view of the world. Potential relationships between attention deficits and creativity are explored, including the effects of certain stimulants. We then discuss the impact advertising has on sensory perception and conclude the chapter with a brief discussion on the utility of measurement systems and how individual perspective is a quintessential component of the presentation of an event.

In Chapter 5, we discuss the idea of what it means to be a "normal" person, and if such a concept is even realistic or worthwhile. Various forms of physical and psychological discriminations are discussed, including their effects on personal development. We discuss what it means to form impactful personal relationships and friendships and how this process changes throughout your life. Different ideas of physical attractiveness are explored both from a personal and biological standpoint. We implore the reader to exercise caution in the application of labels on people, and to exercise sensitivity about the trials and hardships of others. Mental health awareness is a major focal point of this chapter, and the relationship between mental health and creativity is explored. Different forms of intelligence are covered, with some popular ideas about them challenged. We conclude by encouraging the reader to celebrate their diversity and individuality.

Chapter 6 illuminates the human decision-making process and addresses the age-old philosophical debate of free will versus fatalism. Are people in charge of the choices they make or do circumstances determine their decisions? We discuss the substantial role the unconscious mind plays informing decisions as well as how difficult times can bring out a different side in people. Another topic addressed in this chapter is genetic memories - the idea that the actions of your ancestors could influence your present habits and decisions. Other sensations, including déjà vu, dream states, and meditation, are covered. We also talk about the issue of indecisiveness and what psychological and neurological mechanisms are responsible for this annoying behavior. We emphasize the importance of mindfulness and its value to experiencing an enjoyable and fulfilling life.

Chapter 7 begins with a detailed overview of early childhood development theory, focusing on the works of Piaget, Vygotsky, Galperin, and Erickson, while presenting counterarguments to these theories, including feminist standpoint theory. We explore the concept of the self in great detail and view its development and subsequent psychoanalysis from many different perspectives, namely the idea that people are not as stable as they appear to be and specific life circumstances or events can dramatically and permanently alter their identities. Finally, we explore the hard problem of consciousness and its role in constructing a unified self.

Each chapter is conveniently broken down into sections. There is also a collection of figures from the text and a brief appendix covering the functional anatomy of the brain and neurons (nerve cells). It is my sincere hope that this book enhances your perspective on the mysteries of the mind. I am certain you will be able to meaningfully apply many of these novel and exciting topics to your daily life.

Chapter 1 – No Space

"Vision is the sense that both operates at a distance, unlike touch and taste, and can be focused and directed, unlike hearing and smell. We can pay attention to certain noises or odours, or try to ignore them, but we cannot blink our ears or aim our nose: the eye is far more active, under far more control. Seeing is our best perceptual tool – our foremost way to engage with the world."[1]

— Damion Searls

Object Recognition

One of the defining features of conscious awareness is your ability to distinguish objects from one another. While it is easy to take this ability for granted, it is no simple task for the brain. The world around you would appear as meaningless static-filled blobs if specific neural networks were not busily firing away, building reality right before your eyes. There would be no way to tell an apple from an orange, an airplane from a cloud, or a person from the couch. Everything would be blended together and nothing would stand apart.

According to research scientist James DiCarlo, the major part of your brain responsible for object recognition is the inferior temporal cortex.[2] As he mentions, "The apparent ease of our visual recognition abilities belies the computational magnitude of this feat: we effortlessly detect and classify objects from among tens of thousands of possibilities, and we do so within a fraction of a second, despite the tremendous variation in appearance that each object produces on our eyes."[3] At the forefront of his research efforts was to lay the groundwork to search for computational algorithms that the brain uses to perform object recognition tasks. If he could determine what these algorithms were and how they worked, it seemed reasonable to surmise that could pave the way for the discovery of similar algorithms for the other human senses of touch, sound, taste, and smell. If scientists understood what these specific pathways were and how they operated, it might be possible for medical researchers to develop cures for sensory-related conditions including blindness and agnosia, the inability to correctly interpret incoming sensory data as a result of brain damage.[4]

The occipital lobes and temporal lobes in the brain are home to critical neural networks responsible for image processing and recognition. The ventral visual stream, which is a region of the brain composed of multiple visual cortex areas, has strong connections to other regions of the brain, including the temporal lobes. Transcranial Magnetic Stimulation (TMS) to the ventral visual stream can cause people to identify objects incorrectly temporarily or not be able to recognize them at all, especially with facial recognition tasks.[5] The inferior temporal cortex (IT) processes data from the ventral visual stream, and if it is functioning correctly, it can accurately and efficiently identify objects in the visual field. The IT is also able to filter out meaningless sensory data that is not relevant to image processing. Facial recognition and facial discrimination are among the more prominent features of the IT. DiCarlo et al. hypothesized that simple weighted summation of mean spike rates of electrical activity in axonal connections of neurons is what ultimately leads to object identification working together with several other high-level noise and object recognition filters.[6]

The researchers believed that object recognition happens through a variety of non-linear data processing and probability weighting functions occurring across different subgroups of cortical neurons. Each of these subgroups is responsible for only coding familiar patterns and shapes and not focusing attention on irrelevancies and other "noise" patterns in the visual field. The idea is that objects are temporarily stationary long enough for retinal cues (from the eye) to transfer sensory data to these distinct visual substreams which then work together to formulate the "best guess" of the object based on potentially thousands of previous encounters with similar ones.[7]

A few years later, researchers Majaj et al. tested these hypotheses about neuronal image recognition by setting up a series of experiments that measured human performance on challenging object recognition tests.[8] This study was necessary from their viewpoint because earlier studies into object recognition were mostly qualitative and inconclusive and their goal was to introduce a quantitative analysis into this one to elucidate how the brain performs object recognition so seamlessly. One of the hypotheses of their study was that human performance on these 64 rigorous object recognition tests would be equivalent to data gathered from monkeys.[9] It is worth noting that the tests they employed did not focus on low-level visual processing and that there were also known inconsistencies in the perceptions of these objects. They tested a variety of scientific hypotheses and acknowledged that "Each neuronal linking hypothesis is a postulated mechanism of how downstream neurons integrate ventral stream activity to decide which object label the observer will report in each image."[10]

Their method was to use a database of 5760 achromatic images based on 64 distinct objects. To construct this database, they altered the viewing angle of the object as well as its background. They applied mathematical transformations to faces so that they might be seen from the front, side, or another angle while being projected against various backgrounds. As Majaj et al. mentioned, "Each trial started with a central fixation point that lasted for 500 ms, after which an image appeared at the center of the screen for 100 ms. After a 300 ms delay, the observer was prompted to click one of eight 'response' images that matched the identity or category of the stimulus image."[11] Following both state and federal animal welfare guidelines, they obtained similar data from rhesus monkeys in laboratory conditions. They used standard operant conditioning on the monkeys and gathered data on visually-provoked electric potentials via carefully placed electrodes in their scalps (in the neighborhood of the ventral stream and IT) and used a smaller, but a significant, battery of images to evoke and measure neuronal responses from the monkeys' brains.

Through mathematical and statistical analyses of their experiment results, the researchers were able to conclude that their initial hypotheses that learned weighted sums of randomly selected average neuronal responses spatially distributed over monkey IT (LaWS of RAD IT) "perfectly predicted the human behavioral performance across all 64 object recognition tasks."[12] Moreover, they were able to identify that object recognition in humans takes place across a distributed network of approximately 60,000 IT neurons. They found that with facial recognition, specific face-specific neurons and "face patch" neural networks were activated in the distributed network of IT neurons. It is also fascinating that monkey neuronal population responses were very accurate predictors of human population responses because that suggests that there is direct evolutionary conservation in these neural pathways across the two species. Both primates and humans appear to share a non-verbal visual representation of different shapes and features that allow them to identify incoming visual sensory data correctly. What is currently unclear, however, is how much of this is due to innate neurochemistry and how much of it is caused by life experience and learned behavior. Remarkably, your brain can filter out sensory data in this way, not just with visual stimuli but with other sensory stimuli as well. Without a reliable and robust filtering mechanism, you would not be able to identify objects at all, and the world would appear filled with nothing but static and visual snow. Object recognition is a necessity for survival.

Anthropomorphism

Closely related to object recognition is the tendency of humans sometimes to misapply human traits, appearances, emotions, and feelings to otherwise inanimate or non-human objects or beings – a feature known as *anthropomorphism*. Philosopher David Hume believed that anthropomorphism was a universal human trait. According to him, "There is an universal tendency among mankind to conceive all beings like themselves, and to transfer to every object, those qualities, with which they are familiarly acquainted, and of which they are intimately conscious."[13] This view has been held as valid until recently when psychological researchers conducted a study demonstrating that Hume's anthropomorphism theories about the universality of anthropomorphism, while socially and neurologically significant, might be scientifically unsubstantiated.[14]

Other researchers, for instance, have identified deficits in anthropomorphic abilities in populations, including individuals on the autism spectrum and people with brain damage to their amygdala.[15] Waytz et al. (2010) define anthropomorphism as "[going] beyond *animism*—simply attributing life to a nonliving object. The essence of anthropomorphism is, therefore, attributing capacities that people tend to think of as distinctly human to nonhuman agents, in particular, humanlike mental capacities (e.g., intentionality, emotion, cognition)."[16] So anthropomorphism moves beyond just attributing human-like physical traits to objects and animals and is more concerned with the formation of perceived human-like behavioral characteristics in them.

There is some thought in the scientific community that anthropomorphism serves a functional purpose in helping children develop the ability to reason about mental states. Advertisers are keenly aware of the implications of anthropomorphism in their marketing campaigns, as commercials that bring certain products to life can be very alluring for potential consumers. Similarly, inventors and product developers can also use the principles of anthropomorphism in designing user-friendly products.

Waytz et al. developed a test called the "Individual Differences in Anthropomorphism Questionnaire" (IDAQ) with the goal of better understanding the individual, cultural, and socio-economic differences in how people anthropomorphize objects and non-human living beings. One of their other goals was to provide a standard, reliable metric on this subject for use by other researchers. In developing the IDAQ, researchers considered four essential dimensions of commonly anthropomorphized things: "nonhuman animals, natural entities, spiritual agents, and technological devices."[17] They took each of these traits and paired them with five human and five non-human characteristics.

Over a thousand total participants completed the IDAQ across a series of separate trials, each measuring something different about anthropomorphism. Based on extensive data analysis, the researchers deduced that some people have more of a tendency to anthropomorphize than others. One interesting finding was that cultures who anthropomorphize nature are often found to be more environmentally conscientious than those who do not. The IDAQ was also able to accurately predict that people who anthropomorphize non-human objects were more likely to report trust in a polygraph test than a human interrogator when it came to the investigation of a suspect accused of committing a crime.

People typically act more socially appropriately when other people are around them and watching their behavior compared to when they are alone because they care about what others think of them and desire to make a good impression. Similarly, people who anthropomorphize God (or another deity) compared to those who do not tend to perceive God as more judgmental than those who worship a God they do not recognize as human-like. They are also more likely to cooperate if they feel that a human-like god is observing them. People also behave better when faced with a human-like computer interface than when they exposed to a more machine-like interface. The researchers set out to determine if the IDAQ scores would be predictive of these philosophies, so they gave out the IDAQ to participants and then asked them to respond to a battery of questions on a computer screen delivered by an anthropomorphized robot named Kismet.

Waytz et al. found that people were more likely to behave in a socially acceptable way when there was a human-like interface. As they explain, "These results suggest that anthropomorphism may increase the social influence of nonhuman agents. Being watched by others matters, perhaps especially when others have a mind like one's own."[18] This data is useful for product designers, law enforcement, and other professionals because it strongly suggests that an individual's behavior is subject to the influence of the character of the device. Encouraging the responsible use of more human-like tools and products might be beneficial toward providing for a more peaceful and productive social landscape. Researchers even found that support robots, who act human-like, were found to be a reliable source of emotional support for the elderly, helping them to lead a happier and healthier life.

Kuz et al. conducted a study using fMRI imaging to analyze the different neurological behavior of people visually interacting with two types of robots, one anthropomorphized, and the other one not.[19] These robots were presented by video to participants who were asked to use a 5-point scale to rate the human-ness of each robot with five being the most human-like and one being the least human-like. Both the robots and anthropomorphized robots that appeared in the videos were simulated using a combination of computer programming and an infrared optical tracking system. The researchers sought to answer the question of whether the human mirror neuron system (MNS) activates more strongly in robots that are strongly anthropomorphized compared to traditional non-humanized robots. Mirror neurons are neurons that are associated with both mimicking, interpreting, and relating to the gesturing and body language of others.

They focused on fMRI data from one exemplary subject who participated in the study and found that the non-human robots activated slightly different regions of the brain than the anthropomorphized robots did, even though there was some overlap between the two models. The non-humanlike robot activated the right temporo-occipital lobe and the left-temporo-occipital lobe while the anthropomorphized robot activated the mesial-parietal lobes. As Kuz et al. explained, "Most importantly the observation of humanlike movements activated the fronto-parietal MNS stronger than observation of robotic movements. Whereas the observation of robotic movements activated the left inferior-parietal cortex."[20] The results of this study suggest that the brain responds differently to human-like movements and expressions even if they are known to originate from a robot. Both types of robots activated different areas of the visual and parietal lobes, regions responsible for visual and sensory data processing, but the anthropomorphized robots were responsible for activating the MNS. The brain, therefore, has a built-in network for distinguishing human versus non-humanlike movements.

Not only does the human brain possess different neurological mechanisms for reacting to human versus non-human movements, but humans are finely tuned from birth to seek out faces. According to Nicholas Day, six-month-old babies can recognize faces not only across different people but across primates as well. They do not discriminate nor have any preference amongst these different faces. Around nine months, babies undergo a phenomenon known as *perceptual narrowing*, where they develop strong preferences for human faces and view other faces as being foreign to them.[21] At three months old, babies generally prefer human faces of their race, but up until then, they do not discriminate. So, a two-month-old baby would not react strongly to a person of different ethnicity, but a four-month-old very likely would. Babies cannot genuinely be racist and lack the mental capacity for sophisticated forms of discrimination, so there must be an alternate explanation for their preference.

In his article, Day explains that one time while his wife was studying abroad in Nanjing, his wife's Chinese roommate asked her how she can tell people apart from one another back in America because, according to her, all white people looked the same. This remark was surprising to his wife, who could not possibly understand how someone could say that. What was even more surprising to her, however, was that after she returned to America from the mainland, she found herself unable to discriminate amongst people of her ethnicity because she became conditioned to being around Chinese people. She was finally able to understand why her roommate in China made that remark, strange and discomforting as it may have seemed at the time.[22]

The desire to see faces is so strong that sometimes people see faces or familiar shapes where none exist. This phenomenon is referred to as *pareidolia* (Figure 1) and refers to the psychological condition of viewing patterns in random objects.[23] Some of the more famous examples of this phenomenon include a woman who noticed the face of the Virgin Mary on a burnt grilled cheese sandwich, people seeing a human face projecting out of some hills on Mars or viewing a man on the Moon. Pareidolia also extends to other senses too, as people have frequently reported hearing hidden messages in songs or being able to make out voices in static noise on the radio.

What is it that causes people to see or hear things that are not there? In terms of seeing faces, there is a region in your brain called the fusiform gyrus that is responsible for facial recognition. According to Susana Martinez-Conde, "The 'face neurons' in people with healthy brains are so overactive that they scream FACE! in many situations where there are no actual faces to be found. Those sophisticated face-detection skills, combined with our brain's compulsion to extract meaning from the sensory chaos that surrounds us, is why we see faces where there aren't any."[24] Skilled artists take advantage of this phenomenon and often embed images into their artwork that are likely to evoke this sensory phenomenon and lead people to extract a deeper meaning out of their artwork.

Pareidolia is a perfectly normal phenomenon, and researchers have shown it to occur slightly more frequently in women than in men with the reason likely being that women have a heightened social awareness and greater receptivity to facial expressions than men do. Highly religious and superstitious people were also prone to higher levels of pareidolia than non-religious and skeptical people. The reason for this is likely because the former group is more open to the suggestion that there could be faces in material objects. People experiencing high levels of fatigue or people having specific neurological ailments such as Lewy Body Dementia are also prone to higher levels of pareidolia than the general population. Even rhesus monkeys demonstrate this phenomenon, although it is unknown if other primates or non-primates experience it too.[25]

Perhaps one of the most controversial assessments of pareidolia is the Rorschach test, created by Hermann Rorschach in 1921.[26] Although the use of this test has declined over the years, there are still a significant number of psychologists who use it to understand the minds of their patients better and it is still taken very seriously by the judicial system (its results are admissible in court) and it can even be used to screen out job candidates.[27] The task is simple enough. Show a patient a series of ten cards dotted with various inkblots. The images are ambiguous and straightforward enough to tap into the patient's subconscious and unconscious mind and reveal things about them that might otherwise lay dormant or completely undiscovered.

Rorschach quickly discovered that people with different personalities showed significant differences in the ways they interpreted the inkblots. The test requires participants to say what they see on the cards without a time limit. They are asked, however, to refrain from telling a story about the inkblots and the therapist administering the test should not interfere with or otherwise obstruct the patient's interpretations.[28] Interpreting the test results is not entirely open-ended, as Rorschach compiled detailed criteria for each image. He even went so far as to code specific responses, patterns of response, or whether people saw movement or not as being evidence suggesting the presence of a particular mental disorder. Some therapists have used the test as a means to an end, making a diagnosis either solely or partially based on the test results.[29]

Research recently uncovered the reasons why people sometimes see more images in certain inkblots (Figure 2) than in others. Images that have more fractal complexity are less ambiguous than those that have less of it. Fractal complexity is loosely defined as the amount of fine structure in an image containing edges that are self-similar upon magnification.[30] The surprising reason why less-complicated inkblots might lead to a broader range of interpretations might have to do with the way the human visual system processes visual imagery. According to Taylor, "Traditional measures of visual patterns quantify complexity in terms of the ratio of fine structure to coarse structure… the increase in number of induced percepts between the different blots might be linked to a reduction in their fractal complexity."[31] Experiments mentioned by Taylor et al. further confirmed this association between decreased inkblot complexity and perceived image variety. This mathematical phenomenon led some people, including Abbott, to challenge the validity of the test because the variation in interpretations may not be as subjective as first meets the eye. While this skepticism of the Rorschach test is undoubtedly warranted, by no means does it present an exhaustive criticism.

To confirm the psychological theories of Rorschach, a team of Japanese scientists experimented with subjects viewing a series of ten inkblot images and recorded brain activity on an MRI machine equipped with a voice scanner. The inkblot images were fed to the participants while they were in the MRI tube, and they were asked to describe what they saw on them. The researchers confirmed via the MRI analysis long-held suspicions about the Rorschach exam. According to Damion Searls, "The study demonstrated that seeing something in a 'standard' way uses more instinctive, precognitive brain regions, while 'original' vision, requiring a more creative integration of perception and emotion, uses other parts of the brain."[32] People who are more creative and unique in their thinking abilities are therefore more likely to view the images in more imaginative ways than those who are not.

Although the Rorschach test is not without its significant critics and detractors, there is an excellent value in the test for learning more about human visual perception. As Searls asserts, "Seeing is an act of the mind, not just the eyes. When you look at something, you are directing your attention to parts of the visual field and ignoring others."[33] For vision, sensory data is processed from nerves in the eye and into the brain and then back to the eyes. Social, cultural, and personality factors can also influence what you see when confronted with ambiguous visual data such as that encountered in the Rorschach test.

One such prominent example of the utility of the Rorschach test in clinical practice Searls mentions is that of a young child Basia, the daughter of a Russian immigrant single mother, who was sexually molested by her 40-year-old landlord. When the police showed up to confront the suspected perpetrator, he fled the city and flew his small plane directly into a mountain, killing himself instantly. Basia's evaluation by her psychologist was troublesome because of her tendency to shy away from providing details about the trauma and minimizing any impact it had on her. It was not until Basia saw a battery of Rorschach images that the trauma she endured as a child began to unfold.

One of the interpretations that stood out the most to her psychologist was how she responded to the first inkblot image. She saw a bat, as most people do who view that image, but she commented extensively on its broken features and noted how it had holes in it. She concluded that the bat must have been attacked and damaged from how it should have otherwise looked. Through her interpretation of the images, the psychologist concluded she had been substantially emotionally traumatized by past events despite her apparent calmness and denials of how badly the events affected her. Eventually, Basia sued her perpetrator's estate for civil damages and their defense attorneys argued that she was not as traumatized as she claimed to be due to her consistent denials of suffering any ill effects from the abuse. Fortunately, Basia's therapist was able to use the Rorschach test as evidence of how deeply traumatized she was despite her outward façade. In 2008, the state awarded her $8.4 million in damages.

The Rorschach test is just one example of how individuals can attribute detail and meaning to otherwise meaningless inkblots. If you think more deeply about it, the entirety of perception in the world works in this way. Nothing in the world around you should have any meaning at all without a reliable label and characteristics that clearly distinguish it from everything else around it. The world is, of course, not a collection of random inkblots, but it also does not naturally operate with the type of order that you might ascertain it does. Certain perceptual puzzles, often found on social media, can be viewed as different things depending on how you are looking at them. Optical illusions and brain puzzles can cause people to form order out of otherwise random patterns. There are numerous ways to trick the brain into believing it is seeing something that may not be present.

The Sound of Silence

The ability to correctly identify an object requires you to distinguish it from its surroundings, which can be a background, wall, table, floor, or even the air around it. Being able to view a sequence of objects requires you to acknowledge the empty spaces in between them. Keep in mind, however, that those spaces are not truly empty. They only appear to be because your brain naturally filters out the minutiae in between objects and also in between you and another object. There are millions of specks of dust, viruses, and bacteria floating around in the air, but they are too minuscule to be seen by the naked eye. If you could see these particles in such fine detail, how you view the world would be radically different. Fortunately, there is no purpose to being able to see these tiny particles, so the space in between objects appears to be empty.

For many years, scientists have postulated that there is, in fact, no such thing as emptiness but proving such a theory has been tremendously difficult. A team of research scientists led by Professor Alfred Leitenstorfer from the University of Konstanz was recently able to detect faint signals from pure nothingness in a quantum vacuum using a specialized laser system.[34] This system generates such incredibly brief light pulses that it can detect electromagnetic fluctuations even in complete darkness. Their instrumentation is so sensitive that they can filter out any background noise effects when measuring the quantized energy. They also found that when fluctuation amplitudes are decaying in one position, they are increasing in another as the way traffic builds on a freeway with cars slowing down behind the ones where traffic is beginning to let up.

If pure emptiness does not exist, then there is no space in between anything. There is energy everywhere around you, even if it is mostly undetectable to the human body. The concept of space is a complicated one, and what it refers to depends on its context. A better definition of space would be one that refers to the apparent emptiness between things you can perceive. For practical purposes, this definition of space should suffice because it is the *perception*, or illusion, of space that matters most. You see what you are meant to see via the constraints and boundaries of your human brain and eyes.

Another sense in which the perception of space is important is your sense of sound. Auditory perception is highly sensitive to pauses, whether it be during a conversation between two people, while listening to music, or just hearing the environmental noises around you. As Adam Blumenfeld remarked, "Rhythm is a series of pauses. Rhythm is a pattern of absences of sounds. The brain likes patterns. Your brain won't be able to process a constant streamline of information."[35] Dr. Victoria Williamson, a respected authority on the psychology of music, asserts that pauses and silences in music are essential in setting the overall mood and feel of the piece. Breaks build musical tension for the listener, and it is up to the musician to best determine how to proceed from that pause, whether it be to elicit a sharp transition or to introduce a lofty tone. A long pause of silence is sometimes the only indicator that a musical piece has terminated. If the piece does not feel complete, that silence may conjure up feelings of anticipation or unrest. On the other hand, if the piece came to its logical conclusion, then the silence at the end will feel appropriate and satisfying.[36]

Professor Elizabeth Hellmuth Margulis of the University of Arkansas studied the effects of musical context on the perception of silence. She defines silence as "the periods during which the acoustic signal descends below some threshold of detectable volume."[37] There are programs which can detect the presence of silence in a musical piece when the sound signals fall beneath the lower threshold for human hearing capability. Acoustic silences are defined to be "the one-dimensional gaps consisting purely of duration; the duration from the end of the previous sound to the start of the next."[38] The perception of silence can vary greatly depending on the context, even when the temporal signature of it is precisely the same in two different pieces.

In her experiments, Margulis recruited subjects with limited or no musical background from a university-level introductory music class. In her first experiment, she shared excerpts from commercial recordings with participants from a variety of classical composers containing an instance of musical silence. They were then asked to identify the beginning and end of silent pauses accurately, utilize a moving slider to determine their perception of levels of musical tension throughout the piece, and finally to answer a series of questions concerning their experience with the silence and the musical excerpt. Margulis asked if they noticed beats during the silence, how many beats they inferred, how surprised they were with the silence and what followed it, how noticeable the silence was, how well it fits into the overall piece, and how relaxed or tense it was in the context of the music.

In the second experiment, a different set of participants were asked to listen to a more carefully controlled musical piece and perform the same tasks as in the previous trial. The idea behind the first experiment was to analyze how subjects would perform in a more authentic musical setting like ones they might encounter outside of the laboratory whereas the second experiment focused on observing the effects of silence in a controlled laboratory environment. For this experiment, participants listened to excerpts from a series of 23 monophonic, diatonic melodies produced using Adobe Audition software. Because the tones were all so similar in structure, the researchers prompted the participants with random questions during the sessions so that they could ensure their continued attention, a problem they did not experience with the first experiment.

One of the results of the first experiment was that variations more strongly influenced the reaction times to the onset of silence in pitch than temporal variations. Accelerating or decelerating the tempo of the music did not seem to affect the reaction times as much as varying the loudness of the music piece did. The researchers also found that listeners were more likely not to notice a silence if it followed a sustained note, a result supported by earlier research suggesting that people tend to perceive silences and long notes similarly.

An interesting finding from the second experiment was that due to the melodic, repetitive, and predictable nature of the musical tones, participants missed silences because they likely extended these notes in their imagination during the silence. Variation in tonal qualities either before or following a silence resulted in different perceptions of the silences as either tense or relaxed. Participants generally overestimated the length of silence when it occurred as the closure of a piece as opposed to a pause in the piece.

Margulis noticed some general trends across both experiments. One of these was that the way people perceive musical silence depended heavily on their context in the piece. While there is absolutely nothing to objectively distinguish one period of silence from another in a piece, their perceptions were influenced by what preceded them and what followed. In particular, the interpretation of silences was highly sensitive to the pitch context directly before it even though silence itself only occurs in a temporal, or time-dependent, sense. According to Margulis, "The occurrence or nonoccurrence of tonal closure (in the form of a melodic descent to the tonic pitch, or a cadential arrival on the tonic chord) immediately before the silence is perhaps the most significant factor in the shaping of that silence's sound."[39] The *tonic pitch* refers to the first note of a musical scale, and the *cadential arrival* refers to a progression of musical notes that leads to some tonal conclusion or rest.

The results of Margulis' study suggest some neurological mechanism by which people, even those with little to no musical background, potentially utilize certain stylistic norms or otherwise familiar patterns to fill in the gaps between silences. Silences can create anticipation, closure, fear, excitement, and many other emotions, which is remarkable considering the nature of silence is the *absence* of any auditory stimuli. How can people experience so much passion and feeling in complete silence? While the musical piece might technically be at rest, the listener's mind is still busy generating sounds and feelings to fill in the gap. This phenomenon by which the brain emulates auditory data in its absence is fascinating.

Auditory imagery is a term that describes the subjective experience of hearing music or other noise inside your head in the absence of sound or additional auditory stimulation. A team of researchers conducted an experiment in which subjects were played music while they were in an fMRI machine.[40] The researchers then muted the music and noticed that the auditory cortex remained quite active despite the silence. The brain attempted to compensate for the gaps in music by recovering lyrical or tonal memories and continuing the music through auditory imagery in the absence of actual music. Auditory cortex responses were stronger in subjects when music was played from familiar songs compared to non-familiar ones, regardless of whether lyrics accompanied the songs or not. This observed phenomenon is the same thing that happens in your brain when a random song gets stuck in your head for seemingly no reason. Auditory imagery is similar in some ways to visual daydreaming, and there is neurological evidence to support this.[41]

People use auditory imagery in a variety of contexts, from remembering phone numbers to utilizing mnemonic devices to help them remember facts or details. Sometimes random songs pop in your head for seemingly no reason or exposure to a specific environment reminds you of a familiar tune. Rhythm, whether real or imagined, can help people get through their day. Silence is but a golden opportunity for the natural rhythm of the mind to take over. Silence is also an essential tool in both written and spoken language. The blank spaces between words distinguish them from each other. Symbols, including periods, commas, and semicolons, indicate written pauses. There are even instances where individual letters and symbols are silent such as the "e" in "become." If it were not for these silent markers and spacings, it would be challenging to decipher or interpret forms of written communication. The silences in writing provide meaningful pauses like they do in music.

The perception of silence in oral communication and speaking depends heavily on context, the tone of voice of the person before and following the silence, and whether it indicates a sense of pause or closure in the speech. Silence can also occur when there is a failure of language to adequately or articulately communicate something. As author Melanie Sard of Macalester College explains, "In this case, silence itself is what is meaningful since it indicates that experience even as it fails to express it."[42] Sometimes ideas are lost in translation. The world's languages are so diverse and complex that an idea expressed in one language might not have a precise translation into another one. One example of this difficulty in translating is the Japanese word *shoganai*, which is used to express a humble acceptance of the unfortunate circumstances that often present themselves in everyday life. There is no equivalent word in the English language that translates into shoganai, so if a native Japanese speaker were to try to use an equivalent word in English, they would most likely resort to silence, at least temporarily, until they tried their best to explain the definition of the word as clearly as they could.[43]

A language is a tool with inherent limitations. Most languages develop around the cultural, social, geographical, and economic needs of the people and serve the purpose of conveying ideas to each other. Some languages, including German and Russian, are particular and descriptive while other languages such as English are less specific. Translating between words in this way can be very difficult and lead to challenging moments of silence in a conversation. An idea that is crystal clear in one language might not translate well to another. The only thing that all languages have in common is the concept of silence. Different languages go about the expression and notation of silence and pause differently, but the experience of it is universal. Although the notion of silence has been at times cast in a negative light and viewed as a complete absence of anything useful in conversation, some people see silence as one of the great arts of communication. So much can be communicated without saying anything despite the paradoxical nature of silence. "Silent communication" sounds like an oxymoron, but it can be just as deep with meaning as the conversation surrounding it.

Michal Ephratt from the Department of Hebrew Language at the University of Haifa deeply examined the functions of silence and delineated different forms of silences from each other.[44] The first type of silence he described is the *referential silence*. This type of silence implies something that is not explicitly stated but can be figured out from the context in which it occurs. For instance, if asked how many children you had and you answered, "Three girls," it means that you have zero male children even though you never explicitly indicated so. Another example of this type of silence occurs during traditional marriage ceremonies when the officiant asks the wedding parties and guests if anyone objects to the marriage. If nobody answers, that silence is assumed to collectively represent agreement among everyone that they do not have any objections. Authors who intentionally leave a page blank even though it is part of the book use that blankness as a visual reference for the reader to infer something about the story, possibly something dark or dreary. In this case, the blankness is a type of verbal silence that refers to something of significance.

The second function of silence is as an *emotive* force. Silence is used during religious ceremonies and funerals to express feelings of sorrow, reverence, deep contemplation, or joy. As Ephratt explains, "Silence in such cases is the socially built-in means whereby one expresses one's empathy as in cases of loss and sorrow, or one's admiration, reverence or bewilderment in the presence of the mighty."[45] When words or other gestures are unable to express emotions, silence can be the only logical expression. Applause is a traditional way of expressing gratitude following a speech or performance, but there are times where the moment is so overpowering with emotion that clapping is not appropriate. It is in these moments that a brief silence is necessary.

Silence can also be a form of *enactment*. It is often preferable for someone to verbally express feelings of hatred and enmity compared to silently expressing these feelings through a violent altercation. While the presence of silent moments in communication can seem unnerving or awkward, there are times when quiet moments represent feelings of warmth and comfort. Ephratt references the case of a psychotherapy patient who frustrated her therapist with her long moments of silence, but when he probed the patient about it, she remarked that her silence was a reenactment of her comfortable relationship with her deceased mother. She coped with her loss through silence, and it was this expression that allowed her to grieve and make peace with her significant loss.

Procedural silence refers to the type of silence that occurs during a transition between speaking and listening. In this context, the silence serves as an unwritten invitation for the listener to take their turn and speak. The silence itself is not the official marker for turn-taking, but it is a meaningful pause between the end of one discourse and the beginning of another one from a different speaker. There might be other verbal or non-verbal cues directly following the speech from one person in transition to the silence preceding the other person's turn to speak.

Another type of silence is that occurring in a direct speech act. For instance, someone might threaten another with silent treatment for not paying off debts. The punishment, in this case, is outside the range of spoken language and is an implied reference to a lack of communication, support, or whatever else the silent treatment suggests. This type of silence can be crippling to the person experiencing it even though the direct act of it is not physically or emotionally caustic in any way.

Silence can also come in the form of a *right* or a *concession*. The opening statement in the Miranda rights is, "You have the right to remain silent."[46] The fifth amendment of the Constitution protects against self-incrimination and preserves an individual's right to be silent about their legal case.[47] Unfortunately, a person's silence can sometimes be interpreted as an indicator of guilt, even if they are innocent. The silent can be presumed guilty because of their lack of verbal defense against the accusations.

One of the most primitive functions of silence is the *phatic function*.[48] Phatic conversation includes meaningless small talk, chatter, babbling, or other utterances to fill the aching void of silence. It can be something as simple as asking, "How are you?" to a stranger. Phatic expressions and utterances help people to avoid the inherent discomfort in silence around others. Over time and in the right circumstances, people who were once uncomfortable around each other and engaged in phatic conversation to avoid silence might reach a point at which silence around others is embraced rather than shunned and communication becomes meaningful. The Chinese culture, for instance, embraces silence and expects that if you have something to say, that it better be worthwhile.

Poetic silence[49] is used to build up tension, express certain feelings, or to indicate the unknown. Poets suggest silent moments in a variety of ways, from using symbols including caesuras, ellipses, dashes, and blank lines, or by clumping or truncating words to express action. The expression of silence in poetry is an art form not unlike the artistic use of blank space in painting, and while silence can be eloquent and poetic, it can also feel suffocating and uncomfortable. An anechoic chamber is a particular type of room insulated heavily with foam blocks and other materials designed to completely absorb acoustic vibrations and deaden sound as well as prevent external noises from entering the chamber. There seems to be some unofficial rule about the chamber that a person stuck in there for more than 45 minutes in complete silence would go crazy and start experiencing auditory hallucinations to fill in the silent void.

Clinton Nguyen put this hypothesis about the 45-minute time limit to the test when he visited Cooper Union's anechoic chamber in New York.[50] This chamber, while considerably smaller and less fancy than other ones throughout the world, was enough to challenge the prevailing theory about losing your mind to silence. He received permission to spend 45 minutes alone in the anechoic chamber with all the lights turned off. While in the chamber, Nguyen noticed that he could hear natural sounds and functions that would typically be imperceptible. He was able to listen to his eyelids blinking, joints creaking, and his skin rubbing against his clothes. After 30 minutes in the chamber, his typically imperceptible tinnitus (ringing in the ears) become very loud and annoying. Overall, he handled the 45 minutes in the chamber well and did not feel as if he were going to lose his mind, although he was annoyed by some of the acoustic sensations. Since then, similar experiments involving anechoic chambers have shown comparable results.

NASA utilizes an anechoic chamber to prepare its astronauts for the vacuum in outer space.[51] The chamber is the closest thing here on Earth that can prepare them for the strange silence of space. Sometimes people cannot handle the chamber because it makes them feel claustrophobic and uncomfortable. In these circumstances, it is not advisable to send these people into space because once they are out there, it is not easy for them to come back to Earth if they experience anxiety in the strange silence.

Sensory deprivation tanks which are sometimes called "float tanks," are commercially available for people who wish to experience the sensation of acoustic and visual deprivation for themselves.[52] Clients get into a tank filled with warm water and Epsom salts and then close the lid and turn off the gentle blue light inside. They float on top of the saltwater in complete darkness and silence until their time is up. The silence experienced in the float tank is not as extreme as that of the anechoic chamber, but it is enough for people to experience relaxing sensations while they are in the tank. Unfortunately, some people experience paranoia and terror in the darkness as what is pleasant for one person might not be for another.

As famous musicians, Paul Simon and Art Garfunkel once mused, "And the sign said, 'The words of the prophets are written on the subway walls and tenement halls' and whispered in the sounds of silence."[53] Just as there is no such thing as complete emptiness, total silence does not exist either. Even in the most acoustically insulated environments, you cannot escape the sounds of your own body. Sensory deprivation alters your perspective and your brain fills in the gaps by amplifying the normally dormant sounds around you. Perhaps this amplification is an evolutionary tool for survival, to keep you on alert during times where you feel threatened or in danger. The lack of silence is the greatest reminder that you are alive.

Chapter 2 – No Point in Time

"Time present and time past are both perhaps present in time future, and time future contained in time past. If all time is eternally present all time is unredeemable. What might have been is an abstraction remaining a perceptual possibility only in a world of speculation."[1]

— T.S. Eliot

The Mind's Clock

Time is something that everyone is aware of, but nobody truly comprehends. The past is a series of memories encoded in the brain. The present happens now, and the future is a potential series of events that have not happened yet. Poet T.S. Eliot purports that time may not exist in the way most people think it does, but that it instead all exists at once, or perhaps not at all. It is more likely your perception of time that passes instead of actual time itself. The measurement of the passage of time was a human invention, and the brain contains neuronal mechanisms for perceiving, interpreting, and managing the passage of time.

The suprachiasmatic nucleus (SCN) in the brain is part of the hypothalamus and is directly above the optic chiasm. The SCN is primarily responsible for regulating circadian rhythms and providing people with a sense of time. Researchers demonstrated that the SCN is not a simple isolated neurological mechanism, but is instead a complex heterogeneous neuronal network with multiple pathways throughout the brain designed to regulate specific homeostatic processes including the sleep-wake cycle and control physiological responses to exposure to light.[2] Most of the studies conducted were on animals, particularly mammals including mice and hamsters. In the early 1990s, putative "clock" genes were discovered to be particular molecules at the core of the SCN responsible for providing a fundamental oscillatory mechanism consisting of two interacting feedback loops leading to a natural circadian rhythm.

The three genes transcribed in one of these loops include the *Period (Per)*, *Cryptochrome*, and *Timeless* genes.[3] Of these three distinct types of genes, the most extensively researched ones are the Per genes which oscillate with a circadian rhythm. *Per* gene levels are higher during the day and lower at night and are photoinducible, meaning they activate through exposure to specific levels of natural or artificial light. Studies in mice revealed that these genes were not localized but existed throughout their entire SCN. Based on their observations, researchers theorized that there must be a linear signal pathway in their SCN in which "axons of specialized retinal ganglion cells form the retinohypothalamic tract (RHT) in the optic nerves and release glutamate at conventional synapses onto SCN 'clock' cells."[4] Retinal ganglion cells are present in the eyes and are responsible for receiving visual information and relaying it to the brain via the optic nerve. This transmission of information and associated chemical reactions occur on the RHT, creating a connection between incoming visual stimuli and physiological responses. Glutamate and other essential proteins are stored and transmitted throughout these retinal terminals and then deposited into the SCN to activate different stages of the circadian rhythm.

Damage to the RHT can result in dysfunctional or shifted circadian rhythms that are out of sync with normal rhythms. It is also worth noting that not all cells in mammal SCNs respond homogeneously. Some are more photoreceptive than others, and some react more rhythmically than others to incoming visual data. The circadian rhythm does not result from a singular entity, but rather from a collection of both rhythmic and non-rhythmic photoreceptive cellular responses in hypothalamic tissues. Some circadian rhythms get damaged by lesions or other forms of disease and disorder. Micro-lesions in a particular non-photoreceptive region of the hamster SCN caused a complete loss of circadian rhythm activity even though the endogenously rhythmic Per-expressing cells were undamaged.[5] These results suggest that circadian rhythm stability is highly location-specific and the behavioral and functional effects of damage to the SCN depend on the exact locations of atrophy and disorder.

As Silver & Schwartz (2005) explain, "These kinds of data have stimulated a new model of SCN tissue organization, in which retino-recipient non-rhythmic 'gate' cells provide resetting and synchronizing signals to individually rhythmic 'clock' cells with different intrinsic periods."[6] This bidirectional feedback loop is what powers circadian rhythms. Non-rhythmic cells act as switches to activate and deactivate networks of photoreceptive rhythmic cells and then, in turn, these cells regulate the photoreceptive non-rhythmic "gate" cells. SCN circuits consisting of sets of random oscillators modulate their overall behaviors to form cohesive units that maintain rhythmic outputs. In this way, cells can cluster together to develop robust neural networks that express "clock" genes and self-regulating behavior.

The SCN provides scientific evidence that humans and other mammals possess an internal clock that regulates everything from their body temperature to the complicated sleep-wake cycle. Most of these processes are autonomic and function seamlessly in the absence of significant environmental changes and neurological or psychological disorders. The brain has a remarkable ability, however, to adapt and rewire itself in the presence of certain diseases and other disorders that alter circadian rhythms. In this way, the human body has a physiological sense of time.

Although the SCN is the locus of the circadian rhythm, other physiological processes also have their important rhythms. The cardiovascular system, for instance, is regulated by a person's heartbeat. The rate at which the heart pumps oxygenated blood throughout the body has a profound effect on overall health and wellness. If it pumps too quickly (tachycardia), that can be a sign of dehydration, anxiety, or high blood pressure. If the heart pumps too slowly (bradycardia), that can be an indicator of exceptional physical fitness or possible electrical issues. Irregular heartbeats can be a warning sign of an underlying disorder such as atrial fibrillation or an impending heart attack, heart failure, or stroke. These cardiac arrhythmias are the result of different stresses or conditions affecting the heart, and they demonstrate the importance of the heart maintaining appropriate rhythms in specific circumstances.

Timed processes in the body occur through rhythmic oscillations of SCN neural networks and other physiological processes. Psychologically, time takes on an entirely different meaning. Time is the tool that forms the narrative of your life, but the perception of time varies throughout the brain. According to researchers Fontes et al., "The perception of time is the sum of stimuli associated with cognitive processes and environmental changes. Thus, the perception of time requires a complex neural mechanism and may be changed by emotional state, level of attention, memory and diseases."[7] The frontal cortex, basal ganglia, parietal cortex, cerebellum, and hippocampus are all brain regions implicated in the individual perception of time. These regions gather and interpret sensory information and process it along with associated emotions to formulate a time perception. Time can appear to pass more quickly or slowly, depending on individual circumstances. Waiting in anticipation of a significant event such as a wedding or birthday celebration can make time appear to pass more slowly, whereas being thoroughly engaged in a fun and exciting activity such as a party can cause the time to seem to move more quickly. To better understand and summarize the way time is perceived and acted upon neurologically and psychologically, researchers conducted an in-depth 25-year literature review of time perception drawing upon numerous case studies, original papers, and reports. They acknowledge that there is still an incomplete understanding of the physiological and psychological processes behind time perception, but that there are some robust theories about how they work.[8]

One of the most popular theories about time processing in the brain is via the pacemaker-switch-accumulator mechanism.[9] In this model, a neural switch activates via the presentation of a visual or auditory stimulus that needs to be temporally perceived. As the brain processes the stimulus and the pacemaker temporarily closes the switch, the accumulator stores the event in long-term memory or discards it if it is deemed irrelevant. Once the stimulus has temporally processed, the switch re-opens again to allow in more stimuli. The number of impulses recorded during a given interval of time determines the perception of how much time passed. Individual factors including age, emotional or mental state, cognitive ability, and memory quality can thus alter the perception of actual time and either make a time interval appear shorter or longer in duration than it is. The brain is also inherently limited in how much information it can process at any given moment and these brief, but significant gaps in attention can alter the personal narrative of the individual distorting their perception of the actual amount of time passed.

Chronostasis is the illusory phenomenon that it takes longer for a second to pass visually on a clock than it should take.[10] The reason for this illusion is saccadic eye movements that are not in sync with the second-hand movements. A similar equivalent phenomenon happens when someone listens to and focuses their attention on the audible ticking of the second hand on a clock. In both cases, the passage of time will appear to slow down, although what is happening is a psychological, sensory processing illusion. Intently focusing on the passage of time makes it seem to pass by very slowly, so the worst thing someone can do if they are bored is to stare at a clock.

Past, Present, and Future

The brain's ability to envision and contemplate the past, present, and future is known as *chronesthesia*. The ability for humans to engage in this form of mental time travel may have evolved as a survival method, allowing early people to sharpen their hunting and gathering skills and learn from their past mistakes and improve upon them to refine other personal abilities and survival skills. Scientists refer to these mental experiences as occurring in subjective time because these events occur psychologically and are not part of the real time-line of natural phenomena.[11]

Researchers L. Nyberg et al. set out to better understand the neurological correlates of the consciousness of subjective time. According to them, subjective time "cannot be the same 'clock and calendar' time that figures prominently in physical sciences and governs many practical affairs of everyday life, because 'past' and 'future,' necessarily defined with respect to a sentient observer, do not exist in the physical reality but are products of the human mind."[12] It is particularly noteworthy that the researchers mention that the concepts of *past* and *future* must be defined concerning an individual's observations and cannot function independently of them. They provide sequencing to the view of personal and physical events as they occur in the individual's frame of reference.

The researchers conducted an experiment in which participants in an fMRI scanning machine were asked to imagine the same event, taking a short walk in a familiar setting, in four distinct time frames. Three of these imaginary time frames included "yesterday" (PAST), "right now" (PRESENT), and "tomorrow" (FUTURE).[13] The final time frame was used to elicit episodic memory by asking the subjects to specifically recall a time when they performed the walk in the highly familiar setting (REMEMBER). The researchers also provided the subjects with a few other reference conditions for the experiment, including counting backward by threes from a three-digit number (COUNT) and resting with their eyes closed (REST). They were curious if imagining the short walk in the three imaginary time frames would elicit electrical activity in different brain regions corresponding to an imaginary flow of time, and they also hypothesized that the brain regions that might be involved in this activity would include the medial prefrontal cortex, hippocampus, and parietal cortex.

The left lateral parietal cortex near the intraparietal sulcus, left frontal cortex, right cerebellum, and thalamus activated during the PAST and FUTURE imaginary time frames. Sensorimotor functions, including the planning of eye movements, grasping, reaching, and protective head and forelimb movements, are among the functions of the intraparietal sulcus. The left frontal lobe is associated with executive decisions, including planning, decision making, attenuation, and judgment. The right cerebellum is responsible for maintaining a sense of balance and coordination on the right side of the body. The thalamus regulates different states of consciousness and relays sensorimotor signals. Interestingly, neurological activity during the REMEMBER event was like that of the FUTURE one, suggesting a common neurological pathway for mental time travel and the experienced event. The hippocampus, long considered to be the memory center of the brain, was surprisingly not active during the subjective time travel. The researchers hypothesized that this might have something to do with the conscious temporality of the experience.[14]

The main reason the parietal cortex activated during the PAST and FUTURE subjective time frames is because of the episodic memory retrieval functions of this brain region. Retrieval of old information and memories or even the subjective impression that memory is old causes heightened activity in the parietal cortex. The researchers hypothesize that this region may be the neurological center for chronesthesia, which in turn appears to be a robust neural correlate of subjective consciousness. According to them, "Conscious visual experiences reflect increased activity in dorsal frontal and parietal regions, and the parietal cortex was found to be part of a distributed network interacting with prefrontal regions in relation to awareness in sensory learning."[15]

Successfully interacting with others and with the surrounding environment requires the ability to visualize scenarios and situations, often calling upon memories to assist with planning out actions in both novel and familiar situations. Some call this "daydreaming," but this may be one of the essential features of active consciousness, allowing you to time travel through your memories to make the best decision or judgment at any given moment. Chronesthesia may be one of the key ingredients of what gives you an awareness of being in the present moment because of the ability to place it in between an imagined past and a distinct imagined future.

Subjective awareness of time is one of the primary aspects of active consciousness. A psychophysics researcher Marc Wittman explains, "The contents of consciousness are phenomenally present – now. This temporal aspect of phenomenal consciousness – its nowness – is inherent in all our experiences: I see, hear, feel, and think at the present moment. What is experienced is experienced now. Conscious experience is not static and unchanging; the passage of time is often described by a stream or a flow."[16] Accepting the idea that you can experience awareness of the present moment while simultaneously experiencing the continuous flow of time seems paradoxical. While in the present moment, it should be impossible to simultaneously perceive things like motion, environmental and chemical changes, or even the passage of time.

This apparent logical paradox hinges on the assumption that the present moment is a static and discrete unit devoid of any duration and utterly distinct from other points in the time surrounding it in the past and future. That is, time is akin to a dimensionless point on a continuous line, and occurs in complete isolation from other moments surrounding it. Due to the inherent contradiction in this line of logic, there must be another explanation as to how the present moment works. The alternative is to consider the present not as a singular moment, but as existing on some continuum of experience stretched across time.

Wittman explains a classical theory by German philosopher Edmund Husserl that provides a tripartite structure to the present consisting of the three elements of *retention, impression,* and *potention.* [17] *Retention* refers to the act of calling up information from memory to make sense of incoming sensory data, experiences, and social interactions. As data enters your frame of reference through your five senses, it leaves an *impression* on you that gets filtered and encoded by your brain. Depending on the nature and content of the incoming data, the experience may get encoded in your memory or activate specific brain regions, which may elicit certain thoughts, emotions, feelings, or sensations. Finally, the reaction to the impression is *potention* which is the anticipation of a future event that naturally leads again to retention, and the process repeats indefinitely so long as the individual is consciously aware of themselves and their surrounding environment. In this sense, the present represents a stretched out or exaggerated moment consisting of multiple sensorimotor and neurological processes. One stretched out moment seamlessly flows into the next – this is the *specious present*.

In trying to explain further how the brain processes time, Wittman alludes to three distinct and progressive temporal processing tools that help make sense out what he calls "the present moment" and "experienced presence." The first of these tools he refers to as the *functional moment*, a fundamental temporal unit of perception that is only a few milliseconds in length and whereby distinct individual events at this extremely brief duration appear to coincide. One of the main characteristics of temporality is the brain's ability to differentiate two stimuli to determine that they are separate entities in time. The detection threshold for non-simultaneity of events varies depending on the nature of the stimuli. Experimental data revealed that auditory stimuli have a much lower detection threshold than tactile or visual stimuli with non-simultaneity of different auditory stimuli being detected typically around 2-3 ms and the non-simultaneity of visual or tactile stimuli detected around 30-50 ms.

One important thing to keep in mind, however, is that being able to tell apart two stimuli does not automatically imply that you can place them in order and reliably discern which event happened first. Wittman explains that the interstimulus-interval (ISI) where an individual can determine the temporal ordering between two distinct events lies around 20-60 ms (depending on various parameters) and is remarkably consistent among the different senses. There is a minimum of a roughly 20 ms ISI for someone to be able to identify the correct temporal order between two distinct acoustic events, indicating that there is some minimum activation threshold for the perception of temporal order. Below this threshold, which is where functional moments occur, it is impossible to determine the temporal order of neural events subjectively.

According to Wittman, "Ultimately, the notion of time is based on the elementary temporal relation of two events, A and B, which can be judged in their temporal order, 'A occurs before B' or 'A occurs after B'."[18] Auditory tools including music and speech are only meaningful if the correct temporal order is present during a musical piece or dialogue. The brain must encode both the stimuli and the temporal order in the memory for you to be able to recall a conversation or recite a song from memory accurately. The preservation of temporal order thresholds must be present, or it will be impossible to accurately process something such as the contents of someone's speech.

If the temporal order threshold is abnormally heightened, then speech may sound garbled and would be very difficult to interpret. Individuals suffering from aphasia or other language-learning impediments reveal the importance of temporality in understanding speech. People who experience these disorders experience a higher-than-normal temporal order threshold. These individuals struggle to discriminate consonants in spoken language because of their increased temporal order threshold, so they may need others to speak more slowly and deliberately for them to be able to comprehend the content of the conversation accurately.

Wittman mentions that the current theory is that the anterior insular cortex, a brain region typically credited with the processing and expression of visceral emotions and feelings, creates a continuity of subjective conscious awareness by integrating temporal building blocks of neural events. Electrophysiological recordings have demonstrated evidence of "atoms of thought"[19] corresponding to 125 ms neural microstates which are critical periods in which various neural events are integrated into a functional moment. Many neural events may be processed together during a single functional moment, but because they fall beneath the minimum threshold for temporal ordering, they are experienced simultaneously as a single moment that has no *subjectively experienced* duration to it.

For example, during speech processing, various neural signals are transmitted throughout the left and right auditory cortices. Each of these brain regions specializes in interpreting, identifying, and constructing speech input through the ears with visual cues processed by the visual cortex simultaneously. All these processes are occurring in stages of duration less than the temporal ordering threshold, and when they integrate into a functional moment, there is no conscious awareness of each of the individual steps of neural integration that had to take place for you to understand and process necessary auditory input. To you, it seems as though all these complicated neural processes happened at the same time, even though they did not occur that way physiologically. You consciously cannot be aware of each of the individual steps involved in piecing together a single moment of language comprehension. There are very likely countless other neurological processes in the brain that operate this way in functional moments that you experience without any duration to them.

The nature of subjective consciousness is not characterized by discrete moments, but rather by the seemingly continuous flow of events. The second of Wittman's temporal processing tools is the *experienced moment,* which he defines as a "segmental processing mechanism [which] creates temporal windows that provide a logistical basis for conscious representation and the experience of *nowness.*"[20] Conscious perception and interpretation of events are entirely dependent on the proper placement of those events in a temporal context, especially with auditory perceptual processes such as the processing of language and music.

In a phrase of music or language, specific content (such as notes or words) only make sense in the greater context of the piece by referring to what came directly before it and what comes after. The anticipation of a familiar word or note revolves so tightly around the perception of an individual unit of music or language that they automatically get mentally clumped together. One example of this is the song "Ventura Highway" by America.[21] When they land on the word "Highway," the word "Ventura" is retentively present even though it is no longer there. Likewise, the word "Ventura" creates a protensive presence of the word "Highway" because of its anticipation at this point in the song. This example illustrates that the recent past and anticipated future endemically influence the perception of the present moment.

A metronome is a musical tool that plays a steady beat to assist musicians in helping then maintain a steady rhythm. When listening to a metronome at a moderate speed, the brain automatically inserts a subjective accent after every nth beat. For instance, if you were listening to a 1-2-3 metronome beat at 60 beats per minute (bpm), you would automatically accent the note occurring after each third beat. This accenting creates a subjective grouping to these beats, which objectively happen in isolation of one another. Wittman mentions that there are temporal boundaries to the perception of subjective grouping with an ISI between successive notes of 250 ms to 2 s. Consecutive metronome notes occurring too rapidly in succession (with an ISI below 250 ms) will synchronize and will be heard as one long note whereas people hear successive metronome notes, spaced too far apart in time (with an ISI over 2 s), in complete isolation from each other.

Wittman (2011) comments that further studies revealed that the "sweet spot" for the formation of a subjective imaginary rhythm with successive bursts of sound occurred between 250 ms and 2-3 s for the ISIs.[22] Within these temporal parameters, people naturally moved their body to the sounds. If the sounds occurred too far apart, people found the music too difficult to relate to and could not move their body rhythmically to it. Likewise, if the sounds occurred too close together, no discernable rhythm was heard, so the subjects were unable to feel or express a natural rhythm.

Researchers Yi-Huang Su and Elvira Salazar-Lopez studied the phenomenon of rhythm perception as it relates to meaningful dance movements. According to them, "Rhythm perception entails tracking the underlying periodicity, such as a beat or pulse, in a temporal pattern of (often auditory) events."[23] Cortical motor systems are engaged by perceptual auditory timing, suggesting an underlying neural connection between purely sensory auditory stimuli and physical movements. There are two modes of auditory timing that work in unison to provide a unified sense of rhythm. Interestingly, this system closely mirrors Wittman's *experienced moment*, providing a window in which meaningful synchronized motor movements occur. The *duration-based* mechanism is responsible for timing the ISI between beats and the *beat-based* mechanism times an interval based on a perceived beat.[24]

The researchers hypothesized that the visual perception of rhythmic human body movements might strengthen the perception of timing and elicit similar neurological responses to strictly auditory timing mechanisms. They specifically chose to focus on human dance movements as opposed to artificial moving stimuli because dancing typically occurs in timed sequences to musical rhythms. They also felt that observing dance movements would be more likely to activate internal motor representations because this activity involves movements of the whole body. Periodic limb and torso trajectories such as hip movements, rhythmic tapping, and leg movements might serve as cues for visual temporal perception.[25]

The researchers designed three different experiments to test their hypotheses. During the first experiment, they tested whether visual arm or leg movements with periodic trajectories were better timed than those without them and if these effects varied across different tempos. They modified the movements so that some of them were circular, non-circular, or a mixture of both. For data comparison, they used an auditory stimulus recognition test where one contains a beat, and another does not. In both cases, participants were required to memorize the sequence and then reproduce it from memory.

In the second experiment, they presented subjects with dance movements that contained both periodic and non-periodic rhythmic movements of both the arms and legs to see if the actions of one of the limbs dominated the subject's perception of the timing of the whole-body movements. The third experiment focused on presenting subjects with auditory interference sounds during moments of impact with the visual dance movements to determine if the beat advantage in visual timing was independent of the sound of the impact. The researchers wanted to know if beat-based timing neurologically transformed into auditory experiences.

The overall results of all three experiments strongly suggested that visual periodic limb movements, especially those of the legs, were the most critical factors in stimulating beat recognition and that this phenomenon occurred regardless of the frequency of auditory impact since the dancers did not clap or tap the floor with each beat.[26] Subjects visually inferred a whole-body rhythm from the limb movements, even in the presence of auditory interference. These results strongly suggest that participants subconsciously assume an overall rhythm to the visual piece based on the temporality of individual periodic limb movements. Furthermore, the visual rhythms adopted by the subjects had a structure that closely represented auditory rhythms with an underlying beat. Variations in tempo affected participants' abilities to extract a temporal rhythm out of the dance, and similar factors can most likely explain this to the limitations of the experienced moment. A tempo that is either too slow or too rapid prevented observers from being able to discern a rhythmic beat from the piece accurately.[27]

These experiments suggest the importance of the *experienced moment* in beat recognition and explore this phenomenon beyond the perceived beats formed by listening to a simple metronome, suggesting that meaningful rhythms occur in both visual and auditory contexts (Figure 3). You do not have to observe a dancer to discern rhythm – people walk and jog rhythmically every day. Even certain nervous tics, such as restlessly shaking your leg while sitting down can appear to have a beat to them. Rhythm provides a visual and auditory means of perceiving and experiencing subjective temporality.

Ambiguous figures are drawings (or other objects) that elicit roughly an equal probability of perceiving two or more different images despite its properties remaining constant. One of the most famous examples of an ambiguous figure is psychologist E.G. Boring's "Old/Young Woman" figure, which depicts different faces depending on how you look at it. One of the faces is that of an old lady and the other is an old woman (Figure 4). According to researchers Kornmeier & Bach, "In all of these cases, the brain states corresponding to the two interpretations become unstable and spontaneous perceptual reversals can occur although the external stimulus stays unchanged."[28]

The brain has evolved to disambiguate sensory information and to keep unstable brain states as brief as possible. Kornmeier and Bach reveal that multiple distinct regions of the brain work together to form a perceptual artifact. Following the perceptual identification of an ambiguous figure, the transient stability of the perception gradually fades slowly over seconds into maximum instability. EEG data on research subjects viewing ambiguous figures implicated the right hemisphere as being involved in the destabilization of these images. The period of transition from a state of maximum instability to a stable perceptual artifact is very brief, on the order of 40-60 ms.[29] The temporal period of image stability, where the figure is unambiguous, seems to correlate well with Wittman's *experienced moment*. A key component of meaningful conscious awareness is the stable perception of material objects and other visual and auditory artifacts. Problems with the disambiguation of perceptual stimuli may be present in specific mental health and neurological disorders.

The *experienced moment* forms the foundation of the experience of *nowness*, which is characterized by the conscious representation of the present.[30] These brief 2-3 second moments of temporal processing are the building blocks for meaningful conscious awareness. Wittman mentions a theory that temporally disorganized functional moments are integrated into the subjective present through a series of three stages, each occurring roughly at 30 ms, 300 ms, and 3 seconds.[31] The first stage corresponds to a reaction to a stimulus and formation of the *functional moment*. The second stage is the temporal integration of successive *functional moments* which is the lower threshold for the genesis of conscious experience and the third stage is the upper threshold for the *experienced moment* and serves as a transition point into another *experienced moment*.[32]

Individuals experience temporal intervals that are longer in duration than 3 seconds differently than the briefer *experienced moments*. The integration of these *experienced moments* into a continuous series forms the basis for Wittman's concept of *mental presence*, which "involves the experience of a perceiving and feeling agent ("my self") within a window of extended presence, a phenomenon that is based on working memory function."[33] The feeling of *nowness* is in the *experienced moment*, but *mental presence* unifies a collection of these moments over time into a unified conscious experience over a longer duration. Wittman uses the example of two people engaged in a conversation where the person most recently talking to the other one pauses for a few seconds to gather their thoughts. If the pause goes on for too long, say six seconds or more, then that silence may be experienced as being uncomfortably long. The focus of the conversation at that point is on the silence.

Memories

Working memory is a blanket term that refers to a multitude of structures and processes that are involved in the storage and recall of information on a relatively brief time scale.[34] Short-term memory, being limited in its capacity, consists of the ability to process and recall information in 10-15 second time intervals and usually involves no more than seven distinct items. Knowledge will be quickly lost if the working memory system does not effectively process it. There are techniques, including rehearsal, that can improve short-term memory by repeating data that might otherwise be lost so it can integrate into short-term memory for more extended periods. New content entering short-term information or other types of memory interferences can cause the displacement of existing knowledge so that old information is quickly lost. Neurologically, forgetting short-term information corresponds to a nerve impulse ceasing its transmission through a neural network associated with that information.

The prefrontal cortex is the brain region most heavily implicated in the effectiveness and function of working memory. The central executive part of this cortex contains two neural feedback loops, one of them linked to the visual cortex and the other connected to the auditory cortex. These loops are what are responsible for different types of short-term memory storage, one corresponding to visual sensory data and the other one primarily concerned with incoming language. Other brain regions implicated in working memory include the frontal lobes and parietal cortex. Information likely goes through some vetting process whereby it is either discarded or entered into long-term memory storage.

Memory consolidation is the process through which short-term memories become encoded into long-term memories. Techniques, including rehearsal and meaningful association, can assist with this consolidation process. The formation of long-term memories is physiologically associated with the creation or alteration of neural networks through biochemical modification of neural cells.[35] Repetition of data recall through these neural networks strengthens and reinforces the connections between them, making them more robust and formidable for the long haul. The hippocampus is presumed to be involved in the early consolidation process of long-term memories and responsible for some of the first neural network changes that occur. Unlike the fickler nature of short-term memory, long-term memories are not easily forgotten and can be recalled for decades after they first formed in the absence of any memory-altering disease or disorder.

Anterograde amnesia is a loss of the ability to form new long-term memories following a traumatic neurological event. Retrograde amnesia, on the other hand, is characterized by the loss of existing long-term memories. Damage to the hippocampus is often associated with the development of anterograde amnesia, as it makes the formation of new long-term memories impossible. Damage to both the thalamus and hippocampus are associated with retrograde amnesia.[36] Some older memories may still available, depending on their storage location in the brain, but the effects of both retrograde and anterograde amnesia on the afflicted individual's temporal awareness can be quite remarkable. People with anterograde amnesia live within a brief window of *mental presence* where they can perform everyday tasks and socialize with others, but after a few minutes, they will be completely unable to recall what just happened. People who have retrograde amnesia may have the same subjective temporal awareness as someone without it, but parts of their past will seem to have never occurred to them, not much different than what happens to people when they wake up from a night of sleeping and cannot remember their dreams.

Famed neuroscience researcher Oliver Sacks discussed one particularly fascinating case study of someone with both anterograde and retrograde amnesia. Jimmie G. was a 49-year-old patient of his who seemed completely lucid, logical, and capable of rational conversation when Sacks first met him in the seventies.[37] Sacks diagnosed him with Korsakoff syndrome, a disorder caused by a lack of thiamine in the brain. Despite his outward appearance, Jimmy believed that he was still living in the past. He was unable to form new memories due to his disorder and even did not recognize himself when shown a mirror – he thought it was a cruel joke. As Sacks explained, Jimmy was "isolated in a single moment of being.... he is a man without a past (or future), stuck in a constantly changing, meaningless moment."[38] Unfortunately, Jimmy could not experience normal emotions since anything he felt would be completely gone a few moments later, and he was also unable to live independently or adequately take care of himself.

Wittman would probably argue that Jimmy did not have a stable *mental presence* because of his inability to form new memories. There is a temporal horizon[39] defined by the filtering effects of short-term memory reconciling with ongoing mental processes and long-term memories. This horizon represents the limitations of short-term memory where information is either forgotten or stored in long-term memory before it expires. The tools of language enable people to articulate, identify, and narrate their memories so that they become part of their conscious, self-aware personal narrative, which defines a continuous *mental presence* that evolves and changes over time.[40] On a fundamental level, *mental presence* could be equated to working memory, as it integrates data from multiple brain regions simultaneously and then uses the tools of language and visualization to form the personal narrative that underlies daily decision-making and other internal thought processes.

Wittman believed that the fundamental temporal properties of working memory underlie the individual subjective perception of the time duration of experiences and are what he refers to as, "a gradual dissolving of representation with increasing duration."[41] In other words, the information contained in the short-term memory stores gradually fades away as new sensory data enters the brain. You can experience the world around you for just seconds at a time, and much of the information that comes in is discarded and forgotten, but significant parts of the limited information that are attenuated to become a part of your ongoing personal narrative. The passage of time is equal to the adoption of recently formed memories, and both working memory and long-term memory act together to establish a clear sense of self living in a continuous series of moments. Based on his research, Wittman concluded that the present moment is not experienced as a discrete point in time, as the brain cannot even perceive such a thing. Instead, *functional moments* of a few tens of milliseconds fuse to form an *experienced moment*, which is the locus of the present, experienced a few seconds at a time.[42] These moments are integrated to form *mental presence*, in which you can use your knowledge of the past and what is currently happening to best plan for the future.

It is common for people to imagine their lives speeding up as they get older and for the past to seem as though it happened much more quickly than it did. This phenomenon occurs because memory is selective, and significant chunks of time are forgotten about or not called up to mind due to personal irrelevance. It is equally common for people to plan for an imagined time in the future by making sacrifices and other concessions in the present. An example of this would be cutting daily calories in your diet to lose a certain amount of weight by a specific time in the future. Similarly, to obtain a large sum of money in the future, you might cut your spending habits down now and live with less money temporarily so that someday you can reap the financial benefit of your sacrifices.

The subjective past for an individual is their collection of long-term memories, and to some extent, the subjective future is an *experienced moment* constructed from imagining potential outcomes based on past experiences. The subjective future, therefore, can get encoded into long-term memory through a combination of verbal thoughts and visual mental imagery that occurs in the present. Think about them long enough (i.e., rehearse these thoughts) and they can become a part of the past. In other words, it is impossible to dream about the future without using the past as a distinct frame of reference. In this way, the past becomes the future, as old information synthesizes into possible moments, and the future becomes the past where thoughts about these moments store in long-term memory.

The Effects of Drugs on Time Perception

Due to their numerous effects on the brain, drugs can significantly impact an individual's subjective time perception. A team of researchers studied the impacts of morphine-derived drugs on perceptions of time, including time reproduction, time estimation, and time discrimination. For this study, they recruited 30 drug-addicted and 30 non-addict individuals. Those individuals selected for the drug-addicted group were evaluated by an expert from the Drop-In Center of Kerman University of Medical Sciences in Iran and deemed to be drug-addicted subjects with no desire to quit and who were not currently undergoing treatment. Each of these subjects was currently exclusively consuming morphine-derived drugs including opium, opium sap, and heroin either through direct consumption, injection, or smoking. The participants, using only a laptop and a mouse, were instructed to make subjective judgments about time without using any other external or internal tools, including finger tapping, clicking, or leg motions.

In the time reproduction test, participants were shown a virtual lamp on the computer monitor that would remain on for intervals between 2-24 seconds. Participants were distracted by a series of emotional questions that appeared beside the lamp so they could not count out loud. Following its disappearance, the subjects were instructed to press down and hold a computer key corresponding to the estimated length of time that the lamp initially appeared on the screen. This process repeated a total of seven times for each participant. The researchers used the term "underestimation" to refer to time intervals that were deemed shorter than they were by the subjects and they used the word "overestimation" to refer to time intervals considered longer than they were.

During the second test (delay estimation test), subjects were shown a red dot on a computer screen. The dot rotated in a circular pattern until two-thirds of the way through when it disappeared behind a dark blue cover. The participants had to press a key to determine when the red dot would reappear again. The researchers calculated the amount of time overestimation or underestimation that occurred over ten trials per participant.

The third test was the time discrimination test where participants were asked to form judgments about how much longer one stimulus remained on a screen compared to another one. Researchers presented a collection of typical images and images related to drug abuse to the subjects, and the difference in duration was in milliseconds. In the first part of this test, an image from nature was placed on the screen for less than three seconds and then after a picture of drug abuse or related tools to overcoming it appeared. They underwent 13 trials of this activity, and following each pair of images, they had to press one of three buttons to determine which of the pictures had a longer duration (or if they were equal). During the second part of this test, typical images occurred in pairs with a one-second time delay between them. The first image had a fixed on-screen duration of 2380 ms, and the second one has a fixed on-screen duration of 2000 ms. The minimum threshold for visual image discrimination at this level was determined to be close to 380 ms. In the third part of the test, images containing drugs or drug-related content were posted sequentially under the same parameters as the second part of the test.

The results overwhelmingly showed that the drug-addicted participants committed overestimation errors on the time reproduction test and the delay estimation test. The only exception to this finding occurred during the time discrimination test, where there was no discernible difference in performance between the drug-addicted and non-drug addicted individuals. Interestingly, they found that non-drug addicted individuals consistently underestimated the time duration of the drug-related images.[44]

The researchers hypothesized that the reasons for the consistent overestimation of time by the drug-addicted participants in the first two trials have to do with the cumulative effects of drug use on slowing down reaction times.[45] Morphine-derived drugs are known to have adverse effects on cognitive performance and data processing of visuospatial tasks, so it does not come as a surprise that slower neurological reaction times would lead to overestimation errors.

The most likely cause of the underestimation in time duration of the non-drug addicted individuals to the drug-related images was that these images elicited negative connotations, and this caused the non-drug addicted individuals to react emotionally by psychologically shortening the perceived time duration of these images.

The latter results superficially contradict previous research on time perception involving negatively-connoted stimuli.[46] The researchers cite, as an example, studies involving time perception of faces where individuals overestimate the amount of time a negative face (i.e., angry, sad, depressed) appears on the screen compared to a positive one (i.e., joyful, loving, happy). This same phenomenon also occurred in studies involving negative auditory stimuli. Their explanation for this difference has to do with both types of stimuli engaging a fear-based survival instinct causing periods to appear longer than they are and thus giving endangered individuals proper focus to react and evade imminent danger quickly.

Another team of researchers studied the effects of micro-doses of LSD, a potent hallucinogen, on time perception.[47] One of their inspirations for this research was a previous study conducted on the impacts of another drug, psilocybin, on the subjective perception of time.[48] The results of that study showed that psilocybin caused individuals to underestimate the amount of time that passed, making time seem to move more quickly than it did for supra-second intervals of 4-5 seconds. Since psilocybin is a serotonin agonist, the researchers concluded that serotonin production and dopamine inhibition are two critical factors in human time perception. Serotonin is a neurotransmitter that is thought to regulate mood, social behavior, gastrointestinal function, sleep, memory, and other autonomic functions. Dopamine is associated with feelings of reward and pleasure, typically in response to unexpected events. Yanakieva et al. (2018) noted that while there were many subjective reports of LSD altering perceptions of time, very little rigorous research had been carried out on its effects or its neurological correlates.

To investigate the effects of micro-doses of LSD on temporal perception, the researchers set up a study involving a randomized, double-blind, placebo-controlled experimental design. They recruited 48 older consenting English-speaking adults between the ages of 55 and 75, and each of them received either 5, 10, or 20 micrograms of LSD or a placebo. About three hours after receiving the dosages, the participants were asked to complete a series of temporal reproduction tasks spanning both sub-second and supra-second intervals (800 – 4000 ms). Their first task was to estimate the time duration of a blue circle on a computer monitor and hold down the space bar afterward to reproduce the time interval of the circle. This task repeated for time intervals of varying duration spanning the range of 800 – 4000 ms.

Directly following the blue circle experiment, participants were asked to respond to a battery of 22 questions concerning the subjective effects of LSD on their mental state. These included questions about whether they felt high, if their immediate surroundings appeared different, or if they were experiencing unusual thoughts. Participants used a visual analogue scale (VAS)[49] to respond to these questions. The VAS is a psychometric scale used for situations where an objective data measurement is not possible, and experimental subjects select subjective ratings on a continuum. In this study, participants were asked to answer questions using a scale from 0-100.

The results of the study showed that participants overestimated supra-second time intervals, specifically those between 2000-4000 ms, and these effects notably occurred at a dosage of 10 micrograms of LSD. Furthermore, this subjective temporal expansion occurred independently of extraneous psychedelic effects.[50] Most surprisingly, these results were mostly inconsistent with earlier research[51] which examined the effects of larger doses of LSD on individuals. In that study, subjective underestimation of time intervals occurred, although the authors note that this was likely due to the psychedelic effects of larger doses producing significant changes to conscious states of mind and diverting attention away from the prescribed experimental tasks.

The researchers hypothesized that micro-doses of LSD *enhanced* the individual's attenuation abilities, increasing their ability to focus on the task and thus causing the over-estimation of time duration. Subjective reports from LSD micro-dose users partially confirm this finding, as they reported increased ability to focus attention for the first day with a diminishing effect over a short period.[52] Due to LSD's likely role as a dopamine agonist, individuals under the influence may experience positive attenuation effects initially, but those effects would likely wear off with repeated dosages as their drug tolerance builds and they require higher dosages to achieve a similar effect as before.

The Effects of Mental Illness on Time Perception

Cristián Oyanadel and Gualberto Buela-Casal examined the effects of severe mental illness (SMI) on subjective time estimation (TE).[53] For purposes of this study, SMI included such mental disorders as major depression, bipolar disorder, schizophrenia, and other personality disorders, some of which contain psychosis as a feature of them. According to the authors, TE is an individual's estimation of the duration of a time interval. TE can occur from the present perspective (in the case of an ongoing task or event), or from a past perspective involving retrospective time estimation.

The researchers mention that one study showed that individuals with depressive symptoms in bipolar and schizophrenic psychosis tend to underestimate time compared to controls,[54] while another study implicated depression as a factor in overestimating short time intervals and mania as a factor in minimizing long ones,[55] and yet another study reported a direct relationship between the severity of depressive symptoms and underestimation of time intervals.[56] The natural aging process very likely slows the internal clock down and can also be a contributing factor in depressive patients' underestimation of time.[57]

Oyanadel & Buela-Casal defined five time-perspective (TP) dimensions, as first proposed by Zimbardo & Boyd.[58] The first of these is the *past negative* (PN), which is defined by a negative perception of the past based on emotionally or physically painful experiences. The *past positive* (PP) is the positive perception of past events based on fond or joyous memories. The *present fatalistic* (PF) is a pessimistic view on life and a generally negative attitude. The *present hedonistic* (PH) is a joy and pleasure-seeking position. Finally, the *future* (F) is an orientation toward success and future planning. Individuals with high PP, moderate F and PH, and low PF and PN were considered to have a balanced time perspective (BTP) while others with the opposite configuration had a negative time profile (NTP). Individuals who did not classify in either the BTP or NTP groups formed a third subgroup known as RISK – named for the possibility of them eventually ending up in one of the other groups.

Time perspective therapy (TPT)[59] was developed to help individuals with post-traumatic stress disorder (PTSD) to encourage them to think differently about their perspective on time. One of the difficulties with PTSD is a tendency to have an NTP and be fearful or hopeless about potential future events, fearing that past stressors may repeat themselves or that the future is hopeless and bleak. The features of an NTP include suicidal ideation, so effective therapy measures are essential. TPT takes a group therapy approach to shift elements of an NTP or RISK to characteristics of a BTP in patients with PTSD. By conquering PF and PN ideations about time, therapists were able to reduce suicidal thoughts in PTSD patients, and this type of therapy has also shown potential for assisting individuals coping with major depressive disorder.

Oyanadel & Buela-Casal designed an experiment to examine TP and TE among individuals with SMI and compare them to individuals of sound mental health. Another goal was to explore how participants' TP profile influenced their overall quality of life in people with SMI. Their initial hypotheses were that there would be a significant difference in TP and TE among the two groups and that individuals with SMI would orient more toward an NTP than those of sound mental health. They also conjectured that people with a BTP would experience a higher overall quality of life and that people from the clinical sample with an NTP would be more likely to underestimate time intervals in a TE test.

One hundred sixty-seven clinical inpatients ranging from ages 19-70 from the Hospital de la Serena in Chile participated in this study. The afflicted individuals had either major depression, bipolar disorder, schizophrenia, or another "cluster B" personality disorder following the DSM-IV-TR criteria. All clinical participants were undergoing treatment, including the use of certain mood-stabilizing or antipsychotic medication. A sample of 167 participants of sound mental health also participated in this study and was broken down into four groups to match up with the various SMI categories from the clinical inpatient groups.

The instruments used in this study included a Zimbardo Time Perspective Inventory (ZTPI), a survey of health indicators, the Stanford Sleepiness Scale (SSS), a health questionnaire, assessment with the Beck Hopelessness Scale (BHS), and a Time Estimation (TE) study. The ZTPI is a 56-item question inventory with a range of 1-5 for each question that assesses participants on a variety of the five time-perspective dimensions of PP, PN, PH, PF, and F. The Health indicator survey assesses individual health factors including BMI, frequency of alcohol and cigarette use, frequency of drug use, amount of monthly exercise, and frequency of physical illnesses.

The SSS was used to evaluate participants' subjective state of sleepiness using a self-evaluation tool with responses that ranged from "very active and alert" to "almost asleep." The Health Questionnaire had eight measurements of physical and mental health, including a detailed summary measurement of each which together form a health-related quality of life (HRQL) measurement. The BHS is used to assess present and future negative thoughts as well as an individual's expectations of their coping capacity for future events. Through 20 questions, an overall "hopelessness" score was computed based on the factors of feelings toward the future, motivational factors concerning a lack of motivation, and a cognitive factor about future expectations.

Finally, participants took a TE test using a highly accurate chronometer to assess retrospective (past) time estimations as well as a prospective (future) measure of production at 10 second (E10) and 60 seconds (E60) empty time intervals. For the retrospective TE, participants were asked to use the chronometer to estimate an event that had already occurred, and for the prospective TE, they were asked to use the device to estimate a time interval of a certain specified length.

In terms of comparing the clinical group with the control group, the experimental results showed an elevation of PN and PF scores in the clinical group compared to the control group, which illustrate the importance of understanding how a negative attitude about the past and a pessimistic outlook about the future play a significant role in SMI. The participants with schizophrenia only significantly differed from the control group on the PF score, most likely due to the clinical symptoms of this disorder causing emotional and perceptual issues with the present, including paranoia and delusional thoughts.

There was no significant difference between the two groups on the F scores, which might be due to traditional therapy methods helping patients with SMI to better plan for the future. The authors acknowledge that this hypothesis is currently unsupported, but that therapeutic measures involving future planning are useful because they significantly reduce suicide risk and usually increase personal health factors. The clinical group also underestimated time intervals on the TE test, with the most notable differences found in the E60 intervals. The authors claim that this result is consistent with other study results that demonstrate "the acceleration of the biological clock" in individuals with SMI.[60]

As expected, the BTP individuals had better measurements of well-being and health, while the NTP individuals had different measurements. Although researchers predicted more significant underestimation of time for the NTP group, it turned out that the RISK group was the one who experienced it. The researchers inferred that this surprising result might have occurred because people in the RISK group were anxious and excitable which may have sped up their internal clock while those in the NTP group may have experienced a sense of hopelessness that slowed down their internal clock. The BTP group overestimated time, which could be explained by their mindfulness of the present moment and their conscious awareness of time passing. The significant differences in TE occurred in E10, where time estimation processes are more heavily dependent on attentional factors.

The overall results of the study suggest that an unhealthy time perspective can be a major factor in SMI and the goal of any successful therapeutic approach should include cognitive and emotional strategies that help shift an NTP or RISK into a BTP. The hopelessness of the NTP, which is closely associated with suicidal risk factors, should be addressed in therapy along with other factors that make time feel like it is passing by slowly and without purpose. By helping these individuals build a more healthy time-perspective and providing them with convincing reasons for having hope, ideally in both individual and group therapy, they can lead more productive and fulfilling lives.[61]

Unconscious Time

Another area where psychological time distortions regularly occur is at night during both dreaming and non-dreaming states of unconsciousness. Neuroscience researcher Perrine M. Ruby associated the phenomenon of time alteration in dream states to decreased activity in the dorsolateral prefrontal cortex,[62] a brain region that is extensively involved in working memory processes and executive cognitive control. The individual sense of time perception in dreams can vary significantly, with some people experiencing dreams that seemed longer than they were or others experiencing dreams that felt shorter than they were.

Unfortunately, there is no reliable method that can be used to measure time estimation processes in REM dream states, as dreaming is inherently subjective and there may be memory lapses and other confounding factors that prevent accurate measurements. In dreamless non-REM sleep states, people do not experience time passage at all. They wake up feeling as though hours passed in the span of a quick moment with no explanation for the lost time.

The relationship between consciousness and time perception is so strong that you could potentially argue they are the same. Similar to the concepts of *functional* and *experienced moments* and *mental presence* is the idea of "time slices" posed by researchers Herzog et al. of the Brain-Mind Institute in Lausanne, Switzerland.[63] Time slices provide a discrete bridge between unconscious and conscious states of mind. Instead of arguing for a continuous stream of consciousness, the researchers present a theory that consciousness instead consists of discrete sets of quasi-continuous filtered unconscious moments that are presented simultaneously as conscious experiences.[64]

One of the counterexamples to a continuous model of consciousness is the "color phi phenomenon"[65] in which a green-colored disk appears on the lower-left quadrant of a computer screen followed immediately by its disappearance and re-emergence of a red dot in the upper right-hand quadrant of the same screen. To the observer, it appears as if the dot moves between the two positions and changes color somewhere in the middle of the screen, which is impossible; however, as there are only two distinct dots so the motion of them is entirely illusory. There is no way to experience the color change before seeing the second disk, so the idea that it changes before the second disk has reached its final position is logically impossible. Therefore, the conscious percept of the moving dots must have been formed retrospectively, meaning that the unconscious mind must have processed the dots and applied imaginary continuous motion to them before you even consciously noticed them. The authors mention that there are also cases where people are presented visual stimuli in a particular order, and they perceive it in a different order, suggesting an unconscious ordering to the events, making their conscious temporal ordering appear utterly different than the objective temporal ordering of them.[66]

Feature fusion[67] describes what happens when two individual events occur in such rapid succession that they appear as a single event. For instance, if a green dot is flashed on a screen and then very rapidly followed by the flashing of a red dot, the dot will be perceived as a single yellow dot. A transcranial magnetic stimulation (TMS) study[68] revealed that objects presented below the 400 ms time threshold will be unconsciously perceived and integrated into a single conscious percept. This phenomenon is not exclusive to visual stimuli but also occurs with other types of sensory data, including acoustical and tactile stimuli.

In another illustration of feature fusion, Herzog et al. presented subjects with one Vernier (pair of vertical bars spatially offset to the left or right) followed by another one within a total time interval of 60 ms. The observers, however, were only able to view the pair of Verniers as a single fused entity. The TMS modulated the unconscious integration of the two Verniers, which occurred for 400 ms before the conscious recognition of the objects. Even though it only took 60 ms to present the pair of stimuli to the observers, it took nearly seven times as long for them to observe it as a fused entity. They were consciously unaware of the integration process, which caused the illusion of object fusion. The conscious perception did not match up with the original presentation. TMS applied to the occipital cortex influenced the perception of the dominance of one of the Verniers over the other one so that the perceived fused object appeared more like one of them than the other.[69]

Another example of feature fusion is the *cutaneous rabbit effect*,[70] whereby there is rapid and successive stimulation of the wrist and elbow, which creates the illusion of points of touch along the entire arm even though only there were only two unique locations of stimulation. This example illustrates how the unconscious mind evaluates tactile stimuli in series below the conscious threshold and then delivers an interpretation of them, as a set of discrete percepts, to the conscious mind. Once again, conscious perception does not match up with reality.

An example of feature fusion in auditory language processing occurs during the presentation of homonyms in spoken sentences. Consider the two sentences "the band was repaired at the jewelry store" and "the band booked their show for the weekend." The meaning of the noun "band" cannot be known in the preceding sentences until the verb "repaired" or "booked" is heard. At that point, the word "band" is interpreted either as a wedding ring or a collection of musical artists. Conscious interpretation of the nouns delays until the entire sentence is complete, which appears to happen asynchronously once the sentence has formed into a conscious percept.

The meaning of the words is unconsciously processed together before you consciously understand the sentence.

These examples demonstrate that conscious perception is not a continuous process, but it does not explain the nature of unconscious integration and the subsequent formation of conscious percepts. To clarify how visual conscious perceptions arise from an unconscious mind, Herzog et al. proposed a two-stage visual processing model.[71] In this model, the unconscious analysis takes place for the elements of a visual scene. According to them, this process can last for up to 400 ms and includes a detailed breakdown of stimulus features, including object color, orientation, shape, and depth. Within this period, temporal characteristics are processed, such as object duration and object simultaneity. Color detectors assign a specific color to the object, shape detectors assign a shape, and the duration detector assigns a period to the duration. Herzog et al. explained that "Upon completion of the analysis, the features are integrated into a coherent, conscious percept. All features become conscious simultaneously, and the percept contains all the feature information derived from the various detectors."[72]

The process of temporal resolution in sensory systems is multifactorial in scope and depends on a progressive series of sensory and neurological functions. First among these is the conversion of sensory input into a neuronal signal. For instance, light energy causes a series of electrochemical reactions in the eye, which then, in turn, activate specific neural networks in the brain via the optic nerve. These signals are then processed to detect and differentiate changes within the sensory data. A similar process occurs for other types of sensory data, including auditory and tactile stimuli.

Herzog et al. described three distinct types of temporal resolution, each of which is necessary for people to function effectively.[73] The first type, *same system/same channel,* involves the ability to distinguish the repetition of a periodic signal and accompany the perception of flickering lights or the sound of vibrations. The time thresholds for successful detection of temporal separation of stimuli vary depending on the type of sensation involved, but generally speaking the two stimuli need to be 1-3 ms apart for auditory clicks,

10 ms apart for two tactile taps, and 25 ms apart for two visual flashes. Visual or auditory flickering is a sensation where a series of sensory stimuli appear in such quick succession that they almost appear as a singular pulsating entity. The impression of visual or auditory flickering ceases with approximately 16 ms ISI in between stimulus presentation.

The second type of temporal resolution is *same system/different channels*, which involves being able to distinguish among two or more sensory stimuli coming from different directions or locations in a sensory field. For instance, this ability underlies you being able to identify successive loud beeps occurring near either your left or right ear or a series of bright flashes occurring across different locations in your visual field. Being able to discriminate the order of the different stimuli, called "temporal order judgment," (TOJ) typically requires a 20-50 ms ISI between stimuli.[74] Researchers David Alais and John Cass found evidence that visual order temporal order judgments are consistently less precise than auditory ones,[75] likely because the auditory timing mechanisms are located early in the auditory sensory pathways in contrast to the visual timing mechanisms which operate at a later stage in optical data processing than their acoustic counterparts.

The third type of temporal resolution mentioned by Herzog et al. is *different systems/different channels*, which is the ability to distinguish between two or more sensory inputs occurring across two or more distinct neural networks. For instance, you should be able to tell the difference between a loud beep heard by your ears (auditory sensory system) and a raindrop hitting your nose, which would be felt by the tactile sensory system. The TOJ for this kind of temporal resolution is similar to the *same systems/different channels* one (20-50 ms), but this similarity does not necessarily imply that there is some supra-sensory timing mechanism at work behind the scenes. If anything, there is still much uncertainty about how TOJ works neurologically, and there appear to be many different neurological timing mechanisms located at various points throughout different neural pathways.

Unconscious feature integration is the process by which object and stimulus properties, including their temporal resolution, are encoded in the brain and then presented to you consciously all at once in a single moment, a conscious percept.[76] This percept can be consciously presented to you sometimes several hundred milliseconds after the initial stimulus presentation to your unconscious mind. What is not certain is if the conscious percept continues until the next one is presented (even if they are only milliseconds apart) or if there is an undetectably brief moment of unconsciousness before the next percept appears. If the latter is true, consciousness would still appear subjectively as a continuous phenomenon because unconsciousness is inherently undetectable, especially if it is only occurring for just a few milliseconds (or less) in between the discrete moments of conscious perception.

To further illustrate the concept of discrete-time percepts, Herzog et al. drew a comparison to a digital watch. Compare the time display of the watch to conscious awareness and the inner workings of the watch to the unconscious mind. On the outside of the watch (the only part directly visible to you), it displays the time, say 1:07 PM. Inside the watch is a vibrating piece of quartz that matches up oscillations of the crystal with time. Although the quartz crystal is rhythmically oscillating continuously, the outside display of 1:07 PM remains constant until 60 oscillations have occurred, at which point it switches over to 1:08 PM. You can think of the passage of time on the face of a digital watch as being like the discrete conscious percepts presented to you by your unconscious mind which is like the oscillatory quartz and associated gear mechanisms behind the changing of the outward display.

The comparison of human consciousness to a digital watch display is only meant to serve as an oversimplified model of how unconscious processing begets conscious moments, but it does not suggest that these conscious moments occur rhythmically with constant duration. Herzog et al. emphasize that their two-stage model does not work like a camera, with a series of discrete snapshots making up your conscious perception of your environment. Instead, they argue that unconscious processing operates quasi-continuously in the background until some of it reaches an "attractor state"[77] which develops into a conscious percept. These attractor states represent events that occurred during the unconscious processing phase and are now being described a short time consciously after they occurred. In this way, the conscious present is a representation of the unconscious past. Sensory data that is deemed irrelevant remains in the unconscious mind and is not presented to the conscious mind.

The methods by which the brain decides which sensory data is relevant for conscious processing are not well understood, but hints about how this process occurs can be found in the study of ambiguous figures. If someone is provided with a specific context, verbal clues, or their attention otherwise shifts, they can see an ambiguous figure change instantaneously right before their eyes into something else entirely. Herzog et al. would refer to this as a change in attractor states wherein unconscious processing alter the state of temporal perception. When viewing an ambiguous figure, it is impossible to see two different perspectives simultaneously. In the case of the ambiguous figure, the unconscious brain pieces together an interpretation and then the unconscious data converges to a different attractor state than the one before it.

Unconscious feature integration into discrete time-percepts makes a lot of sense when you think about how complicated sensory processing is, especially when it comes to vision. Herzog et al. used the example of watching a football game to illustrate why this theory of consciousness is the most logical explanation for what occurs during moments of conscious awareness. Twenty-two players are moving around during any moment of play. Each of these individual players has a unique motion trajectory across time and space, which requires a tremendous amount of mental processing to compute. To further complicate matters, some of the 2-D projections of these paths cross each other in your retina, creating significant ambiguity as to how the corresponding 3-D interpretation of the football scene should appear. The brain uses complex unconscious processing of the visual data to put together the most likely scenario, which then becomes your conscious perception of the event. It would be confusing if you were consciously aware of all the different possible 3-D interpretations.

The researchers caution that the length of the unconscious scenario computations depends directly on the complexity of the incoming sensory data, so not all calculations will take a long time to execute into conscious awareness. For instance, automatic "fight or flight" reflexes or motor responses can occur milliseconds before the formation of a conscious percept, indicating that specific physical or psychological reactions can be provoked exclusively through unconscious processing.[78] The ability for your body to react instinctively in such a way is a remarkable feat of evolution and an excellent survival skill. In these situations, the brain makes complicated calculations in mere milliseconds, so the moment of reaction occurs just slightly before you are aware of your behavior. It is impossible to be mindful of the passage of time when you are unconscious of it. With conscious time slices presented to you at brief, irregular time intervals, you can only be aware of what your brain determines is relevant and accurate at any moment. Once the time slice vanishes, there is a hidden period of unconsciousness until the next conscious percept appears, and the process repeats indefinitely for the rest of your life.

The Role of the Imagination in Time Perception

The ability to produce, process, and manipulate mental imagery is an essential part of reflecting on past experiences or planning for the future. Balancing out the contents of your imagination within the complicated framework of conscious perception can help you with effective decision making, task planning, and engaging in creative endeavors. Mental imagery is quite capable of simulating the physical world, in that scientists can analyze and decode activity in the visual cortex to accurately discern the contents of visual perception, visual imagery, and dreams.

Researchers Alexander Schlegel et al. used a modern medical imaging study to try to determine the neurological processes and networks at work behind the generation and processing of complex mental imagery.[79] They hypothesized that multiple brain regions, including the frontal, parietal, and occipital cortices, work together to form a mental workspace for visual representation. In their study, they asked a group of 15 participants to engage in tasks that involved the maintenance or manipulation of visual imagery as an fMRI machine collected data about areas of heightened neural activity. They developed a set of 100 abstract geometric parts which could combine in different ways to form two-dimensional figures consisting of four pieces each. Participants were instructed to either remember a pre-constructed figure or set of parts, mentally put together a composite figure from four parts, or to mentally deconstruct a pre-assembled figure into its four components. After seeing the images, they were given a task with a six-second delay in which they were asked to perform a specific mental operation on the composite figure or parts of the figure. Immediately following the time delay, participants had two and a half seconds to select the correct response to the task out of a selection of four distinct possibilities, three of which were incorrect choices.

For the fMRI data analysis, the researchers utilized an "entire-brain univariate general linear model" to analyze regions in which brain activity differed between the mental manipulation (construction/deconstruction tasks) or mental maintenance (maintain parts/maintain figure) tasks. Eleven areas of interest were identified by the fMRI data analysis, with only two areas more heavily implicated in the mental manipulation tasks than in the mental maintenance ones - the medial frontal cortex and the medial temporal lobe. A subset of these 11 regions is responsible for providing the temporal information required to perform these tasks while connections among different areas are responsible for carrying out the tasks. Specifically, connections occurred between the precuneus and posterior temporal cortex with certain frontal and parietal regions during manipulation tasks and stronger relationships within the medial temporal lobe and other areas were observed during the maintenance tasks.[80] According to Schlegel et al., their data shows that "a distributed set of regions mediates mental operations but also that these regions communicate in an information-processing network. The network switches between two connectivity profiles depending on whether mental representations are maintained or manipulated."[81]

While the results of this study focus on how visual imagery manipulation and maintenance occur across two distinct distributed neural networks, it is plausible that the formation of conscious percepts may also involve these networks during their emergence. For instance, a construction worker putting together the framing for a house may need to stare at the wooden beams and visualize where they are going to move to next. This mental diagramming, or planning, would undoubtedly involve many of the same neural networks elicited during the study. In mentally visualizing what he needs to do next, the construction worker's brain analyzes the visual input and synchronizes it with long-term memory stores to piece together a visual narrative of what he needs to do to proceed with his project. The plans are quickly brought to his conscious awareness so that he can move to the next step and execute the construction process. It is very likely that the processing, storage, and manipulation of other sensory data, including auditory and tactile data, involves the activation of similar dual-channel distributed neural networks.

Aphantasia[82] is characterized by an inability to visualize mental images. Researchers Adam Zeman, Dewar, and Della Salla, mention that two known types of visual imagery impairment sometimes occur as the result of visual memory disorders and "imagery generation deficits"[83] that selectively disable imagery. Following their case study of a 65-year-old man reporting to have aphantasia following a coronary angioplasty procedure, the researchers received written correspondence from over twenty individuals affected by aphantasia. These people claimed that they have never been able to imagine visual imagery and in response to these claims, the researchers designed a questionnaire to explore the subjective nature of this characteristic further.

Subjects generally reported noticing the signs of aphantasia in their teens or twenties, when they became aware that their peers possessed an ability to use their minds to experience internal mental imagery voluntarily, but they did not. Some of the respondents claimed to experience episodes of involuntary mental imagery, most often during dreams but also during wakefulness. Approximately 70% of respondents also reported difficulties with autobiographical memory. Some of these individuals also claimed that they had compensatory abilities in other areas including language arts, mathematics, or other logical subjects, but mentioned that these abilities were a result of memory, previous knowledge, or other non-visual mechanisms.

According to journalist James Gallagher, some individuals are quite distressed by their aphantasia.[84] He documented the story of Neil Kenmuir from Lancaster, UK. Neil claimed to have suffered from aphantasia his entire life and recalled when his step-father told him to try counting sheep when he was having a bout of insomnia, and he was unable to do so because he could not picture the animals in his imagination. Although he does not feel disabled by this condition, and he feels that he otherwise lives a healthy life, he is frustrated by his inability to visualize mental imagery. Whenever he tries to picture his fiancée in his head, he is unable to do so and is only able to remember certain features about her. Another individual Gallagher interviewed also felt flustered and isolated by his inability to imagine things. He complained about his friends not being able to sympathize with him and telling him that he was weird. It made him feel depressed and like there was something seriously wrong with him.

Zeman et al. estimate that aphantasia might afflict up to 2% of the world population and that his research has shown that this charateristic can be congenital or come as the result of a traumatic physical or emotional event, and it also appears to operate on a spectrum with some people only experiencing minor impairments to their visual imagery.[85] Some symptoms include being terrible with directions and navigation, and other people experiencing more severe deficits, including not being able to recognize faces (prosopagnosia) easily. There also appears to be no direct link between aphantasia and creativity, as some of the brightest minds at Pixar (an animation studio) report to have these type of issues with reduced visual imagery despite their prolific artistic talent. Blake Ross, the co-founder of Mozilla, wrote the following on his Facebook page: "I have never visualized anything in my entire life. I can't 'see' my father's face or a bouncing blue ball, my childhood bedroom or the run I went on ten minutes ago. I thought 'counting sheep' was a metaphor. I'm 30 years old, and I never knew a human could do any of this. And it is blowing my goddamned mind."

On the other end of the spectrum is *hyperphantasia*,[87] a characteristic marked by having an overactive and extremely vivid imagination. Gallagher interviewed a popular children's fairytale book illustrator, Lauren Beard, who experiences vivid mental images when reading from the text. She claims detailed, dramatic, and colorful images instantly populate her mind as she reads from stories, allowing her to draw upon her active imagination and create compelling visual scenes for her books.[88] While it might seem like more of a talent than a curse, hyperphantasia can become overwhelming with the constant influx of vivid and detailed mental imagery. There is no way to turn it off and its effects are persistent and impossible to ignore. Nonetheless, Lauren tries her best to use her heightened visual imagery to produce beautiful and inspirational artwork.

Researchers Stefania de Vito and Paolo Bartolomeo acknowledge that while some instances of aphantasia might be due to underlying neurological or genetic causes, a significant portion of these might be partially or entirely due to psychogenic factors[89] – especially those cases reported as having a sudden onset. To illustrate their point, the researchers discuss the case of Monsieur X,[90] who presented his symptoms as an immediate and complete loss of ability to construct mental images. Based solely on his symptomology, he received a diagnosis of a "hypothetical circumscribed cerebral lesion"[91] In the late 19th century, the medical equipment, knowledge, and technology necessary to properly recognize aphantasia was absent, so a diagnosis was made in the absence of a thorough medical examination, and no post-mortem examination occurred either. This hypothesis was not unreasonable, considering the current knowledge about distributed neural networks, including those located in the frontal, parietal, and temporal lobes, being involved in the maintenance and manipulation of mental imagery.

At the time of onset of Monsieur X's mental imagery condition, he also experienced a sudden and drastic change in his mood, becoming deeply depressed, anxious, and feeling isolated. He developed the "Cotard delusion,"[92] named after the prominent 19th-century neurologist, where he believed that he was dead due to his sudden inability to form mental imagery. It is not clear if the psychological symptoms occurred before the mental imagery loss or concurrently with it, but this is not the only case of associated depressive and anxious symptoms. In 1906, a Portuguese neurologist António de Sousa Magalhães e Lemos documented another instance of visual imagery loss in a woman with associated depressive and anxious symptomology.[93] Like Monsieur X, her symptoms were also presumed to be exclusively of neurological origin even though she co-presented with severe psychological symptoms.

Cotard had two patients who also presented with similar psychological symptoms of depression and anxiety and lost their ability to form or manipulate mental imagery voluntarily. He hypothesized that there might be a connection between the misinterpretation of mental imagery loss and the delusion of an individual's state of non-existence.[94] Cotard's (1884) theory agrees with other 20th-century case studies involving individuals with mental imagery loss and associated anxiety disorders that involve depersonalization and derealisation, two dissociative conditions that cause the afflicted to qustion their personal identity or existance..

Further studies[95] have shown that visual imagery loss is not a common symptom in individuals with organic neurological disorders, but it is a common complaint in people with functional, psychological disorders. Some researchers who have revisited the case of Monsieur X believe that his loss of visual imagery resulted from a psychological problem and not a neurological one. Even Sigmund Freud felt this way about Monsieur X, postulating that he suffered from neurosis and that was the cause of his symptoms.[96] Although aphantasia as an individual characteristic has only been recognized recently based largely on anecdotal evidence concerning subjective mental imagery loss, more research needs to happen to establish it being of organic or functional origin firmly. Future neuroimaging and clinical studies will help determine the root causes of aphantasia and will hopefully lead to a better understanding of this characteristic.

An interesting question is how individuals with aphantasia or hyperphantasia perceive the passage of time. To date, no studies on this topic have occurred, and there is no available anecdotal evidence of subjective time distortion. The ability to form mental imagery may be a significant component of time perception in some individuals, but not as significant in others. The brain is highly adaptable, and can often rewire itself to carry out its necessary functions. Nonetheless, it would be fascinating to better understand the minds of those individuals who experience aphantasia or hyperphantasia, and to learn from them what mental tools they use to reflect on the past and plan for the future.

Does Consciousness = Time Perception?

The experiences of conscious awareness and time perception are heavily intertwined. The present moment as a discrete-time percept requires the finely-tuned coordination of distributed neural networks across the brain. If the time-percept theory of consciousness is correct, then the subjective continuity of present experience is a finely tuned illusion. What is more frustrating is the difficulty in discerning the true nature of conscious awareness – the brain sees what it sees, and there is nothing you can do about it. As neuroscience professor Hakwan Lau explains, "When it comes to conscious perception, there seems to be something strangely persistent about what we see, hear and feel. Even when a perceptual experience is 'wrong,' we can't just mute it."[97]

To illustrate how conscious perception works, Hakwan com-pares it to a generative adversarial network (GAN). This type of sys-tem uses artificial intelligence (AI) to train two competing networks to discriminate among data sets to identify one as authentic and the other as simulated. Hakwan identifies a type of GAN in which one network, a *generator*, is programmed to simulate images of cats as accurately as possible. The other network, a *discriminator*, is then trained to tell apart real pictures of cats from simulated ones. The two systems are then set up to compete against each other.

The generator tries to fool the discriminator with fake pictures of cats, and the discriminator tries to catch the manufactured images successfully. Setting the networks up to compete enhances the performance of each one, not altogether unlike two very skilled chess players scrim-maging against each other repeatedly. Over time, the efficiency and accuracy of both networks increases.

The neural networks in the brain work in a similar way to a GAN. The neurons that fire when you imagine a cat are the same ones that activate when you see a real cat, so it is crucial that the brain can discriminate between the real and imagined objects. Sometimes signals in neural networks can fire at random and other times their activity is directly elicited by an external stimulus, so the brain must be able to discern the source of the event immediately. This discriminatory process is known as *perceptual reality monitoring* and involves what Hakwan refers to as "sensory self-monitoring" wherein specific neural networks in the brain act as a discriminator along with its adversarial rival (the simulator) to finely tune and develop a predictive coding mechanism for internal versus external perceptions. Most likely, these are distributed neural networks whose parts can vary depending on the nature of the incoming sensory data.

Hakwan theorizes that the GAN model provides an accurate analogy for how human consciousness works. If the discriminator neural networks interpret incoming sensory data as being an authentic dog, then you will see a dog in your visual field regardless of what is there, which could explain why certain illusions, including mirages, grid patterns, imaginary contours, illusory motion, are so persistent even if you are aware of the inauthenticity of the visual impressions they elicit. Successful magicians and illusionists make a living this way, by fooling your discriminatory neural networks into thinking that what you are seeing or experiencing is real. Phantom limb pain is another illusion where amputees and people missing limbs feel pain or other unpleasant sensations in places that do not exist. The pain is genuine and is undoubtedly not imaginary, but the afflicted individuals cannot just shut it off. In this case, the perceptual discriminator malfunctions so the simulated pain is felt in the limb area as if it were real.

Some perceptual illusions can reverse themselves once you are aware of how they function, but others such as phantom limb pain[98] cannot be easily corrected. It is not immediately clear which perceptual illusions are easily reversible and which ones are not, but most likely it has to do with the type of distributed neural networks involved in the hypothetical GAN. It is conceivable that all conscious perception consists of the use of GAN-like mechanisms, as incoming sensory data is analyzed and compared against information in short-term and long-term memory stores before conscious percepts are formed and become part of your conscious awareness.

Distributed neural networks, including the hypothetical GAN, reveal how adaptable and flexible the brain is. Discriminating among objects based on their features, textures, and their surrounding context and correctly identifying them is just as complicated as accurately estimating time intervals, but the brain makes these abilities seem effortless. Regardless of the presumably discrete nature of conscious perception, the world appears to stream right before your eyes continuously, and it is this continuity of conscious perception that might be the grandest illusion of all time.

Chapter 3 – No Infinity

"What is infinite is not finite. What does not end, does not end. What cannot be encapsulated, cannot be encapsulated. What does not fully converge, does not fully converge. What has no boundaries, has no boundaries. What cannot be completed is never completed."[1]

— Steve Patterson

Counting

One of the first skills you learn as a child is how to count objects. Counting not only gives us a sense of how many items we are dealing with but also it provides a somewhat indirect way of distinguishing one set of things from another. For instance, if you have a bowl containing 12 pieces of fruit, you could break that collection into its components – four oranges, three apples, two pears, and three pomegranates.

There is a lot more to counting objects, however, than meets the eye. Being able to count objects relies on a great deal of information processing in specific regions of the brain and the delicately coordinated pathways among them. To count objects, you have first to be able to distinguish them from one another. The brain accomplishes much of this task in the visual cortex using a combination of edge recognition, spatial mapping, texture rendering, and color coordination. Memory also plays a role in distinguishing objects, as the brain works in concert with all the senses to make its most educated guess as to what an object is.

In a recent study, researchers demonstrated that numbers encode in the brain through specific neuronal responses.[2] One of these responses is purely a reaction to a particular digit. For instance, the digit "2" evokes a different pattern of neuronal responses than the digit "3." It seems that the brain encodes digital numeracy, something also observed in other primates, although it is important to note that the symbolic number system is unique to humans.[3] People learn digits differently than they learn other characters such as alphabetical ones. There is neurological evidence of this distinction from alphabetic characters in how neuronal responses to digits are slightly affected by their surrounding digits.[4] For instance, the neuronal response to a "2" in the number 23 would be somewhat different than the neuronal response to the "2" in the number 28. It is neurological responses like these that contribute to your overall number sense. Researchers Esther Kutter et al. found evidence that number symbolism and associated numeracy functions occur in the medial temporal lobe and parahippocampal cortex, a region also associated with "selectivity to pictures, responses guided by familiarity, responses to spatial factors, and responses to mirror actions."[5]

Digits evolved to process quantities. For instance, the digit 2 represents "two-ness," and the digit 5 represents the quality of "five-ness." Enumerations of amounts might be a relic of your ancient ancestors. Counting was a necessity to barter goods, but there were different ways of doing it. One specific Brazilian culture, the Pirahá, uses less precise concepts for dealing with counting. Instead of referring to a precise quantity of objects, they use the terms *hói* (one or a couple) and *hoí* (a few).[6] The Pirahá are not any less intelligent than other cultures; however, they do struggle more with numeracy and provide insight into how humans may have dealt with issues of counting long before modern digits existed. Contemporary cultures, such as the Pirahá, demonstrates that number sense is not as innate as it might seem.

The fact that humans have five fingers on each hand is probably the most reasonable explanation for the traditional ten-digit number system. Early humans may have used their fingers to compare quantities, noticing that when the number of objects matched the number of digits on their fingers that meant that there was the same number of things. The etymology of "five" in several cultures has its origins in the concept of "hand" because of the convenience of using the natural amount of digits on a person's hand.[7]

Ancient cultures, including the Babylonians, Egyptians, Indians, and Mesopotamians developed tools and systems to deal with quantifying, some of which led to the development of the traditional number systems people use today.[8] The Mesopotamians had no concept of "zero," but instead used a series of rudimentary symbols for the ideas of 10 and 1. To interpret what the number was, you had to pay attention to it in context. Ancient Egyptians used hieroglyphs to represent different powers of 10. The Babylonians used a base-60 number system and are partially responsible for modern concepts of time (60 second minutes, 60 minute hours) and degree measure (360 degrees in a complete revolution). The exact numerals used for counting and enumerating have their origins in ancient Indian culture, where mathematics was an integral part of their society. According to author Peter Schumer, "These ideas were further developed and gradually transmitted to the Western world via Islamic scholars. That's why we now refer to our numerals as the Hindu-Arabic numeral system."[9]

Numbers are for counting objects and representing quantities. Finite quantities are those that can be specifically enumerated. On Earth, everything observable is finite. For example, although it is practically impossible to count the number of tiny grains of the sand on the beach, you can say with certainty that there must be a finite number of them. There is a finite number of every living creature on Earth even though it often can feel like there is an endless number of insects and other bugs around you. Referring to everything on Earth as finite, however, is entirely dependent on your definition of a quantity.

Consider the following alternative perspective to the idea of enumeration. There is a transformative nature to that which is finite, and it can be quite perplexing to quantify. This issue has to do with how people identify the objects themselves. For instance, consider five glass bottles on a wooden counter. There are a few issues that can arise from this seemingly simple situation. One issue is that none of these glass bottles could be precisely the same due to slight variations in their shape and size, even if they were all made to be as perfectly uniform as possible. Each bottle occupies a different location in space and has different dust particles on it, has clear blemishes and scratches, and may also have slight discolorations. Are these then the same bottles? Could they be counted as such? Someone could argue that they are not the same bottle, and they are all different. If you accept this argument as valid, then the same could be said for two or more of any objects – nothing is the same as anything else and trying to categorize two or more of anything is merely applying a contrived label to them.

Another issue to consider is that the physical state of these seemingly homogeneous glass bottles changes over time. The glass bottle could easily shatter into hundreds of pieces of glass shards if it were tipped over and it fell on a cement floor. Now one item has transformed into hundreds of new items made up of the same substances as the original cohesive unit. A single piece has turned into multiple units via a change in its physical state even though the original bottle consisted of the various parts all bound together by strong physical forces. The brain seeks order, and the enumeration of objects depends on your five senses using the available sensory data to determine where an object begins and where it ends, thus defining it and categorizing it for counting purposes.

Your brain does not typically notice the subtle chemical or physical changes in an object, nor does it care what an object is made up of or what forces are holding it together. If it looks reasonably like another object, there is a good chance that you will categorize these objects as being the same (Figure 5). As mentioned earlier, the act of counting can be heavily context-dependent. If distinct objects share enough common traits for a conventional categorization, then they can also be counted together. For instance, one apple, two oranges, and five bananas can be counted together as eight pieces of fruit. There is no restriction on counting objects, as you can even decide to count completely unrelated items together if it makes sense for you to do so. How you categorize objects can be completely arbitrary from one context to another.

Counting is, therefore, not entirely instinctual – it is a skill that needs to be learned and developed. It is a tool that humans invented to cope with quantifying things around them. Over time, counting became the basis for economic and other business transactions, from basic bartering to modern currency systems. It also became the basis behind arithmetic and most advanced mathematics. Like any tool, counting is not without limitations. There is not much utility in trying to count all the tiny grains of sand on the beach, and even if you did try to do so, you would never be able to arrive at an exact number anyway – there are too many grains of sand to count. Even the whole numbers are not entirely countable, as there is no highest number. The set of whole numbers is said to be countably infinite, meaning you could count them forever. The same is true of rational numbers, or fractions.

The Challenge of Infinity

Ancient civilizations, including the Greeks, wrestled with the idea that something might not be finite, but they had difficulty accepting this fact, as it was quite difficult to fathom.[10] In the seventeenth century, English clergyman and mathematician John Wallis developed the symbol for infinity to represent the concept of unboundedness, or something having no end to it, based on the idea of an unbounded curve.[11] The idea of infinity was not rigorously defined, however, until the eighteenth century by mathematician Georg Cantor. According to Alasdair Wilkins, "Cantor provided a stunning and instantly controversial proof that not only defined the nature of infinity, but it also revealed that *multiple* infinities existed, and some were larger than others. What made his achievement all the more remarkable was that he had built the entire thing out of an old and seemingly useless branch of mathematics known as set theory."[12]

The *cardinality* of a finite set is the number of elements it contains. For example, the set {1, 2, 3, 4, 5} has a cardinality of 5 because it contains five elements. Cantor argued that there were different sizes of infinity, and he used the symbol "aleph-null" to denote the smallest cardinality of an infinite set. Larger infinities are defined by having cardinalities of "aleph-one," "aleph-two," and so on. For instance, the set of all integers {... , -3, -2, -1, 0, 1, 2, 3, ...} has cardinality aleph-null. The set of all real numbers has cardinality aleph 1, which is larger than aleph-null, which implies that there are more real numbers than there are integers in each of these infinite sets. Cantor developed a theory known as the *continuum hypothesis* to explain these size differences among infinite sets.[13]

One of the exciting consequences of Cantor's theory is that different sets of numbers can have the same size, even if they do not appear that way. For instance, the set of all even whole numbers {2, 4, 6, ...} and the set of all whole numbers {0, 1, 2, 3, 4, ...} have the same cardinality even though it seems like the latter set should be higher. Likewise, the subset of the real numbers [0, 1] can be shown to have the same cardinality as the entire set of real numbers, just one of the many counterintuitive consequences of Cantor's theory. It is dumbfounding how an infinite set that appears to be smaller than another one ends up being the same size.

Another interesting idea from Cantor is the ternary Cantor set. The concept behind the Cantor set is simple to understand, but the implications of it are quite dense and counterintuitive. Imagine an interval of real numbers of length one, abbreviated [0,1]. Now imagine removing the middle third of this interval (1/3, 2/3), leaving only the sets [0, 1/3] and [2/3, 1] remaining. Then repeat this process on the remaining sets by removing the middle third from each of them. This will leave us with the sets [0, 1/9], [2/9, 1/3], [2/3, 7/9], and [8/9, 1]. This process repeats infinitely many times. Interestingly, any interval of points resulting from each of these subdivisions has a cardinality equal to the size of the whole set. For instance, the size of [0, 1/9] is equal to the size of [0, 1/3], and is also equal to the size of [0, 1].

The mathematics behind the properties of the ternary Cantor set are beyond the scope of this book, but you do not need to have an advanced understanding of mathematics to appreciate the complex nature of this set. As you divide this set up in the way described above, the set approaches something that has no intervals, an uncountably infinite number of elements, is closed and bounded, and nowhere dense. This set becomes almost impossible to visualize and comprehend at this point because of its inherent complexity and contradictory nature.

Understanding the infinite is so tremendously tricky that it has nearly driven some people to insanity. Many philosophers, mathematicians, and others have tried to make sense out of the infinite through various theorems, examples, and thought experiments. Some of the most famous and intuitive examples are Zeno's Paradoxes, believed to have been imagined by the ancient Greek philosopher Zeno of Elea. To visualize Zeno's Dichotomy Paradox,[14] imagine you need to travel one meter, but you are going to make this journey by first taking a half-meter step. Before you take this half-meter step, however, you must take a quarter-meter step (which is half of the first half). Before you take the quarter-meter step, you must take one eighth-meter step, and so on. The idea here is that to complete the journey, you would need to eventually cross over all these steps – an infinite amount of them.

A consequence of Zeno's paradox, therefore, is that all motion is impossible because in any journey you would need to cross over an infinite number of position markers.[15] Zeno's paradox of dichotomy is just one example of how people misinterpret mathematics in the physical world. Mathematically, the sum of the infinite mini-distances approaches the total distance over an ever-increasing amount of time. Traveling the overall length is therefore equivalent to traversing the sum of the mini-distances. Another problem with Zeno's paradox is that it assumes that there exists a being that can make itself infinitesimally small to cross these ever-shrinking mini-distances. This action is practically impossible, as all living creatures have a finite size that would prevent them from being able to shrink their bodies down to scale out these microscopic distances. The exciting part of this paradox, however, is the mind's ability to play tricks on you into thinking about an idealistic situation that is practically impossible.

Why does thinking about the infinite conjure up so much confusion and difficulty? According to Steve Patterson,[16] discussing the infinite is so mentally challenging because endless things do not exist. He argues that there is a central contradiction at the core of mathematics that assumes that infinite things could exist when, in fact, they cannot. The very nature of infinity is that it contains no boundaries, but anything that does exist automatically has limitations, making the idea of infinite things absurd. Patterson elucidates on the fallacy of the infinite with the following thought experiment: "Try to imagine a circle with an infinite radius. The radius isn't really big – it's actually infinite. Is this possible? I am certain you cannot imagine such a thing. I will demonstrate why; it's the same reason you cannot imagine a square circle. The concept is incoherent."[17] Put another way, all circles with a finite radius have curvature. If you were infinitely extending out the radius of the circle, its curvature would disappear, and the circle would become a line. The problem with this argument, however, is that circles are not lines. By definition, circles have nonzero curvature. There is no such thing as a circle that could also be a line.

In the branch of mathematics known as Calculus, specific quantities may converge to a finite number or diverge and increase or decrease without boundary. The concept of a limit builds off the idea that an amount may approach something for sufficiently large (or small) values of one or more of its variables. Consider, for instance, the quantity $1/x$. For sufficiently large values of x, the quantity $1/x$ approaches 0, so you could say that the limit as x goes to infinity of $1/x$ is 0, which does not imply that the quantity $1/x$ will ever actually be equal to 0 – that is impossible. All that this limit reveals are what the long term behavior of the quantity $1/x$ is and what it approaches.

Patterson explains, "An 'infinite thing' is 'a thing which is itself, and more-than-itself at the same time.' An outright contradiction. Think about it: if a thing is not more than itself, it is complete, and therefore finite. Therefore, no things are infinite, by virtue of being things in the first place."[18] What Patterson is pointing out is that the problem with the infinite is the way some people choose to interpret and apply it. Stating that there are sets of infinite size or other actual infinite objects is a logical contradiction and does not make any sense; however, using the infinite as a guide for what the behavior of an object or quantity approaches does make sense. Infinity is inherently about approximation, but it is never exact – it cannot be by its very nature.

Therefore, Cantor was incorrect. There are no infinite sets. Everything in existence must be finite. You cannot imagine the infinite because it does not exist. You can only see what exists. Perhaps one of the reasons why so much of modern mathematics is highly confusing is because of logical fallacies such as the idea that there could be infinite sets. Thoughts like these will drive you crazy because they are built on a logical contradiction and do not make any sense whatsoever. Problems also arise when people try to apply the concept of infinity to the physical world incorrectly.

What is the Size of the Universe?

One of the greatest scientific mysteries is whether the universe is finite or infinite. This question is fundamentally flawed because a genuinely endless universe cannot exist anyway for the same reasons a circle with infinite radius cannot exist. Even if you exclude the idea of an infinite universe from the discussion, it is still reasonable to inquire whether the universe is expanding indefinitely. At every instant of expansion, this universe is always finite. The universe began as a infinitesimally dense singularity and will end in some way by either burning itself out due to indefinite extension, potentially collapsing in on itself in a Big Crunch, or through some alternate physical means.

Another question in cosmology that frequently arises is whether there could be an infinite number of universes, another logical fallacy because there is no such thing as an endless number. There could be an ever-expanding number of universes through a variety of means, possibly some through black holes and other objects not connected to this universe. These hypotheses are mere speculation, but even if there were quadrillions and quadrillions of other universes, there still could not be an infinite number of them.

What about space itself? Isn't it the case that the Universe is expanding into endless, all-encompassing space? Nope. According to Charles Choi, "The universe did not expand into space, as space did not exist before the universe, according to NASA. Instead, it is better to think of the Big Bang as the simultaneous appearance of space everywhere in the universe."[19] This concept is difficult to grasp because if there was no space around before the birth of the universe, then it is not clear what, if anything, was there before the big bang.

Thinking about what existed before the birth of the universe is like trying to imagine your own life before the moment you were born. Since there was no "you" around to know of your impending existence, it stands to reason that, at least for you, there was nothing before your birth. This idea of nothing, however, is easy to misinterpret. Before his death, world-renowned physicist Stephen Hawking tried to explain that the universe formed from a tiny singularity that was so small that the modern laws of physics and time did not apply there. This initial singularity was infinitesimally small. Instead of traditional time existing there, imaginary time existed as the universe became smaller and smaller but never shrank out of existence. Something was always there, no matter how tiny and insignificant it may have been.

As Hawking put it, "There was never a Big Bang that produced something from nothing...it just seemed that way from mankind's perspective."[20] It was at this singularity that real-time and imaginary time converged. You can imagine the expanding Universe as a seemingly endless sphere emerging from this singularity. Imaginary time is a type of time that is just as valid as real-time, but it is not something that can be experienced by humans. It is just a type of time that exists near the singularity. Some scientists predicted that the universe would end in a Big Crunch, the opposite of a Big Bang.[21] The matter will contract back toward the state of singularity, real-time will end, and imaginary time will begin until the process reverses again. This hypothesis does not mean that time will flow backward during the contraction phase. Real-time will still flow as it always has until being replaced at a critical point by imaginary time.

You can imagine the universe existing in a cycle of continuous birth and death, but each time a completely different universe emerges from the singularity and each time it collapses, it does so into an entirely different singularity than the one that existed before it. This process could theoretically go on forever, but unfortunately, nobody will ever be around long enough to find out. Just how many universes exist is currently unknown, but many theories point to black holes being a possible origin of new ones. All matter that enters a black hole approaches a state of singularity which may, in turn, emerge on the "other side" of a black hole in the form of a white hole, which would represent another Big Bang. Real-time is not traceable backward from this new white hole any more than the end of real-time cannot exist inside the black hole. If this is the case, it may be impossible ever to detect the existence of another universe because there would be no mathematical or scientific way to measure or identify it.

The universe appears to be unbounded, in that it has a finite volume but no three-dimensional edges, which means that if you were to travel faster than the speed of light somehow, you would eventually end up back to where you started. In this way, the universe geometrically behaves spherically, but not in the traditional sense. Since space and time are intimately linked together by special relativity and quantum mechanics, it would be more accurate to describe the shape as a hypersphere. Of course, the idea that the universe looks like a hypersphere is just a theoretical conjecture, and no scientists to date have produced any reliable models of the universe.

Alternative theories, one based on background microwave cosmic radiation being uniform everywhere in the *observable* universe, suggest that the universe is flat. Yet another theory predicts a saddle-like universe with a saddle shape and negative curvature. The problem with these theories is that they rely on data collected only in the observable universe, which represents only a very tiny portion of its entirety.[22] Right before his death, Stephen Hawking and Thomas Hertog postulated that the Universe did not arise from an unbounded state, but that there was a demarcated boundary consisted of the absence of time in the moment of the Big Bang. The Hawking-Hertog theory further postulates that the formation of the Universe was like dough rising in the oven, with all of its bubbles and pockets representing possible Universes. They speculate the Universe can be reduced, in the absence of gravity, to a two-dimensional hologram.[23]

Regardless of the actual shape of the universe, it will most certainly not be infinite, even if there is nothing to limit its expansion. Nothing infinite had ever existed, even before the formation of the universe. You can liken this idea back to how there is no limit to how high you can count, but that does not mean that there is an infinite amount of numbers. There are only as many numbers as you identify at any given point. You name the highest number, and someone could add that number to itself, multiply it by itself, or add a quadrillion to it and you have a new number that is higher than the original one. The variety of numbers you can identify is indeed unbounded but limited by your imagination or by the processing power of a supercomputer. On a long enough timeline, both of those tools will break down and, given more time, the entire universe will likely collapse back to a singularity and numbers will also cease to exist.

It is therefore vital to recognize that numbers are a human invention and just because you can think of an endless amount of them, that does not mean that they exist. You will never be able to purchase a "4" at the grocery store. Even the numbered candle that you might place on a birthday cake is just a representation of the idea of 'fourness' and is not the idea itself of four. Humans invented the number 4 and decided to group four objects together and thus call it a representation of fourness. Numbers do not exist outside of your imagination any more than an infinite universe does.

The concept of infinity is often misused and misconstrued to represent that which does not exist rather than to discuss the idea which it is genuinely meant to identify – that which is unbounded or what something is approaching with increasing time. Applying anything more to that idea and calling infinity something that is reachable somewhere out there is a logical contradiction. There is no getting near infinity, getting to infinity, or going beyond it. There is no infinity.

Chapter 4 – No Perspective

"Some men went fishing in the sea with a net, and upon examining what they caught they concluded that there was a minimum size to the fish in the sea."[1]

— Arthur Eddington

Mathematics is a Human Invention

Conventional knowledge dictates that the tools, formulas, and equations of mathematics arise from scientific observations about nature. Some common beliefs are that Sir Isaac Newton developed his basic ideas about gravity from an apple that fell from a tree and Galileo Galilei developed his law of falling bodies from similar scientific observations. Calculus was another tool developed by Newton and Gottfried Leibniz to deal with physical problems involving the basic mechanics of motion. One American mathematician, Richard Hamming, doubts the official stories of these scientists and mathematicians and believes that the mathematical reasoning developed before approaching the physical problems for which the math was used to solve. According to him, "We see what we look for. No one is surprised if after putting on blue tinted glasses the world appears bluish."[2]

Although mathematics is the language of the sciences, engineering, and other subjects, how mathematics applies to these disciplines is not always clear. Is the math invented first and then applied to the sciences, or does the development of mathematical tools naturally arise out of the sciences? Galileo's law of falling bodies states that two objects, regardless of their size or mass, fall at the same speed, and the distances they travel are directly proportional to the square of their elapsed times. Galileo dropped two cannonballs of identical mass off the Leaning Tower of Pisa and observed that they hit the ground at the same time, disproving Aristotle's earlier hypothesis that the rate at which an object falls is directly proportional to their mass. There is much official doubt, however, as to whether Galileo ever experimented as described in historical lore or if he developed his theory another way.[3]

This "chicken and the egg" problem, whether the mathematics or the physical problem it was used to model came first, is a difficult question to answer. Hamming argues that the earliest development of mathematics must have arisen from pure speculation about the physical world. Primitive humans were deeply concerned with their survival, and once a model of cause-and-effect developed, it is not difficult to imagine how the earliest mathematical methods involving logic may have formed. Complicated chains of reasoning would have developed, allowing people to solve problems in their environment related to their survival.

Hamming believed that Geometry most likely developed to deal with the problems of decorating the human body and other objects (i.e., cookware, clothing, utensils) for various purposes even though the official history lists the subject as developing from the ancient Egyptians need to survey their land following each flood. The idea that this branch of mathematics may have been developed initially to deal with problems involving beauty and aesthetics seems far-fetched at first, but it makes sense if you look at the intricate and ornate patterns in body art, jewelry, pottery, and other items from ancient cultures.

Hamming goes on to state, "The search for proper concepts and definitions is one of the main features of doing great mathematics."[4] In mathematics, *theorems* are logical statements that assert the truth of some statement under the assumption that certain conditions are assumed to be true. The traditional belief (and practice) is that you begin with a theorem and then use logical deductive and inductive reasoning to prove its truth, but it is also possible to either deliberately or accidentally discover some properties or relationships among certain concepts and arrive at a fact that you did not necessarily intend to find. In this case, the theorem arises from its accidental proof, an unintended consequence of deductive reasoning.

Furthermore, to prove a theorem requires both awareness and responsible use of the postulates in the mathematical system you are operating within. The ancient Greeks initially believed in the existence of only the natural numbers $\{1, 2, 3, ...\}$ – numbers that could be counted, added, multiplied, and matched up nicely with the material objects in the world around them. Unfortunately, natural numbers were limited in the scope of what they could do, especially in terms of measurement, so the concept of fractions was developed to deal with this problem. Although fractions were not as convenient as natural numbers, they were quite beneficial for measuring specific quantities. Then at some point, as legend has it, the Pythagoreans wondered about how the diagonal of a square and its side were related, something that neither natural numbers nor fractions could explain, and thus the concept of an irrational number was born.[5] For instance, using a square of side length a=b=1 with a diagonal of length c, and the Pythagorean Theorem $a^2+b^2=c^2$, they obtained the result $c^2=2$, which results in $c=\sqrt{2}$, an irrational number because $\sqrt{2}$ cannot be expressed as a fraction of integers.

Much of what is commonly considered *algebra* initially arose out of ideas from the field of geometry such as the Pythagorean square-diagonal problem. Transcendental numbers, such as *pi*, gradually made their way into the algebraic real number system through a process like the one that the Pythagoreans used, except this time the relationship was that between the circumference and diameter of a circle. *Pi* is the number that represents that ratio even though it is not a number that can be counted or described in any other way except via a mathematical symbol. If you wish to perform calculations using *pi* for practical purposes, then you must approximate it out to a certain number of decimal places.

According to Hamming, "We see that one of the main strands of mathematics is the extension, the generalization, the abstraction - they are all more or less the same thing-of well-known concepts to new situations. But note that in the very process the definitions themselves are subtly altered. Therefore, what is not so widely recognized, old proofs of theorems may become false proofs."[6] Sometimes new definitions and the application of more sophisticated mathematical tools lead to the redevelopment and modification of older mathematics to something more current, precise, and relevant. As these new tools and theorems developed, scientists utilize them for their theories about the way things work.

Albert Einstein was so well-versed in advanced mathematics that he applied much of his knowledge to developing the special theory of relativity. People typically believe that he based most of his theories from scientific observations, but the truth is more likely that his arguments were mostly philosophical and based off the body of mathematics from which they emerged.[7] Einstein had a prescient mind for his theory of relativity precisely because of his mathematical knowledge and his ability to interpret mathematics through the lens of a theoretical physicist. Einstein did not use rigorous scientific experiments to validate his hypotheses, but he instead let the mathematics speak for itself and made use of "thought experiments" to further legitimize his theories. In other words, he used pure mathematics to develop his scientific theories about physical concepts.

Of course, the use of mathematics to a situation is heavily context-dependent, and there are times when the mathematical tools you have at your disposal are insufficient to address specific problems. For instance, the mathematics used to measure quantities (known as *scalars*) do not work when you try to measure amounts that have both a magnitude (size) and direction. *Vectors* addressed this issue and allowed scientists to quantify better the forces that act on an object. People repeatedly develop new mathematical tools to solve the specific problems that current mathematics cannot answer. The over-reliance on mathematical and scientific explanations has led many to believe that these subjects hold the keys to understanding all of nature and everything about the human condition, but this could not be further from the truth. Mathematics is inherently self-limited by its axioms and the necessity of interaction between the observer and the observed limits scientific experiments.

The Problems with Logic

Gödel's incompleteness theorems illustrate the inherent limitations in an axiomatic logical system such as mathematics.[8] His first theorem states that in any logical system containing some arithmetic have statements can neither be proved nor disproved within the system using its arithmetic – in other words, the system must be incomplete or inconsistent. The second theorem asserts that a formal system cannot prove the consistency of itself. Every formal system, including mathematical ones, must inherently contain logical contradictions.

To better understand Gödel's first incompleteness theorem, consider one of the most famous historical examples of its application to Euclidean Geometry. Euclid was an ancient Greek mathematician who theorized five postulates for geometry. The fifth postulate, known as the *parallel postulate*, reads as follows: "If two lines are drawn which intersect a third in such a way that the sum of the inner angles on one side is less than two right angles, then the two lines inevitably must intersect each other on that side if extended far enough."[9] Unfortunately, this postulate is unprovable within the logical system defined by the other four postulates, which implied that Euclid's five postulates were incomplete. Consequentially, other geometrical systems developed in which the parallel postulate was not valid. One such example occurs in spherical geometry, where two parallel lines "meet" at the horizon on the surface of a sphere.

Gödel's second incompleteness theorem implies that the inherent limitations of self-referencing will bind any sufficiently complicated logical system containing arithmetic. According to Loyola Marymount University computer science professor Ray Toal, "In simpler terms, within a formal system for arithmetic, truth is a bigger notion than proof. You simply can't prove everything that's true about arithmetic using a formal system."[10] To think of this another way, imagine yourself. You can create any number of formal systems to describe yourself and how your body and mind function, but none of those systems would *be* you. No description of you can ever possibly be complete so that while you can *be* yourself, you can never really fully *know* yourself.

Gödel's incompleteness theorems address the inherent limitations in any formal logical system, but they do not breach the larger question of the utility of logical systems such as mathematical ones. There are questions that mathematics will never be able to address, such as the true meaning of justice, love, or other humanistic abstract ideas. Hamming points out that, "Just as there are odors that dogs can smell and we cannot, as well as sounds that dogs can hear and we cannot, so too there are wavelengths of light we cannot see and flavors we cannot taste. Why then, given our brains wired the way they are, does the remark 'Perhaps there are thoughts we cannot think,' surprise you? Evolution, so far, may possibly have blocked us from being able to think in some directions; there could be unthinkable thoughts."[11] Mathematics is just one of many human inventions, and although it is subject to continual improvement in its scope, efficiency, and rigor, there will always be fundamental limitations inherent in the system itself.

You do not have to look very far at all to uncover how mathematics is substantially limited in its ability to describe the world around you. Mathematics might be the best tool there is to discuss shapes, objects, and measurements, but that does not mean it without its faults and significant limitations. The key concept to keep in mind is that mathematics is a human invention, and because of that, you are unlikely to find it anywhere in nature outside of the confines of your imagination. All applications of mathematical theory to science and other applied subjects, no matter how appropriate, are *always* approximations to the actual reality.

According to Alan Bustany, "Points don't exist. At least not in the way that physical objects exist in reality."[12] No matter how hard you try, you cannot draw a perfect point. It is simply not possible. Even the tiniest of points, upon further examination, are just geometrical blobs on paper. The period in the preceding sentence and the dot above the letter "i" in each instance that it appears in this book are not actual points. If you were to zoom in closely on the period or the dot above the letter "i" on a computer monitor, you would find that each dot is made up of collections of pixels.

Points exist in a zero-dimensional space, which is an abstract mathematical concept that does not exist in Nature. Your brain processes these random blobs as "points" because of sophisticated pattern recognition skills. It is equally impossible to draw a straight line. It probably seems ludicrous, as to draw a straight line all you would need is a straight-edge such as a ruler, but even a ruler is not straight because it has microscopic grooves and edges that alter its shape. A line generated by a computer software program is still not technically a straight line because it consists of a collection of pixels that are spaced apart and not continuous. The brain cannot detect these microscopic irregularities, so what you end up seeing is a perfectly straight line, but your mind is just calculating its best estimate, or approximation, to what is in front of your eyes. You can apply the same logic to circles, squares, rectangles, and any other regular shape or polygon you can imagine. If it is technically impossible to draw a point and lines consist of points and quadrilaterals are made of lines, and so on, nearly every shape you perceive becomes lost in a certain kind of illusion. Your mind uses abstract ideas and concepts to make educated guesses about the identity and form of the objects in your visual field.

Accepting this observation makes you wonder about the true nature of the objects surrounding you. Mathematics presents a quite orderly world of objects through the lens and tools of Euclidean geometry, but it is more of a philosophical tool than reality. Mathematics is at best a very reliable approximation to the objects that surround you in your everyday life, but the mathematical ideas that model the objects (i.e., a perfect rectangle) and the objects themselves are quite different in their true nature. One is an abstraction, and the other is a carefully arranged set of atoms and molecules under direct observation.

Object Representation and Identification

Objects are what your brain identifies them as, and that depends mainly on your perspective. If you were to study a point of ink and deconstruct it deeply, you would find that it consisted of a vast collection of dyes, pigments, stabilizing polymers, liquid solvents, and other additives. Each of these ingredients consists of groups of molecules arranged in a certain way. Within those molecules are individual atoms which can be broken down even further into subatomic particles. These subatomic particles behave according to the rules of quantum physics, which are a different set of rules from the mechanical laws you have familiarity within your field of vision. The eye is very limited in what it can see, and the brain cannot process or perceive that which it cannot detect through the senses.

A similar phenomenon happens in the way the brain filters out imperfections and other irrelevancies to represent the world in a certain way. People typically do not notice the grooves, bumps, and fading paint off a road unless they stand out. Tile floors have plenty of imperfections, from the spacing of the grout to the depth of the tile, but so long as those details are not too noticeable or indicative of damage, your brain will interpret the floor as being completely uniform. Your mind is designed to ignore irrelevant information in your environment, including slight imperfections and other sensory data that have no bearing on your perception and interpretation of your daily interactions within the world. *Sensory gating* (SG) is the mechanism the central nervous system uses to suppress such irrelevancies during daily waking activities.[13] The purpose of SG is to prevent the higher cortical regions of the brain from becoming overloaded by sensory data. Howard Cromwell and his team of researchers collected EEG data from animal subjects[14] to determine what areas of the brain appear to be responsible for SG activity.

To evaluate SG, Cromwell presented subjects with two identical stimuli S1 and S2 (auditory clicks) separated by a 500 ms latency. An eight-second interval then separates this identical pair of stimuli before researchers provide a new distinct pair of identical auditory stimuli to the subjects. The hypothesis behind this experiment is that the first auditory stimulus stores itself in the hippocampus (or similar memory region) and then the second stimulus is compared to the first one and inhibited due to its repetitive nature and the fact that it contains no new sensory information.

Cromwell operationally defined SG as "the ratio of the amplitude of the response to S2 stimuli to the amplitude of responses to S1 stimuli multiplied by 100."[15] Lower ratios imply better SG activity since the S2 response would be substantially lower than the S1 response showing that the subject did not respond as strongly to the second identical stimulus as they did the first one, which is the novel stimulus. In animal studies, the researchers found considerable variation in SG activity depending on where they placed the electrodes during the EEG analysis. They found that the amygdala and medial prefrontal cortex (mPFC), regions responsible for the processing and moderation of emotions, were highly involved in SG of auditory stimuli corresponding to low ratios of SG. Parts of the basal ganglia, a region highly associated with speech, movement, posture, and emotion, showed no SG at all. Regions in the midbrain, an area associated with movement and regulation of automatic body functions, were varied in their responses with putative GABAergic neurons demonstrating high levels of SG and putative dopamine neurons showing no SG.

SG levels varied not only according to the brain regions containing the measurement of electric potentials, but they also changed for the different types of stimuli presented to the subjects. For instance, there was a strengthening of the SG response in the amygdala in response to an injection of a saline solution (an acute stressor) into rats, implicating the importance of this brain region in modulating and regulating emotional responses, especially in states of high alert and fear. Heightened levels of SG in this brain region serve an evolutionary purpose, allowing the animal to focus on necessary sensory data while quickly filtering out irrelevancies in this state of hypervigilance.

Researcher Chia-Hsiung Cheng and his team studied SG activity in human subjects,[16] which is more challenging to measure because of both the ethical and physiological issues with implanting electrodes in the human brain. One of their goals was to take a closer look at the somatosensory SG and study its relationship to behavioral inhibition control, as well as to determine if this link was modality-dependent or modality-independent. By modality, they meant if the connection depended on whether the sensory stimuli were of auditory, visual, olfactory, tactile, or gustatory nature, although for the study they only tested tactile and auditory responses. The other goal of the study was to determine, using magnetoencephalography (MEG) of the median nerve, if the peak value of gamma oscillations was associated with behavioral inhibition control and somatosensory SG. MEG is a minimally-invasive and safe way to map brain activity using very sensitive magnetometers to record magnetic fields that are naturally produced by the brain. Stimulation of the left medial nerve is known to stimulate the contralateral primary somatosensory cortex (SI) and the secondary somatosensory cortices as well, regions long suspected to be involved in SG.

Cheng et al. recruited 22 healthy right-handed male subjects who had no history of neurological or psychiatric disorders and who were also instructed to refrain from smoking for at least 12 hours before the study. The reasons for these conditions were to avoid confounding variables that could potentially interfere with the integrity of the SG study. For the first part of the study, subjects were situated in a MEG machine and then their left median nerve was stimulated with an intensity 20% above the motor threshold to cause the abductor pollicis muscles to twitch noticeably. These stimulations occurred in pairs separated by 500 ms intervals with a pair interval of 6 seconds. While receiving these electrical stimulations, the subjects focused their attention on a silent movie so that they could try to ignore the sensory stimulation of their abductor muscles. Researchers measured the peak value of gamma oscillations recorded in subcortical regions including SI and calculated the SG ratio (S2/S1) based on the peak values of the gamma oscillations produced in the SI region by the electrical stimulation.

Directly following the MEG studies, the researchers conducted a series of behavioral Go-Nogo experiments on the subjects. The idea behind this type of research is that subjects are instructed to produce a response to specific stimuli ("Go" stimuli) and not to respond to other stimuli ("Nogo" stimuli). To carry out the tactile task, the researchers delivered an electric current to either the second or fifth finger of the left hand and subjects were instructed to press a button with their right hand in response to stimulation of the left second finger and to ignore stimulation of the left fifth finger. The inter-stimulus intervals (ISI) were quite brief, clocking in between 1.0 and 1.2 seconds. Despite the short ISIs, subjects were instructed to complete these tasks as quickly as possible. In the auditory Go-Nogo task, participants were asked to press the button with their right hand in response to low-pitched tones and to ignore high-pitched sounds. Low-pitched tones were delivered more frequently than the high-pitched ones. The ISIs were the same as the ones in the tactile-driven Go-Nogo experiments. Researchers used the data collected from these experiments to calculate the accuracy rate for each specific modality (tactile, auditory).

One of their research findings from the studies was that there was a positive correlation between MEG evidence of cortical somatosensory SG and better inhibition control during the Go-Nogo task.[17] They hypothesized that the earlier MEG experiments where the SI was primed ahead of time by the SG activities from the first experiment might have been responsible for the Go-Nogo inhibitory performance success rates. Their study also provided empirical evidence that SG was modality-independent,[18] as the somatosensory SG abilities demonstrated in the MEG experiments correlated well with both the somatosensory-driven and auditory-driven Go-Nogo tasks. Concerning their third hypothesis about the relationship between the peak value of gamma oscillations in SI and SG abilities, the researchers found a positive correlation with only somatosensory SG ability[19] but did not find a direct link with the behavioral performance of somatosensory-driven inhibition execution as demonstrated by the Go-Nogo experiments.

The authors caution not to assume that their experimental evidence demonstrates a clear causal relationship between pre-attentive somatosensory SG and attentive inhibition control. According to

Cheng et al., "Further investigations using pharmacological interventions or virtual lesions induced by transcranial magnetic stimulation, for example, will provide important additional information on the causal mechanisms."[20] They also caution that SI is not the only region in the human brain that is likely involved in SG activity and attentive inhibition control. There is some fMRI evidence[21] from other studies to suggest the involvement of the prefrontal cortex, inferior frontal gyrus, supplementary motor area, anterior cingulate cortex, and inferior parietal cortex in inhibition processing. Furthermore, there is evidence to suggest a causal relationship between GABA concentration and inhibition function in the visual cortex, anterior cingulate cortex, and prefrontal cortex.[22] GABA is the primary inhibitory neurotransmitter in the human brain that is thought to be responsible for effectively modulating neuronal behavior.

There is some evidence to suggest that overall GABA levels decrease with increasing age, and this might explain why it becomes difficult to ignore irrelevancies and distractions in your environment as you get older. Sounds that may not have bothered you when you were younger may suddenly become bothersome, and your ability to concentrate and focus can diminish, which can also interfere with your quality of sleep and potentially lead to depression or other mental or physical health issues. Researcher Declan Jones et al. intensely studied the auditory mechanisms involved in sensory gating using a traditional P50 model in which a sensory stimulus is presented repeatedly to the subject with an ISI of less than one second.[23] EEG recordings were used to study event-related potentials (ERP) P50 occurring during this short period. According to L.A. Jones et al., "The attenuation ('gating out') of the P50 response to the second stimulus is the operational definition of sensory gating to be due to neural excitation of a set of sensory neurons to the presentation of the first stimulus generating P50, while simultaneously activating a second set of interneurons that inhibit any further excitatory response."[24] Optimal functioning of SG occurs with a robust ERP P50 response to the first (novel) stimulus followed by a much reduced ERP P50 response to the second redundant stimulus.

Schizophrenia is a mental health disorder marked by delusional or disorganized thoughts, hallucinations, memory dysfunctions, and other cognitive and psychosocial symptoms. Although there is substantial research suggesting that people with schizophrenia experience significant SG deficits, the researchers caution that cognitive correlates of SG are not particularly well-understood. Impaired performance on tasks measuring sustained attention, latent inhibition, and inhibition of distractions are all characteristics of impaired SG in people with schizophrenia, but how much of this is due to SG compared to other neurophysiological factors remains unclear.

Jones and his research team sought out to better understand the cognitive correlates associated with SG by developing a holistic, comprehensive, and exhaustive battery of SG tests administered to a group of 60 healthy individual subjects. They designed correlational studies in which SG ratios (via EEG data) were associated with individual tests of inhibition including the Stroop task, Simon task, latent inhibition test, negative priming, go/no-go, switch, antisaccade, attentional network, and continuous performance. They performed these tests in addition to other auditory SG tests.

The auditory SG test occurred in a "dimly lit, sound attended Faraday cage."[25] Researchers placed electrode caps on participants' heads (in preparation for the collection of P50 ERP data on an EEG), and they responded to 135 paired-beep trials and 15 paired-click trials. The paired-beep experiment consisted of a conditioning stimulus and test stimulus, and the paired-click trials included the subject fixating on a visual cross on a screen and being asked to press a button every time they heard a click. Researchers calculated the SG ratios in the same way as during previous studies (S2/S1 ratio multiplied by 100).

In the Stroop task, participants were shown a series of words and asked to identify the ink color of the words quickly. Some of the words were colored the same as other ones (congruent), while others were distinctly colored (incongruent). Researchers examined the difference in response times, called the "Stroop effect,"[26] to congruent versus incongruent trials. The Simon task was like the Stroop task in that participants were shown either a blue circle or a red circle in different locations on a screen, and they were asked to press various keys for each one, with the location being irrelevant. Researchers calculated the Simon effect[27] in the same manner as the Stroop effect.

The latent inhibition task consisted of participants examining a geometric figure made of five randomly connected straight-line segments on a white background. Researchers constructed four designs in which they either contained 20 identical stimuli or 19 identical stimuli and one unique stimulus. Subjects were asked to identify if there was a unique element in each presentation. Researchers focused on three distinct presentations of the target and distractor out of seven possibilities and calculated the effect of latent inhibition by measuring the difference in reaction time between the novel and familiar situations.

Similar tasks and measurements of data involving accuracy and response times were carried out across the other experiments. Participants also took Cattell's culture fair measure of fluid intelligence and the OSPAN (operation span) so that researchers could simultaneously assess both individual differences in fluid intelligence (a type of IQ assessment) and individual differences in working memory abilities, respectively.[28]

The researchers found that stronger sensory inhibition abilities correlated closely with higher levels of fluid intelligence and working memory. They also found that individual skills in latent inhibition of irrelevant stimuli varied depending on their backgrounds. Non-clinical high-psychotic participants outperformed their non-psychotic peers at the recognition of a pre-exposed stimulus in a unique environment because they did not filter out the irrelevant information and were thus able to recognize it in a distinct context easily. As Jones explains, "This research suggests that latent inhibition is caused by both the encoding of the pre-exposed stimulus and the subsequent ability to inhibit that stimulus from further encoding through selective attention once it has been deemed task-irrelevant."[29] People who have higher sensory inhibition abilities filter out irrelevant data early on so that if it appears again later, subjects will ignore it due to the initial filtering effects.

People who demonstrate high levels of latent inhibition ability utilize selective attention to filter out irrelevant data so that they can focus on goal-oriented tasks and effectively function toward completing those tasks without being burdened by irrelevant information. In the event they need to access the previously-deemed irrelevant details, it may be quite challenging due to the limited cognitive resources available to complete a given task. Information previously deemed useless or irrelevant will be more difficult to recall or recognize even in an entirely distinct context because of SG. Conversely, people with a higher SG ratio (lower filtering ability) may have difficulty sustaining focused attention for periods, but they can more easily recall and recognize previously-considered irrelevant stimuli as a result of lower SG abilities.

Interestingly, effective SG might involve both top-down and bottom-up neurological processes.[30] The priming for SG of irrelevant stimuli might be rooted in individual expectations and the cognitive ability to identify context-specific irrelevant stimuli and information before its presentation. Once the stimuli have been identified and processed as trivial, then the focus shifts to selective attention, or the ability to maintain a goal-oriented continuous information flow with minimal distractions. The auditory cortex is most likely involved in the top-down preparation for SG encoding while the prefrontal cortex is probably responsible for maintaining the continuous focus on relevant information in a goal-oriented setting.[31]

The Link Between Distractibility and Creativity

While it may seem counterintuitive at first, there may be some distinct advantages to having a lower SG ability. There are numerous anecdotes of highly creative people being exceptionally sensitive to noise and other distractions. This failure to filter is involuntary since SG typically occurs 50 ms after hearing the sound (P50 ERP) and it would be contradictory to notice a sound that you are supposed to ignore anyway. The point is that people who successfully filter irrelevant noises would be unable to hear them because they just ignored them.

Although background noise can be a significant annoyance to creative people, the fact that their brains cannot easily filter out these distractions may also explain why they can form deep and novel connections amongst things most other people would not even notice. Psychological researcher Darya L. Zabelina claims, "Leaky attention may help people integrate ideas that are outside the focus of attention into their current information processing, leading to creative thinking."[32] To test this hypothesis about the link between poor SG ability and enhanced creativity, she recruited subjects for an experiment, in which she provided them with a Creative Achievement Questionnaire where they were asked to report on their creative achievements across different domains. Then she asked the participants to complete a divergent thinking test in which they were presented with a series of novel and unlikely problems and tested on their ability to respond to them in a brief amount of time. Immediately following these two tests, Zabelina utilized P50 measurements to test the participants' SG abilities. Subjects were presented with several consecutive series of two identical auditory clicks, spaced 500 ms apart, and their physiological response (ERP) was measured 50 ms following each successive click using an EEG machine in a sound-proof chamber.

People who self-reported high levels of creative achievements were found to have higher SG ratios ($(S2/S1)\cdot 100$) than those who did not. Ironically, participants who demonstrated high levels of divergent thinking on the second test showed lower SG ratios than those who exhibited more moderate levels of divergent thinking. The thought behind the latter result is that efficient divergent thinking is marked by strong problem-solving skills which require enhanced focus, especially under the prescribed time constraints. It could be that the time constraint itself motivates people to focus more deliberately or perhaps the type of creative thinking involved in these exercises is psychologically different from the kind of creativity involved in other endeavors in the self-report questionnaire. Zabelina believes that the reasons for the differences have to do with an individual's ability to exercise cognitive control over SG, and these SG associations disappear following the 50 ms mark on the

EEG machine. Beyond the 50 ms mark, there were no discernible correlations between ERP readings and creative or divergent thinking.

If Zabelina is correct in her thinking that cognitive control is the key to enhanced creativity for specific individuals, then that would imply that some people can switch on and off their sense of intentional focus. When they are ready to be creative, they loosen up and welcome in a wide variety of sensory data so that they can free-associate and make new connections that lead to new and exciting ideas or projects. Then when they need to problem solve, they engage a renewed sense of focus and goal-oriented thinking that allows them to find sensible, logical solutions. She also believes that some people can utilize cognitive control better than others and those individuals who do not possess this ability are more likely to experience problems with focus, attentional disorders, and psycho-pathological disorders. It is also possible that a lack of cognitive control is a significant contributing factor to certain psychiatric conditions, including schizophrenia and bipolar depression. An individual's ability to exercise cognitive control may vary throughout their life due to a variety of external and internal circumstances so that in some instances they may be able to express remarkable feats of creativity and then in others they may fall deeply into apathy and depression.

The Effects of Nicotine Administration on Distractibility

There is a substantial body of research to support the idea that nicotine administration greatly enhances SG abilities and that specific populations of individuals suffering from certain psychiatric disorders including schizophrenia, attention deficit hyperactivity disorder (ADHD), and other schizotypal disorders might instinctively seek out nicotine to help them focus. According to researcher Li Wan and his colleagues, "Smoking may exert positive effects on attention by enhancing sensory gating. Superior sensory gating has been found in chronic smokers."[33] The idea here is that nicotine enhances attentional control in the brain. Few studies, according to Wan et al., have examined the association between attention and SG, so they set out to explore the connection between the two in their study.

Wan et al. used Posner and Petersen's attention model[34] to guide their research on the connection between attention and SG. In this model, there are three phases of attention - alerting, orienting, and conflict. The right frontal lobe and parietal lobe are most active during the alerting phase in which the brain initiates and maintains an attentive state. The orienting phase, believed to be activated by the frontal and superior parietal lobes, is responsible for the brain relying on sensory cues to decide what to focus its attention on specifically. The anterior cingulate gyrus and the lateral prefrontal cortex are responsible for the conflict phase, whereby conflicts resolve among different responses to the stimulus.

The researchers hypothesized that there should be an inverted relationship between SG ability and attentional performance (AP) where lower SG ratios were associated with higher AP levels and vice-versa. They designed a study that tested this hypothesized association by using an attention-level network test (ANT) and a Stroop task. Both tests occurred on subjects with brainwaves recorded by an EEG machine. In the ANT, participants saw an array of four distinct cue conditions. Following each cue, they observed a specific stimulus (an array of five arrows), and they had to press the left or right keyboard key to indicate the direction of the arrow. Researchers recorded their reaction times following each trial.

The Stroop task was used to assess subjects' ability to process relevant information and reconcile conflicting information. During the first 60 trials of this task, participants were presented colorful symbols and were asked to respond, using one of three distinct keyboard keys, which color was present in the symbol. In the next 80 trials of the experiment, subjects saw color words written in a different color, and they were asked to identify the color of the displayed word. These colors were incongruent with the words – for instance, the word "red" appeared in any color except red. The final 80 trials of the experiment consisted of trials in which the subjects saw color-congruent words so that words including "red," were written in red. The researchers collected data on both accuracy and mean reaction times in different tasks.

Researchers collected experimental data for two groups of college students – smokers and non-smokers. For the smokers, they were tested once after abstaining from cigarettes for at least four hours, and then they were tested again after smoking their preferred brand of cigarettes. Non-smokers got tested in the same two conditions (without smoking). Researchers collected P50 ERP data via EEG for both groups during the trials. Participants were further broken down into four distinct groups via schizotypy status: high-schizotypy smokers, low-schizotypy smokers, high-schizotypy non-smokers, and low-schizotypy non-smokers. Schizotypy represents a psychological continuum of personality characteristics and traits ranging from normal dissociative imaginative states (low schizotypy) to clinical episodes of schizophrenia, delusions, and psychosis (high schizotypy).

Researchers discovered a moderate association between SG and AP in the centroparietal region of the brain, the area most closely associated with sensory processing. No significant associations between SG and AP existed in the frontocentral region, an area primarily responsible for movement, decision-making, and planning. They also found that there was one significant relationship between SG and the Stroop test. Lower SG ratios positively correlated with better performance on the Stroop test. These results led the researchers to conclude that "the data generally suggest that sensory gating ability is positively associated with attentional vigilance and precision, and the capacity to resolve attentional conflict."[35] Auditory sensory data takes about 20 ms to reach the auditory cortex, and the SG activity typically occurs about 30 ms following that moment, inhibiting irrelevant stimuli and allowing for accurate information processing.

Another noteworthy finding from the study was that there was over three times the number of significant correlations between SG and attention span in the smokers compared to the non-smokers.[36] The researchers hypothesize that this effect is due to nicotine's enhanced effects on the neurological systems involved in SG. Chronic nicotine administration strongly reinforced that SG-attention relationship and was found to enhance performance and reaction time on the ANT as well as the quality of conflict resolution on the Stroop test. Acute (less frequent) smoking, however, did not establish a significant effect on SG although it did enhance performance on the ANT. According to the researchers, these results are consistent with earlier research establishing that long-term nicotine administration helps people with ADHD better focus their attention and enhances their cognitive skills.

Both the low and high schizotypy groups produced results that were consistent with earlier findings that schizotypy results in reduced SG abilities corresponding to poor performance on the ANT and Stroop test. Levels of schizotypy, whether high or low, had no significant effect on SG abilities, as the presence of this condition is known to impact the SG modality negatively. It was only in the presence of acute or chronic nicotine administration that SG or AP abilities were greatly enhanced. This finding may explain why smoking is typical self-medicating behavior among people on the schizotypy spectrum. Smoking may strengthen their skills to pay attention and focus for sustained periods, allowing them to feel more productive than they might otherwise be without it. It is important to note that this study neither endorses nor condones smoking behavior in affected individuals, but merely confirms the likely existence of a meaningful link between smoking and enhanced SG and AP levels.

The Psychology of Advertising

SG is a crucial neurological tool that allows you to extract relevant information from sensory data to determine what is essential to pay attention to as you navigate through the world. Object recognition skills and SG together play a pivotal role in your sensations and perceptions, but there is more to it than that. One significant idea that is difficult to reconcile is that of perspective. When confronted by objects and incoming sensory data, their context in their surrounding environment plays a vital role in how the brain prioritizes and interprets them. The same item presented in a different context might stand out more in one than another, which can be done intentionally, as in the case of media or commercial advertising, or unintentionally.

Consider the Stroop test for a simple example of how perception influences conflict resolution skills. The word "red" written in blue as opposed to red is more likely to catch your immediate attention because of the conflict in sensory information. You expect to see the word written in the same color as its identity, so any significant deviation from this will very likely catch your immediate attention. Similarly, a person's tone of voice, loudness, and tone will significantly influence how closely you might pay attention to what they are saying to you. It is much more challenging to pay attention to someone who is monotonous and dull than someone lively and entertaining, even if they are saying the same thing.

People are surrounded by and bombarded with advertisements daily. They are inescapable and ubiquitous, appearing everywhere from your television, the internet, freeway signs, to real estate signs in your neighborhood. There is very likely advertising even in your own home, be it the cereal boxes in your cabinet, health and beauty products on your nightstand, or even directly on your clothing. Everyone is competing for a few seconds of your precious attention. Advertisements are intended to lure you in subconsciously and capture your attention, if only for a moment. The best advertisements leave a lasting impression on you and promise to fulfill personal desires and needs, some of which you were not even necessarily aware you had in the first place. Advertising must first overcome your brain's SG filter process to avoid being discarded as irrelevant information and therefore completely disregarded by you. From there, it needs to convince you that the product or service offered is indeed relevant and necessary for your lifestyle.

In their book, *The Psychology of Advertising*,[37] authors Bob M. Fennis and Wolfgang Stroebe describe the different ways in which advertisers target their audience. They present two dominant models of advertising, dubbed the *argument-based* and *affect-based* models.[38] Argument-based models are typically used by advertisers when dealing with products that offer exceptional quality, durability, and value, such as a kitchen appliance or computer. These types of advertisements use rationalization and logic to appeal to the quality-savvy consumer.

Affect-based models appeal to an individual's emotions and feelings and use subliminal psychology to attract consumers' attention. As Fennis explains, "Consumer evaluations of experiential products will be mainly based on affect and will have very little cognitive content. In addition, such appeals require little processing motivation to be effective, so they are particularly suitable when consumer involvement is low."[39] Advertisements for spa treatments, vacation packages, family fun centers, and jewelry come to mind as products for which affect-based models of advertising would be appropriate. Sometimes advertisers target primal fear-based emotions in their consumer outreach. Fennis elucidates on five dimensions of fear-based advertising, including *physical*, *social*, *product performance*, *financial*, and *opportunity*.[40]

Advertisements for products that offer protection or symptom relief from physical conditions, including those for certain medications or protective sports gear, may involve dramatizing specific health maladies or potential injuries and then offering the product for relief or protection from them. For products such as deodorant, shampoos, or breath mints, advertisers may focus on their product as protection from social isolation for people with poor personal hygiene, as they make people fear rejection in the absence of their product.

Name brands rely on product performance fear whereby the advertiser implies that use of a competing brand will result in inferior results. The consumer must use the name brand to experience the full benefits of the product. Investment firms, banks, mortgage brokers, and credit card companies sometimes use financial fear to motivate consumers into using their products or else face the consequences. When consumers notice a competitive product, advertisers can perpetuate this fear by implying that purchasing that product will result in a financial loss because of its inferior quality. The opportunity tool is one of the most ubiquitous advertising techniques used by companies where they suggest that consumers can only get their product for a limited time. They engender a sense of urgency that if the customer does not purchase the product soon that they might miss out on a great deal forever.

One of the longstanding challenges advertisers face in constructing a captivating and effective advertising campaign is understanding the psychology of their intended audience, which can be a time-consuming and costly endeavor involving a great deal of market research, trial-and-error, and product modifications. There are competing theories as to how consumers process information during an advertisement, with some psychologists arguing they are actively engaged responders who should be encouraged to think critically about the product and others suggesting that consumers are passive recipients of information and that advertisements should play to their primal instincts and fears.

The cognitive response model[41] offers up the notion that consumers ought to consciously interact with an advertisement in a way that makes them feel a sense of ownership and pride in their response. According to Fennis, this model "emphasizes the mediating role of idiosyncratic thoughts or 'cognitive responses' that people generate when being exposed to a persuasive message. The consumer is no longer a passive recipient of an advertising message, but instead actively tries to make sense of it."[42] In this model, the credibility of the persuasive message is critical, as a convincing argument grounded by solid facts and reasoning is more likely to elicit a positive response toward the product. The idea is that they will engage in an internal dialogue and continue to persuade themselves that they need this product because of the logic suggesting that it is indeed a necessity or at the very least a good idea to purchase. The consumer ought to recognize the potential long-term value of their investment and feel that it is a "no-brainer" that they buy this product.

The problem with the cognitive response model is that not everyone likes to think about advertisements. Many people watch television, for instance, to relax or unwind after a hard day of work and they might not be interested in anything that requires too much conscious reflection or thought on their part. The *dual-process theories of cognition*[43] formed as social-psychological tools to address conflicting information about attitude formation, social judgment, and persuasion. This theory recognizes information processing, analysis, and decision-making as existing on a continuum with a high-level cognitive reflection on one end of the spectrum and primal low-level unconscious or subconscious stimulation on end the other end.

The most effective advertisements, according to this theory, are ones that encourage responses in the middle of the spectrum. If the ad encourages too much thinking and reflection, consumers might find it to be dull, uninspiring, or not worth their time. By contrast, an advertisement relying too much on factors such as background music, physical attractiveness or natural charisma of the product endorser, or other subliminal contextual messages might not be sufficient enough because of its weak foundation. If consumers invest too little thought into a product, their attitudes can be changed very quickly in the presence of a better advertisement from a competitor. Fennis explains that an ad "invariably needs to 'break through' an almost vegetative state of consumer media viewing, and then deliver a powerful punchline that consumers need to respond to with a well-articulated and favourable stream of thought, strong emotions and in a resource-active manner."[44]

The dual-process theories of cognition present an idealistic middle ground for advertisements where they need enough "bells and whistles" to attract an audience and then just enough of a convincing and thoughtful message to keep them engaged and make them feel like they are receiving useful information about a quality product or experience. This balance between resourcefulness and entertainment in an advertisement is both an art form and a science unto itself. When advertisers implement the proper blend of superficial and deep cognition-inducing qualities into their ads, they give themselves the best possible chance of attracting consumers to their product.

Understanding the psychology of color and sound are equally crucial to presenting an attractive advertisement.[45] The color white is useful for promoting a sense of purity, cleanliness, and creative potential. Blue is associated with feelings of calmness, coldness (if darker), sadness (if dark), or happiness (if lighter). Yellow can convey feelings of warmth, inspiration, joy, and satisfaction. Red is associated with power, sexual attraction, confidence, and boldness. Green is associated with nature, a sense of extraversion and exploration, and peacefulness. There are other ways to interpret these colors and how they are interpreted also depends on their context, hues, brightness, contrast, and other visual factors. Advertisers need to have an awareness of the colors they project in their advertisements and how they might set the stage for their product. The same goes for sounds and music. Depending on the mood an advertiser wishes to set, they may choose a speaker with a soft calming voice or one with a loud authoritative voice. Commercials may also involve classical music (reflective, calming, and classy), pop music (possibly accompanied by dancing), or heavy metal (excitement or aggression).

By themselves, colors represent nothing more than distinct wavelengths of light in the visible spectrum, so it is fascinating that they can be subjectively interpreted with psychology and associated with certain feelings and emotions. The same goes for sounds. An authoritative tone of voice might be off-putting and condescending in one context, but in another situation, it might feel appropriate or even relieving. Context matters and perspective is everything when it comes to interpreting sensory data in any of the five senses.

The Fallacy of Measurement

Precise automated visual and auditory processing are what allow you to interact with the world around you meaningfully. The brain has to approximate order where it might not exist using the tools of mathematics and language processing. Without these and similar processing tools, the world would look and sound a little bit like television static, or worse – like nothing at all. You would not be able to recognize the boundaries of the objects around you nor be able to assimilate the linguistic nuances hidden within vibrations of the eardrum that are necessary to formulate meaningful language.

Every physical object in existence is at best slightly irregular in its shape and composure compared to the preciseness and exactness predicted by mathematics. Every collection of sounds contains slight irregularities in tone, pitch, timing, and resonance. No two people pronounce the same word the same way, yet it is possible for them to understand each other correctly. Mathematics consists of seemingly perfect ideas of measurement, yet you cannot find any instances of this perfection in the world. Even some of the world's most technologically advanced atomic clocks cannot keep time entirely accurately, as they are in some instances off by about a nanosecond each month. Bridges built to exacting standards will most certainly contain minute errors, many of which are well within acceptable engineering tolerances, but erroneous nonetheless.

The concept and practice of measurement have been around almost as long as humanity has kept written records. The basic unit of length in ancient Egypt and ancient Mesopotamia is the *cubit*, a measure of length approximately equal to the length of a forearm. There was considerable variation as to what was considered a cubit, with a small cubit coming in around 18 inches in length and a large cubit measuring approximately 21 inches in length. Modern methods of measuring length include using rulers, tape measures, and even infrared laser beam equipment. The standard units for length come from the metric system and the US Standard system.[46]

The measurement of weight has occurred since ancient times with two primary methods for determining it, using either a balance or a scale to compare the weight of two objects. There is evidence from ancient Middle Eastern cultures using balance beams for this purpose and this method is still standard practice today. The ancient Egyptians used a limestone beam,[47] likely to measure things including the weight of gold discovered in the Euphrates river. They used a *Beqa*,[48] equivalent to between 12.18 and 13.61 grams, as a "standard" weight. Without such a standard of weight, there would be no reasonable way to measure the weight of an object.

In the late 18th century, the unit of standard mass, a *kilogram*, was equal to the mass of one cubic decimeter of water at a temperature of 4 degrees Celsius, an agreed-upon measurement meant to appease King Louis XVI of France in his quest for a standard unit of measurement.[49] 1/1000th of a kilogram is the *gram*, which is the standard unit of measurement in the Metric system. Ancient Roman civilization used the libra as their standard of measurement, which was equivalent to approximately 5040 English grains[50] and was the nominal standard used to weigh items including gold, silver, and other commercial transactions. Britain adopted the libra and referred to it as a *pound* retaining the "lb" as an homage to its name.[51] The pound is the standard of measurement still used by several European countries and the United States.

One ancient measurement of volume (capacity) is the *dram*,[52] which is 1/8th of a fluid ounce. This word derived from the Greek word *drachmë*, meaning "handful." In modern cultures, the word *dram* implies a small quantity of something, especially in the context of a beverage. The *litre*[53] (also spelled *liter*) is the modern metric unit for measuring volume and is equal to one cubic decimeter. The standard English unit of volume measurement is the *gallon*,[54] which is derived from the Medieval Latin word *gallëta*, meaning "jug" or "bucket."

One of the earliest activities carried out by ancient humans was to measure the passage of time, which needed to be done to plan for and coordinate both personal and business activities efficiently. By observing the different phases of the moon, the annual changes in seasons, and the amount of sunlight in a day, prehistoric humans were able to comprehend and measure the passage of time. None of these measurements was entirely consistent because of the inherent variation depending on geographical location and the time of year, but they worked reasonably well for the societal needs at the time. The ancient Sumerians are believed to have invented the sundial, a primitive clock that used the sun's shadow to tell time. Numerous cultures from all over the world used sundials and other primitive devices, but it was the Babylonians that were initially responsible for developing a temporal measurement system that eventually developed into the modern method used today.

The Babylonians used the number 60 to denote the number of seconds in a minute and the number of minutes in an hour because this number has many divisors compared to other numbers. This culture was also responsible for the idea that there are 360 degrees in a circle, so using the number 60 to measure smaller units of time made logical sense.[55] The Babylonian water-clock[56] was a primitive tool used by this culture to tell time, based on their mathematical measurements. This device relied on a steady flow of water, which gradually turned the dial on their clock. Modern cultures still make use of many of these ancient concepts of time measurement, with certain modifications. Atomic clocks are capable, for instance, of measuring the passage of time more precisely than anything else.

Regardless of the method or label applied to it, measurement is ultimately a human invention used for practical purposes to make sense out of the world. Just as a sports game has a set of rules and regulations that players must abide by, measurement systems provide a similar structure for people. Societies must agree upon standard units of measurement to function effectively, and standardized measurement systems are one of the hallmarks of a civilized people. The units and standards of measurement could have been remarkably different if other cultures were responsible for their development, but the concepts would have been the same regardless.

A society with consistent standards of measurement can then progress to similar standards for barter, whether it is goods for trade or units of financial tender. If enough people agree on the value of a unit of economic measurement, then civilized transactions and other sophisticated methods of business become possible. People need to feel that they are being treated impartially and fairly to engage in financial transactions. A standard unit of trade should be of the same value regardless of who takes possession of it. People can still negotiate with others, but the units of financial measurement retain a constant value throughout the negotiation process.

The tools of measurement in their various forms require a group of people to agree upon them for them to be practical and useful. Even though it only takes one person to have a perspective of how something should be measured, once a large enough group of people adopt a certain standard for their society, it gets labeled and used for essential purposes, which is similar to how laws get enacted and enforced. If enough people agree to make rules for a society and they possess the power, financial means, connections, and other resources necessary to implement them, then over time their culture will be conditioned to accept these laws (whether they like them or not) and to obey them. Ideally, the result is not an authoritarian one, such as a dictator might do in a totalitarian government, but even in those situations, the people around the leader must collectively and psychologically accept the legitimacy of the regime.

A Matter of Perspective

The power of perspective cannot be understated, and many visual artists, both historical and modern, exploit the psychology of perspective shifts to construct artistic masterpieces. *Impressionism* was an art movement from the 19th century, whereby artists relied on both subtle and bold changes in color and less on detail to build their artwork. Two artists might paint the same scene, but the results and subsequent interpretation of that scene might be quite different depending on the technique, colors, and brushstrokes used. One famous example of this phenomenon is the impressionist paintings of *La Grenouillere* by Pierre-Auguste Renoir and Claude Monet, two renowned artists from this era (Figure 5 and Figure 6).

La Grenouillere, a family gathering area, surrounded by lush greenery and situated on a gorgeous lake, was a famous vacation spot for working-class Parisians looking for a weekend getaway. Renoir and Monet painted the same scene from this vacation spot but used two completely different perspectives and techniques in their approach, the result being paintings that looked completely different.[57] Monet's goal was to paint a scene full of light and color that highlighted features of nature without focusing too much on the people in it. Renoir, on the other hand, chose to focus more sharply on the people with the result being a more social painting with less emphasis on natural features.

Both artists painted with broad brushstrokes, a defining feature of impressionism, to accentuate the subtle elements of the lake and surrounding nature. The main view in each painting is a small and round floating dock with a large boat floating towards it and several small rowboats around it. There is also a drooping tree limb in the foreground of each painting. Renoir's focus in his scene was on the social features, highlighting the interactions among people and painting a few animals which were absent in Monet's work. Renoir conveyed a sense of lightheartedness and joy in his painting, evident by the vivaciousness and relaxed mood evoked by the colors and social atmosphere depicted by his work. His broad brush strokes were complemented by more sharp strokes that highlighted the details of the larger boat, sunlight reflections off the water, bright clothing, and the dark leaves of the tree limb. When you view Renoir's interpretation of La Grenouillere, you almost feel as though you are there enjoying the relaxing atmosphere with everyone else.

Monet's painting offers a more distant view of the dock with considerably fewer social details and more space taken up by the natural features of the scene, especially the lake and surrounding beach. There is a sense of vastness in Monet's interpretation due to the emphasis on large swaths of the empty lake and less attention to detail and less space taken up by the large boat and dangling tree. There is also a sense of being a detached, perhaps unwelcome, observer in this scene than in the welcoming and playful atmosphere depicted by Renoir. The people seem to be so far away, and although they look relaxed, they seem far less lively than the ones in Renoir's painting. There is a greater emphasis on the empty rowboats in the foreground, and they contain darker tones than the warm tones of the boat highlighted in Renoir's work.

It is remarkable how two painters can observe the same scene yet interpret it in two completely different ways, to the point where it neither looks nor feels the same. One thing you can be sure of is that neither painting precisely depicts what happened that day on the lake because both are entirely subjective interpretations of a landscape and the people, animals, and objects within it. Each artist painted the scene through his point-of-view that was colored by a combination of personal experience, internal psychology, and artistic techniques. In both paintings, you capture a sense of the passing moment conveyed by the broad-brush strokes, giving each picture a seemingly coherent blurriness to it. Despite the similarities, Renoir's painting feels more upbeat while Monet's feels lonely and dreary. Monet used darker colors for the water and other natural objects, while Renoir's painting had smoother blending and lighter tones. You can get a sense for the mindset of each artist from details like these in their pictures.

So, what happened during that moment at La Grenouillere? The answer to that question is indeed a matter of perspective. Supposing each of the people in the painted scenes was truly present that day, each would have their own unique personal account and view on what happened, including the overall mood and atmosphere of that moment. Some of them might not even remember it at all. It would have been especially interesting if someone present that day on the boat or floating dock had painted the artists who were busy painting them, which illustrates the absurdity of trying to determine what happened or the nature of the social atmosphere.

The importance of perspective is not just limited to social scenes such as that of La Grenouillere. Even everyday material objects are a matter of perspective. The same object viewed from different angles, different times of day, or even in fluctuating levels of light will not look the same. As author G.E. Moore points out, "There are two beliefs in which almost all philosophers, and almost all ordinary people are agreed. Almost everyone believes that he and what he directly perceives do not constitute the whole of reality: he believes that *something* other than himself and what he directly perceives *exists* or is *real*."[58] People naturally believe that what they perceive must be real and that there is some objective nature to the things, people, and animals in the world around them. This supposition is not falsifiable either, as any method of measuring the nature of reality relies on an observer to report on it, which makes it inherently biased.

Perhaps the greatest irony of all is how there is no objective way to look at or even to identify objects. Even more strange than that is that an object is always changing and is never in the same state from moment to moment. Take, for instance, a white golf ball. After it has been used on the fairway and beaten and covered with dirt and debris, it is hardly the same ball as it once was. Every strike and action toward the ball adds or subtracts particles from it and alters its composition. While any rational person would never question the object's identity as a golf ball, one could quickly wonder at what point would it cease to be one. Hitting the golf ball into a lava pit would immediately and irrevocably alter the properties of the golf ball. The ball would rapidly disintegrate in the lava and would no longer be identifiable, as all its composite parts would quickly become integrated into the surrounding lava.

The brain relies on properties including colors, edges, contrast, context, familiarity, memory, and shapes to recognize and identify objects and can accurately estimate objects when confronted with visual discrepancies or ambiguities. What your brain cannot do, however, is reveal what the correct perspective to examine an object from is. There are seemingly infinite ways to approach an item, whether it be up close, from behind, the side, at a great distance, or through a microscope. Separating an object from your perspective is impossible.

Now consider a tall oak tree in a grassy field. There is a tree with its firm stump, glorious branches, and dark green leaves. This tree will look very different, even if viewed at the same time, from various observational perspectives. If viewed from ten or twenty meters away, all the defining features of the tree are visible, which is most likely the most appropriate distance to capture a photograph of the entire tree. Step a few hundred meters further back, and the tree will be hardly visible at all. Move closer to the tree, and you will be able to make out more details about it including the texture of the bark, insects crawling around on it, the sunlight reflecting on the leaves, and birds perched on the branches. If you had a superhuman vision, you could theoretically get even closer to the tree and view individual plant cells, bacteria, and other miniature ecosystems within it.

Each perspective of the tree is unique and offers its special features and limitations. Although there is no way to know what an animal or insect with eyes sees when they view a tree, it would most certainly be different than a human perspective. An eagle or crow flying overhead could see it from above while a honeybee would see a pixelated view of it. Everyone considers the tree differently depending on what their eyes can see and their viewing angle and distance away from it. Objects also change form over time, some more quickly than others. Water freezes into ice, and then the ice melts when the temperature is warm enough. Heat water up some more and it boils and evaporates into steam. Even the sturdiest objects change form subtly, as they collect dust, rust, and experience gradual wear and tear. Nothing is safe from the elements, and over time, everything eventually crumbles back to the Earth. No object is the same from moment to moment because of constant changes to it.

The fine line between an object and its surroundings is not always clear because objects are continually interacting with their surrounding environment and subject to the forces and elements within it. Most objects remain relatively stable for long periods such that these changes are subtle and trivial. Nonetheless, it is up to the brain to recognize and identify them appropriately. If objects exist independent of observation, there should be a standard way to measure their size and dimensions. To measure the dimensions of an object requires a standard measuring instrument, but this is not as simple as it may initially seem. Consider measuring the height of an oak tree. Just measure the height from the highest point of the tree to the base. The most reasonable measurement is as close to the tree as possible, but even at this distance, there will be some significant issues trying to obtain an accurate measurement. No matter how close you hold the measuring tape to the trunk and no matter how taut you attempt to make the tape, there are many grooves and edges in the bark that would prevent you from genuinely obtaining an accurate estimate of the height. Even if you were to construct a measuring instrument that could account for all these grooves and edges, it would still be impossible to obtain an exact height for the tree because even these irregularities within the tree have peculiarities of their own that are difficult to measure.

The other issue that prevents truly accurate measurement is the inherent errors in the measuring instrument itself. A measurement is only as good as the measuring instrument, and unfortunately, even the most carefully calibrated instruments still possess some degree of error to them. These errors typically fall within acceptable tolerances and are not usually of any practical concern, but they illustrate the limitations of measurement. A measurement device is a tool invented by humans to quantify the dimensions of objects, but as with any device, it is subject to limitations and errors.

Back to the oak tree, there is no way to know how close you need to get to it to measure it accurately, be it just mere centimeters away or a few meters away. Even if you use the same measuring device for two measurements from different distances away from the tree, you will obtain two separate measurements for the height of that tree, and there is no reliable way to tell which one is more accurate than the other. This difference in height would be present even if the two measuring distances were very close together. If objects are genuinely unique, then it could be argued then that an oak tree viewed from two different perspectives are not the same trees – that the properties of the tree change with and are dependent on the angle of observation.

Additionally, the properties of the oak tree are in a constant state of change. Besides the slower change the tree undergoes with the passing of each season, there is a minute, but significant change going on with the tree all the time. Each day the length of the tree roots varies slightly and the cells that make up the leaves, bark, and other parts of the tree, are continuously changing as well. Bark dries up and falls to the ground. Dead leaves detach and fall to the ground in Autumn, and then new leaves sprout from branches near the top during the Spring. The tree is also its ecosystem with countless insects, birds, and other animals hiding in it and feasting on it. Parts of the tree are always falling off into the ground beneath it while new elements are assimilating into and from it at the same time, making it difficult to tell at what point the tree becomes separate from the Earth beneath it.

Perspective is everything when it comes to object recognition and detection. The distance you are away from the object as well as the angle you view it from influences how you perceive it. The stars in the night sky would appear as giant violent fireballs like the Sun if they were closer to Earth. Likewise, if you were living on a distant planet in the Milky Way galaxy, the Sun would appear as one of those faint distant stars in the night sky. Even within your own body, there are microscopic ecosystems full of life. The dust mites crawling on your skin do not know of the larger world around them any more than the ants in your backyard do not know of the house across the street.

According to Alice from the 1951 classic film *Alice in Wonderland*, "If I had a world of my own, everything would be nonsense. Nothing would be what it is, because everything would be what it isn't. And contrary wise; what is, it wouldn't be. And what it wouldn't be, it would. You see?"[59] In a sense, everyone is their own Alice trying to make sense out of the world around them, using labels from other people's imaginations to identify objects, animals, and other material things. If everyone were to come up with unique labels, forms of measurement, and ways of identifying objects, then each person's world would be completely different from one another. No two people would share the same labels or perspectives. In some sense, this is what is already happens, as no two people share the same view. Everything is not what it is to another person.

Chapter 5 – No Normal

"The world is made up of two kinds of people: the ones who think they're normal and the ones who know there's no such thing."[1]

— Will McAvoy

Discrimination

There are the eccentrics, the geeks, and the freaks. There are the crooks, the liars, and the cheats. There are the crazy, the lazy, and the meek. It is easy to judge the people around you. Everyone is different, and some people take great liberty in judging others and labeling them, perhaps to make them feel better about themselves or as a way of distancing themselves from others. Few people strive to be "normal" as a goal, yet others are all too quick to point out when someone is not acting in the usual way. Stray too far away from normal behavior, and you might be considered abnormal. This label of "normal" is carelessly and thoughtlessly tossed around, but with little regard to what it means. According to Merriam Webster, the primary definition of the word "normal" is "Conforming to a type, standard, or regular pattern."[2] Interestingly, the tertiary definition of normal is, "Of, relating to, or characterized by average intelligence or development. Free from mental illness: mentally sound."[3]

These definitions are challenging to apply to people for a variety of reasons. What is considered socially acceptable in one context might be offensive and inappropriate in another situation. There is also a subjective nature to intelligence, as there is a broad and varied spectrum to it. Some people are mechanically inclined but not skilled scholastically, while others are very intellectually oriented but not particularly handy. Mental illness also tends to occur on a spectrum, and a person's level of sanity can vary significantly given different contexts. Trying to normalize people can be both ignorant and dangerous. Adolf Hitler famously tried to eradicate entire social classes of people for a variety of reasons, but chief among those was to eliminate undesirable traits from the population to produce a master race of humans only containing specific physical and mental characteristics. The Holocaust was one of the darkest events in human history and one of the most infantile displays of bigotry and hatred.

Time and again, despots have arisen in various nations and coerced their populations into mental imprisonment, conditioning them to feel and believe certain things about other people that only serves to divide them and create a sense of hostility amongst each other. Aldous Huxley famously said, "This concern with the basic condition of freedom — the absence of physical constraint -- is unquestionably necessary, but is not all that is necessary. It is perfectly possible for a man to be out of prison and yet not free — to be under no physical constraint and yet to be a psychological captive, compelled to think, feel and act as the representatives of the national State, or of some private interest within the nation, want him to think, feel and act."[4]

Casting artificial labels on people can serve a useful purpose if trying to organize a group project for work. One person is the project manager, the other one is the marketing director, and yet another is the content manager. For the time that these people work together, their labels help them to complete their tasks and provide a sense of organization to the entire group. Names like these serve a useful purpose and can be very productive, but other types of labels can be misconstrued and applied in a divisive or derogatory manner. Racial divisions have haunted human history since the dawn of humanity. According to author Simon Worrall, "The characteristics of normal human variation we use to determine broad social categories of a race—such as black, Asian, or white—are mostly things like skin color, morphological features, or hair texture, and those are all biologically encoded."[5] These characteristics are mostly superficial and ignore the myriad genetic variations that exist among people. The author mentions that there is so much genetic diversity in Africa, for instance, that two people from that same continent are likely to be more genetically different compared to each other than compared to anyone else on a different continent.

Modern studies in paleo-genetics have revealed that human ancestry weaves like a beautiful tapestry through at least three certain sets of ancestors including Neanderthals, Homo Sapiens, and Denisovans. There is also some inconclusive evidence of a potential fourth ancestor.[6] These species all interbred many times over in the past, and each acted in part to contribute to the modern human. All people share a common ancestry and therefore are relatives of each other, no matter how distant. While modern genetic studies have come to be revered recently due to their historical and predictive powers, people have gotten carried away in their illogical reverence for genetics. Worrell points out, "There is a genetic basis to human behaviors. But there is also an environmental component. We used to say nature *versus* nurture. But we might say nature *via* nurture."[7] Genetics is neither an excuse nor an explanation for evil human behaviors or traits. Human behavior is a complex system of both psychological and social interactions sprinkled with an element of random circumstance.

Racist attitudes are not a result of genetics. People develop racist thoughts and patterns, mostly out of fear and ignorance. Rather than try to understand another's socio-economic or cultural conditions, they build blanket statements and judgments about them to avoid interaction or feelings of inferiority. Unfortunately, these feelings can become validated in the collective and lead to civil violence, discrimination, and condemnation. Once formed, prejudices can be difficult to overcome and lead to toxic alienation and feelings of hatred. Racism and bigotry become the social norms in these communities and lead to an environment of exclusivity and isolation.

Most ironically, discrimination is a vital and necessary skill for human survival, as people are naturally inclined to categorize people and objects. This skill enables people to learn about and how to navigate complex physical and social systems. Children need to be able to discriminate among the different letters of the alphabet and know how to manipulate them together to write and form words and sentences. A doctoral student in medicine must be adept at discriminating amongst the various organs and systems in the human body to be competent at diagnosing and treating illness.

Discrimination is an endemic and necessary quality of human survival, but just as is the case with any condition, it can serve both a beneficial and harmful purpose. In the case of racism, people learn to discriminate amongst people in what psychologist Gwendolyn Keita describes as, "the result of deep-seated, destructive generalizations about a certain group. In such cases, people harbor unrealistic, disparaging beliefs about a group and its members, while also maintaining a sense of the moral or intellectual superiority of their own group."[8] There is almost a cult-like nature to the perpetuation of racist generalities and the need for collective validation to continue with the harmful and destructive behaviors associated with these beliefs.

One of the most prevalent forms of discrimination is microaggressions. According to the American Psychological Association, "Microaggressions are everyday, seemingly minor verbal, nonverbal, or environmental slights or insults that may be delivered intentionally or unintentionally. These messages provide a glimpse of the communicator's conscious or unconscious assumptions and prejudices."[9] How a white cashier at a convenience store might instinctively shriek away from a person of color purchasing liquor is an example of a microaggression. Although the cashier is not blatantly demonstrating a racist attitude, his action indicates some deep-seated beliefs and experiences such as people of color have criminal tendencies. This same cashier very likely will not display the same behavior when approached by a fellow white person purchasing liquor.

These microaggressions transcend all levels of society, including race, gender, disability, class, and other traits beyond the individual's control. An example of a gender microaggression would be referring to a dominant female politician in a derogatory manner while lauding the behavior of an equally high-ranking male politician. Both the male and female politicians might behave similarly, have similar viewpoints, and even share a common platform, but the female might get labeled and also treated differently because of microaggressions from her constituents.

Someone holding a door open for a person with paraplegia in a wheelchair might seem like a goodwill gesture, and indeed it very well could be, but the assumption that they cannot open the door by themselves might be a type a microaggression. A way to avoid this simple act from being taken the wrong way is to ask the person if they would like assistance with the door and only open it for them if they oblige. Providing them with a choice in the matter allows them to ask for help and will likely not make them feel any less able because they can reply politely with "no thank you" if they do not wish to have the door opened for them.

A wealthy customer might treat a person working as a cashier at a fast-food restaurant with an entitled attitude because of feelings of superiority of social class over them due to their perception of having an elevated social status. The wealthy individual may know nothing about this individual but makes assumptions based on their place of employment and possibly also based on their attire. There is a subconscious bias at work here that influences the wealthy individual's attitude toward the cashier.

Microaggressions do not have to be exclusively unidirectional. Often, they are bidirectional, and it is the combination of competing microaggressions that can lead to conflict among individuals. In the previous example, it could be the case that the cashier carries prejudices about the wealthy customer based on his attire or attitude. He might feel threatened or intimidated and act rudely toward him for no reason. After that awkward interaction, the customer might notice that the cashier is friendlier to the customers behind him.

In this case, there was a dualistic nature to the microaggressions, which can lead to a total communication breakdown. The wealthy individual made certain assumptions about the cashier as part of his entitled attitude. Simultaneously the cashier made assumptions about the wealthy person that led to him treating the customer differently. These competing microaggressions might lead to an escalation in rude behavior between these two individuals that could result in unnecessary conflict. Even if the absence of direct conflict between the individuals, their feelings might be hurt as an immediate effect of the microaggressions.

Microaggressions can also perpetuate across different cultures. What might be offensive in one country might be completely acceptable in another one. An American visiting Australia might give the "thumbs up" gesture of approval to the waiter after eating a delicious meal out at a restaurant without realizing the derogatory nature of that gesture in that culture. The waiter might scoff at him thinking "stupid American" and leave the patron completely confused. This awkward situation is the result of two types of ignorance at work.

The American did not take the time to educate himself about Australian culture completely, and the waiter who took offense might hold certain beliefs and attitudes towards American tourists. Although the action of the patron did not demonstrate any microaggressions, they contributed to the activation of a microaggression in the waiter due to being ignorant about the culture before dining. If the patron was aware of the derogatory nature of the gesture and did it anyway assuming that the waiter would automatically understand what he meant, then that does demonstrate a microaggression on the part of the patron in the form of willful ignorance toward another person's socio-cultural norms.

One of the hallmarks of discrimination is making assumptions about other people. According to Felix Unger from *The Odd Couple*, "When you assume, you make an ass out of u and me."[10] Making assumptions in the absence of factual information represents lazy and uninformed thinking, can be harmful to relationships, and most of all is usually wrong. Many assumptions arise from previous experiences, microaggressions, or ineffective communication. As Professor Beverly D. Flaxington of Suffolk University explains, assumptions can lead to unnecessary conflict in relationships.[11] She recounts the story of a radio show host who wrote out a shopping list for her husband and numbered off the list to make it easier for him to read. When he arrived home, he brought in the groceries, mistakenly believing that the numbers represented the number of items his wife wanted him to purchase. Shocked at this assumption of his, she expressed irritation towards him and he also was frustrated with her not fully explaining what the numbering on the list meant. He could have avoided this simple miscommunication if his wife asked him if he had any questions about the grocery list and if he did not just make errant assumptions about it.

Meaningful Relationships

The two antidotes to making assumptions are regularly engaging in the practices of active and reflective listening. Active listening requires engaging with the person you are communicating with and asking them questions when you feel that you need further clarification about something that they said. When you are listening actively to someone, they will feel acknowledged and be willing to provide greater detail to their explanations. Reflective listening is when you demonstrate to the person you are communicating with that you understood what they said. You can do this by paraphrasing what they said to you in your own words and making sure that you understood what they intended to communicate to you. If you did not understand everything, the other person should be able to clarify some details so that there are no misunderstandings.

Practicing active and reflective listening with people can help reduce microaggressions and lead to more positive and uplifting relationships.[12] Instead of making assumptions about individuals or groups of people, you can ask questions and learn about their personality, habits, and culture. The best part about having this attitude toward people is that it significantly reduces feelings of insecurity and loneliness because people like to feel validated and that you are genuinely interested in them.

It is all too easy to judge someone based on their culture, physical appearance, social or marital status, material possessions, or hobbies, but all that does is reveal insecurities and fear on the part of the person making assumptions about the other person. Taking a genuine interest in someone requires effort and a willingness to engage with them actively. In some cases, it means stepping outside of your comfort zone and risking vulnerability to get to know someone better. At least if you make a genuine effort to inquire about someone's personality, you can feel validated if you end up not wanting to pursue a friendship with them. The reasons why you did not wish to associate with them would not be purely superficial or based on erroneous assumptions. More likely than not, you will find yourself having more good experiences with people than bad ones if you are putting in the effort to get to know them.

Concerning relationships, there is no rule about the number of friendships a person needs to have. The number of friends in an individual's life should not indicate a metric for social success. Some people prefer only a few close friends, and others enjoy socializing with large groups of people. Some friendships are only there for a brief time, and others can last a lifetime, but all of them add some value to your life. Friends are there to learn from each other, to share experiences with, and to be there for one another. They are the people you can count on to not judge you for your character flaws but to call you out on them when they are harmful to yourself or others. They are also the ones you can be around comfortably when nothing is going on at all. As David Tyson puts it, "True friendship comes when the silence between two people is comfortable."[13]

Friends are there to ease your struggle through this challenging world and to help you discover the beauty and happiness of the moments of your life. They are there for you in times of need and allow you to be there for them when they are experiencing hardships as well. True friendship is all about learning how to balance out the "give and take" in life. Unbalanced friendships rarely last as resentment can build an impenetrable barrier between two people. Nobody likes to feel taken advantage of by someone else. The best bonds consist of interactions that make each person feel happier than they were before. Having friendships like these adds quality and value to your life that you cannot obtain from anything else.

Trying to find the right friends can be challenging. People come and go, and not everyone is there to stay as a close friend or romantic partner. The idea of compatibility between people is something that many psychological researchers have tackled for years with limited success. What qualities should a person look for in another person to ensure a high likelihood of relationship success? While there is a substantial body of evidence suggesting that people are generally attracted to others who exhibit similar physical and socio-economic characteristics, there is not much data to support that people are attracted to others with the same personality traits. Personality tests, such as the online surveys circulated throughout social media, are a completely unreliable method for identifying interpersonal compatibility due to their inherent subjectivity and confirmation bias.

One of the most commonly accepted self-reported personality tests is the Myers Briggs Type Indicator (MBTI)[14] which was created by Isabel Briggs Myers and her mother Katharine Briggs in an attempt to bring the theory of psychological types explained by Carl Jung accessible to everyone. The MBTI is a four-dimensional test with sixteen possible combinations of characteristics. Each possible combination is considered a distinct type of personality. The first category is used to determine whether an individual is extroverted (E) or introverted (I). People who are extroverted feel motivated and energized by being around others and getting involved in different social activities. People like this are generally considered outgoing, confident, and friendly. Introverts prefer to reflect inward and get their inspiration from ideas, memories, books, and other sources of internal motivation. They prefer to have a few close friendships and are most comfortable being by themselves.

The second category is concerned with whether the individual is sensing (S) or intuitive (N). People who are sensing are reactive and responsive to the world around them. They respond most to the sights, sounds, and smells right in front of them and are most interested in facts and experiences as their primary guides. Intuitive people trust their feelings and intuition to help them make decisions. They are forward thinkers who spend much of their time dreaming and fantasizing about the future. They prefer to take chances and are "big picture" thinkers.

The third category is used to characterize a person as thinking

(T) or feeling (F). Thinking people base their decision-making on a combination of logic, truth, or principles and rules. They can occasionally come across as rude or indifferent to others, but they pride themselves on not allowing their personal feeling and preferences to get in the way. Personal values guide feeling people who seek to understand the perspective of everyone involved in a situation or decision. Although they can come across as idealistic and emotional, they are compassionate and empathetic and will listen to anyone even if they do not necessarily agree with them.

The fourth and final category determines whether an individual is judging (J) or perceiving (P). This category is a reflection of how these individuals come across to others. An individual who is judging will usually appear as someone who is highly responsible for getting things done on time and who excels at planning, task management, and managing resources. Perceiving people typically come across as flexible and open to new experiences. They may tend to procrastinate on deadlines and work best impulsively and spontaneously.

The MBTI is widely considered to be one of the foundational developments in applied personality theory; however, it is not without its criticisms. Modern psychology considers personality traits as continuous and fluid and not as discrete entities. Someone introverted in one situation might be extroverted in another one. Different circumstances call for various decisions, and some conditions can bring out different elements of a person that would otherwise be dormant. Nonetheless, the MBTI did introduce interesting personality delineations that are highly relevant today. People need to exercise caution in how they apply the MBTI and not to interpret the results as definitive and conclusive.

Another problem with self-reported questionnaires such as the MBTI is they exhibit a limitation known as the *reference group effect*.[15] When responding to self-reflective questions, you are most likely to base your answers about yourself in comparison to those around you or close association with you. For instance, if you are naturally a lazy person, but lethargic people surround you, you might think of yourself as a hard-working individual in comparison to those people. On the other hand, if you are lazy and surrounded by a group of overachievers, you will likely rate yourself as being very lazy.

Researchers Wu Youyou et al. discovered through their landmark personality study[16] that people tend to select friends and romantic partners that are like themselves. They conducted an experiment soliciting users of a Facebook application known as "MyPersonality." Facebook users filled out personality questionnaires used for conducting psychological research. Six million people participated in the surveys until being officially closed in 2012. The researchers obtained three samples of participants from the MyPersonality study. They gave each of these participants, across sample group 1 and sample group 2, an International Personality Item Pool (IPIP) Representation self-reporting personality test[17] in which they were asked to describe themselves in relation to the people they know using the well-established five categories of personality - openness to experience, conscientiousness, extraversion, agreeableness, and neuroticism.

Sample group 1 were used to construct a predictive model for personality type by developing a likes-based personality assessment. Sample group 2 were used to construct another predictive model for personality type by developing a language-based personality assessment. The predictive tools created by the first two sample groups were then used to test member dyads of the third sample group for the existence of personality similarities between them. These dyads in the third sample group consisted of both friends or romantic partners based on their declared Facebook relationship status (for romantic partners) or data from friend lists (for friends). Note that only some of the participants in the third sample group took the IPIP test.

The likes-based analysis[18] sought to determine a relationship between liking certain things on Facebook and having a specific personality type. For example, people who liked pictures of people partying might be more likely to exhibit extroversion, whereas people who liked pessimistic political posts might be more inclined to be neurotic. Researchers looked for a relationship between people wanting specific things and having a particular personality type by organizing the like data into a matrix that associated specific likes with categorical personality traits. They ran a statistical program on the vast matrix of data to come up with the predictive model between the participants' self-reported personality data and the digital "like" data. They used this predictive model on participants from the third sample group to predict their personality traits based on their Facebook "like" preferences.

In the language-based analysis,[19] the researchers first identified target words and phrases from participants' posts and status updates. These words and phrases were very carefully selected so that they would be common enough to be found across a broad enough sample of participants. They looked at binary indicators which told them whether a participant used a common word or phrase, and they also examined the relative frequencies of each common word or phrase across the different participants' Facebook profiles. They statistically analyzed this data in a similar way to the "like" data and established a predictive model that associated the use and frequency of certain words and phrases with personality traits. Researchers used this predictive tool for participants from the third sample group to predict personality traits from their written social media data.

One of the study authors, David Stillwell, summarized the results of the study as follows: "We found that, on self-reported questionnaires, couples are no more similar than strangers, but when we measured personality using digital behavior…couples were far more similar than [by] chance."[20] They found that openness to experience was the most commonly correlated trait between friends and romantic partners when it came to data analysis from the self-report, the likes-based results, and the likes-language correlations. Extraversion was the most commonly correlated trait for the language-based results. According to Stillwell, "People date and befriend others who are like themselves, and birds of a feather do flock together after all."[21]

What is not clear from this study is what is the causal nature of the results. It is a sort of "chicken and the egg" dilemma, where it is unclear if people are attracted to each other because of similarities that already exist or if two people become more like each other over time. That is a question that will likely take a very long time to answer and will require more sophisticated methodology, but one thing is clear – the availability of social media data has enabled researchers to revisit established psychological problems and find exciting trends among people based on what they reveal, both directly and indirectly, about themselves online.

Future psychological studies might aim to help develop more sophisticated techniques to help people learn how to utilize social media and technology to search for friends or romantic partners. Matchmaking algorithms for friendship and relationships might move beyond the superficialities of apps like Tinder or the tedious nature of Match.com and similar online dating sites. Then again, the intricacies of human behavior might prove too dynamic and complex for researchers ever to master their properties and guarantee stable, productive relationships between people. Not long ago, there were minimal services or technology available for matchmaking. You would meet the people you met and make the best out of it. Sometimes relationships blossomed, and other times they wilted away like flowers in a field.

Perhaps the best course of action is just to let relationships develop naturally and trust your intuition about them. There is no right way to go about meeting people and no formula for guaranteeing that any particular interaction with a person is going to lead to something more. Compatibility between people is not a static quality, and it takes effort on the part of both participants in a relationship (platonic or romantic) to keep it exciting and meaningful. Like romantic relationships, friendships change and mature over time due to numerous factors including changes in careers, health, residence, habits, and families. When it comes to friendships, there can be considerable variation in how often you interact with your friends. According to Julia Beck, "Friendships are unique relationships because unlike family relationships, we choose to enter into them. And unlike other voluntary bonds, like marriages and romantic relationships, they lack a formal structure. You wouldn't go months without speaking to or seeing your significant other (hopefully), but you might go that long without contacting a friend."[22]

One consistent finding from Beck's research was that people associated quality friendships with their overall happiness level. The beauty of friendship is that it is an entirely voluntary relationship not bound by the same restrictions of a romantic relationship, especially one involving children and family. Friends are with each other because they want to be, and even if a lot of time passes between meetings, they can usually pick right up where they left off as if no time passed at all. That is the remarkable beauty of a healthy friendship. According to her, the most significant drop-off in friendships occurs when people get married. Middle age is also a challenging time with careers, children, and other factors getting in the way of social time. Although most people define friendship as "being there" for each other, the irony is that many working adults cannot find the time to devote to their friends due to all of the competing and more urgent demands in their life. Friendships come and go throughout life, but everyone has a different way of forming friendships and maintaining them. According to Beck, "Some are independent, they make friends wherever they go, and may have more friendly acquaintances than deep friendships. Others are discerning, meaning they have a few best friends they stay close with over the years, but the deep investment means that the loss of one of those friends would be devastating. The most flexible are the acquisitive—people who stay in touch with old friends but continue to make new ones as they move through the world."[23]

Friendships made in middle age are often associated with existing family or work relationships. It might be more comfortable, for instance, to make friends with a co-worker because you already interact with them daily anyway, so it would not require that much effort to pursue their company outside of work. It might similarly be convenient to form friendships with your child's parents because their kids also go to the same schools. Research has shown that the most fruitful associations are equitable, where both people feel that they are putting in a comparable amount of effort into the bond. Some friendships exist off longevity, where an initial investment earlier in life into the association allowed it to still be intact later in life despite constantly changing life circumstances. Beck also noted that the quantity of friendships over an individual's lifespan tends to follow a parabolic curve.[24] People have a lot of friends in their early years through their college years where people tend to live nearby each other, frequently interact due to school and other common interests (such as sports, recreational activities, and studying), and go to a lot of parties and social events. Friendship quantities decline in middle age due to familial and career responsibilities, and then they pick back up again in old age due to retirement, which brings about fewer responsibilities and increased opportunities and time for socializing.

According to Beck, there are progressive behaviors that are necessary for maintaining a friendship in order of closeness. The first behavior is an acknowledgment, which can be as simple as wishing someone "Happy Birthday" on social media or sending them a text message. These mechanistic gestures of affirmation prevent people from forgetting about each other and show them that they are still relevant. The next behavior is to create stable feelings of closeness, which goes beyond the simple acknowledgment and is more in-depth. For example, it could be a detailed message explaining how much you miss your friend, or it could be a heartfelt apology for letting so much time pass in-between visits. By making yourself vulnerable in this way, you are opening the door to a closer friendship, especially if it has been a long while since you last spent time together. The third behavior is to turn the association into a more satisfying relationship, which requires effort from both parties (as do all the other actions) to make time for each other, be it over the phone or in person. Think of it as committing to making time for each other regularly, which moves beyond the online presence of friends on social media and pushes them into reality.

Friendships can cycle through these stages multiple times in your life, and the level of closeness you experience with your friends will depend on how much effort each of you is willing to put into the relationship. Some people are satisfied to have many acquaintances, such as those present on a social media profile. Others prefer activity partners that they meet up with semi-regularly to hang out and engage in everyday activities such as painting, dancing, or hiking.

Others wish to have very close friends who come over regularly and participate in significant conversations with each other. Many people have a combination of close friends and acquaintances.

Beck goes on to explain that there are three significant friendship categories: active, dormant, and commemorative.[25] Active friendships are those relationships in which both people can depend on each other regularly for emotional support, and if you two live near each other, then you make time to hang out and socialize. Dormant friendships are ones that have history to them and were active in the past. In a dormant friendship, you would take time to meet up with your friend if they were in town for a visit, but then you would likely not see or hear from them for a while after seeing them. A commemorative friendship is one in which you think of a person fondly and have good memories with them, but you know that you will likely never see them again.

Friendships solely based on social media or other online platforms are ones that are inherently limited in their ability to breed a sense of closeness and trust. As Beck explains, "If you never see your friends in person, you're not really sharing experiences so much as just keeping each other updated on your separate lives. It becomes a relationship based on storytelling rather than shared living—not bad, just not the same."[26] Since people can project a particular persona about themselves online, these types of relationships tend to be shallow and superficial. There is value in having friends online, but it is necessary to find other ways to interact with them if you want to develop closer and more meaningful relationships.

The best friendships are the ones in which, no matter what circumstances life throws your way, you stay friends. It does not matter if you have to move away for a career change or you have hardly any free time due to raising a family or taking care of aging parents. Friends always find a way to make some time for each other. Good friends care about the people they have memories with and seek to form new ones with them. The definition of a "normal" friendship will depend on the expectations of the people involved in it. If two people are content just sharing occasional text messages and pictures online and that brings some value to their life, then that is a healthy friendship. So long as both parties' expectations are reasonable, and they are both willing to put in equal effort into maintaining the relationship, then it will flourish. There is no average number of friends someone should have, but many researchers agree there is little emotional or personal value by living in complete isolation from others. As Oprah Winfrey once said, "Everyone wants to ride with you in the limo, but what you want is someone who will take the bus with you when the limo breaks down."[27]

Discovering Beauty

The most crucial friendship someone can have is with themselves. You must love yourself before you can show love to others. Unfortunately, not everyone is brought up in the same circumstances, and some people have it much harder than others. Some people inherit physical or mental health conditions that can have a substantial impact on their overall quality of life. It is vital to have empathy for those who are not as well off as others. Everyone faces a unique set of struggles, obstacles, and triumphs in life. Nobody can completely control their life circumstances or destiny, but there are things everyone can do to make their life more bearable or joyful under challenging times.

Discovering what provides you passion and happiness can be an activity of trial and error. Certain people enjoy working with their hands and making crafts. Others enjoy hiking through nature or other forms of physical exercise and activity. Music, art, and literature can provide great comfort and a sense of purpose. Whatever it is that you enjoy, it is essential to make time to do it, and you will almost certainly feel more productive and happier for it. There is no set standard for how many hobbies or interests someone should have. The proliferation of social media has allowed people to showcase their life adventures for every one of their friends to see and it sometimes has the adverse effect of causing other people to experience jealousy and feelings of inadequacy because their life does not seem as exciting as the ones they see on their news feed. This type of behavior harkens back to the days before social media, where celebrity-fueled lifestyles and fashions were the social standards for people. While television and the internet still portray celebrities in the limelight, the problem has gotten more pervasive with social media because anyone can represent or highlight only the aspects of their lives that they want others to see while rarely showcasing the daily struggles and troubles that run through their lives.

People who frequently travel, for instance, might be able to do so because they work for companies that provide them with a stipend for business travel. They might also work very hard behind the scenes making plenty of daily sacrifices to save up for their lavish vacations. They could also have wealthy family members or an inheritance that enables them to afford luxuries that others could only dream of having. Someone who is financially strapped who dreams of traveling but is unable to do so might feel intensely jealous of the people on their social media news feed who are constantly showcasing their travels. Speaking of these people who are always showing off online, who is to say that they are having as much fun as they portray themselves having? They might frequently post to cover up some insecurity, and they feel the need for constant validation from others to convince themselves that what they are doing is as fun as it looks. This need for validation does not necessarily remove the genuine moments of joy they are probably experiencing, but more to point out that nothing is ever exactly as it seems. People post pictures and experiences of what they want you to see, and some are better than others at portraying a particular type of lifestyle. Some people in unhealthy relationships utilize frequent vacations as a distraction from their relationship issues, and others in healthy relationships take trips to add genuinely fun memories to an already blossoming relationship. The point is you must be careful not to read into what you see online in your social media news feed because you can never be genuinely confident as to what is going on behind the scenes.

Social media can also cause you to feel like you are missing out on something in your life or that others' lives are more meaningful and enriching than yours. Some people amass quite a devout following with their popular posts, and others are more reserved or hardly post at all. Whatever the case might be, social media is just one representation of a person's life, and it rarely offers a complete picture of who someone is. Having a social media presence might be of personal value to some people and might be useful as a business tool for others, but it needs to be used responsibly like anything else to be effective. Social media and television frequently distort reality and make whatever is trendy seem acceptable, as people are expected to dress, carry themselves, and look a certain way. Everyday life is not like this. People are more diverse than the way various forms of popular media portray them. This diversity filters its way down to some of the most controversial and complex issues people must deal with – attractiveness and mental and physical health. Attractiveness is a highly complicated phenomenon, encompassing multiple and sometimes overlapping physical, emotional, hormonal, and social constructs. Even in the animal kingdom, creatures select their mates through a similar process to how humans do it. There are animal mating rituals and individual characteristics that they look for in choosing a partner.

One of the most widely perpetuated myths about beauty is that it is an entirely subjective experience. Anecdotally, philosophers and historians alike have attributed beauty to the "eye of the beholder," citing numerous cultural differences and personal preferences for different features as justifications that perceptions of beauty are highly variable and individual. Researchers Anthony Little, Benedict Jones, and Lisa DeBruine challenged this notion of beauty, citing a body of scientific research that demonstrated that specific ideas of beauty are uniform and constant across different cultures and social groups.[28] There is undoubtedly a significant degree of subjectivity in the assessment of attractiveness, but overall, there are specific properties and features common to perceptions of beauty.

Symmetry, the property of one side of something resembling the other, is one of the most critical traits in mating preferences.[29] Numerous studies suggest that individuals possessing high levels of symmetry tend to be healthier and more genetically robust. High levels of facial symmetry, for instance, are associated with lower self-reported levels of respiratory issues. Body symmetry in men and women is generally associated with higher levels of fertility. Facial symmetry was also highly correlated with the perceived attractiveness of a potential mate. Related to symmetry, the idea of "averageness"[30] has scientific support for being an overall predictor of an individual's health. For this purpose, averageness refers to the trait of having enough genetic diversity in your face for it to blend in with most other faces around the world. Faces that strongly deviate from the average tend to be associated with an increased propensity for genetic disorders or health conditions. People generally prefer to be with someone who possesses average-looking facial features because they are then more likely to produce healthier offspring.

Researchers conducted studies in which multiple faces were digitally composed together. The more images put together, the fewer lines, blemishes, and general imperfections there were, and the more the composite face tended toward the average. They found that people consistently favored average-looking facial features over more distinct ones and that averageness was an even higher contributing factor toward overall perceived attractiveness than symmetry alone. According to the researchers, "Women with higher circulating oestrogen have more feminine faces, while men with high testosterone have more masculine faces."[31] Masculine facial features often include a sizeable prominent jawbone, brow-bone, and thinner lips. Feminine facial characteristics are typically petite, smooth, and soft features. Women have more fat in their face, and their cheekbones are more prominent those of their male counterparts (Figure 7). Studies show conclusively that men generally are more attracted to feminine female faces,[32] but women did not demonstrate a clear preference for either feminine or masculine male faces.[33] Perceptions of physical health through skin tone, textures, and colors are also useful tools for determining attractiveness in potential mates. People generally are more willing to trust individuals who possess healthy skin tones than those who do not.[34] Studies also showed that males with more youthful looking skin were not only rated more attractive by others, but they also had lower instances of health issues.[35]

Coloration is another critical factor in mate selection. According to the researchers, "Recent evidence has suggested that primate trichromatic vision is an adaptation to distinguish colour modulations in skin based on blood flow, allowing assessment of the state and/or mood of conspecifics."[36] Individuals can sense the degree of facial health in other people and use that information to judge the person's facial attractiveness. Skin discolorations, mottling, and paleness can indicate information about an individual's health. Men who have more smooth and homogeneous skin color are generally found to be more attractive than those who do not.

The color red is considered to be a dominant color throughout most of the animal kingdom. In general, female primates are more sexually attracted and responsive to male primates who have red coloration in their faces, which is considered a symbol of leadership and dominance.[37] In humans, red has a dichotomous interpretation. It can be positively associated with attractiveness, as in the case of a woman wearing a beautiful red dress against a red background,[38] or it can indicate highly oxygenated blood flow[39] in the face causing the skin to glow and appear healthy. Unfortunately, red can also be associated with aggression and fear.[40] Academic instructors who grade using a red pen can instill a sense of fear and dread in their students. Sports teams wearing red jerseys may appear more aggressive and hence more likely to dominate their opponent. Yellowish skin[41] can be a direct indicator of the presence of carotenoids from a healthy diet rich in fruits and vegetables, making the individual appear more attractive and healthy. Skin color can and does vary over time, with people looking more youthful and appealing at certain times than others.

Specific facial shapes and features may also provide information about a potential partner's personality. According to the researchers, "Increasing the masculinity of face shape increased perceptions of dominance, masculinity and age but decreased perceptions of warmth, emotionality, honesty, cooperativeness and quality as a parent."[42] Faces with a resolutely masculine shape and features tend to convey feelings of dominance and competitiveness, but simultaneously decrease perceptions of empathy, cooperation, and warmth.[43] Feminization of a male face, however, can soften some of these aggressive features and make that person seem more cooperative and empathetic, and likely to commit to a long-term relationship. Conversely, masculinization of a female face can make a woman seem less approachable and more dominant.[44] There is no written standard as to which type of partner is most appealing, as opinions vary considerably as to what kind of facial features are considered to be the most attractive. Some people prefer to be with a more masculine partner and others seek out feminine ones, depending on their own needs and backgrounds.

Attraction levels and preferences also tend to fluctuate, depending on a host of environmental, personal, and other factors. One such factor is a woman's monthly reproductive cycle. Studies have shown that women typically show preferences for men with highly masculine characteristics during ovulation and men with more feminine facial traits during their menstrual cycle.[45] These preferences are not necessarily limited to facial features but can include factors such as body odor, body shapes, and even voices. There are many competing theories as to why these fluctuations in attraction occur, but one thought is that these preferences are evolutionary adaptations.[46] Highly masculine traits exude a sense of vitality and fertility, and feminine traits are associated with comfort and stability. Fluctuating hormonal levels of testosterone, estrogen, and progesterone are all thought to be related to these cyclical preferential changes. Men also experience regular fluctuations in their testosterone levels and tend to show preferences for more feminine characteristics in women when testosterone levels are higher.[47]

Genetic kinship appears to be one factor in perceived attractiveness that overrides other previously discussed factors in determining the attractiveness of a potential mate. Inbreeding has demonstrated to have an overall negative effect on the health and vitality of offspring, so people have likely evolved to avoid mating with others who are genetically like them or part of a similar bloodline.[48] Interestingly, people tend to seek out platonic relationships with others who are genetically similar (perhaps out of familiarity) whereas they typically shun romantic relationships with relatives regardless of the positive archetypal features in their faces.

There are also psychosocial factors at play during attraction. People tend to display a higher sexual preference for people who appear interested in them compared to people who seem indifferent or otherwise uninterested. Positive social cues, including smiling, open body language, positive eye contact, and warm gestures resulted in higher levels of perceived attraction than their opposites. People are wired to select mates who generally look more cordial and socially receptive.[49]

Even though genetic inbreeding is strongly disadvantageous to the survival of the human species, that does not mean that couples should avoid genetic similarities altogether. People are generally attracted to others who resemble themselves and their parents, especially if they had a close and loving relationship with their father or mother. The human brain craves familiarity, especially when accompanied by feelings of warmth, comfort, and positive experiences. Likewise, if someone experienced negative or harmful experiences with an individual, the affected person would be more likely to avoid contact with someone who physically resembles them. The human brain is hardwired to prevent potentially harmful or otherwise disadvantageous situations.

According to the researchers, "Imprinting-like effects may lead to positive assortative mating (pairing with similar partners), at least for long-term relationships, and this may have benefits in terms of keeping adaptive suites of genes together or increasing behaviour compatibility."[50] The neural mechanisms responsible for face processing are highly reactive to the conscious and subconscious value-based judgments of the individual. These neural networks develop archetypes of people you are attracted to as a result of the different types of imprinting caused by a lifetime of exposure to a wide variety of people. People exposed to specific facial traits and features, regardless of how novel they are, will be more likely to find those characteristics familiar and therefore more attractive in the future. These novel features can become part of the individual's archetype for attractiveness due to the early exposure to these features, which in turn shaped their neural networks for facial recognition. In this way, faces that are not considered standard in one context or for one individual might appear highly desirable, attractive, and perfectly usual for another.[51]

Social cues and actions can also influence the mating behavior of individuals. You might have noticed that many women are often attracted to men who are already paired up with someone. This type of attractive behavior is not only witnessed in humans but also in some animals too. Birds and fish both similar exhibit kinds of preferences and will often more readily notice a potential male partner who is already paired up with someone. Some studies have shown that women instantly found a man to be more attractive if he was married compared to if he identified as single.[52] Studies also showed that they were more likely to find a man attractive if he was surrounded by a group of females who were admiring him compared to a group who had neutral or negative body language directed toward him.[53] Similarly, men partnered up with women considered to be more attractive were also perceived by other women as being more desirable. In this way, the male partner's attractiveness radiates onto them, making them more attractive to other women. This same principle is also applicable to men, who will typically find women more attractive if they are paired up with a handsome man.[54] The reason behind these phenomena likely has to do with people subconsciously perceiving value in another individual whom they recognize to have the ability to care for, procreate, or provide for them. These social cues offer details that would otherwise be impossible to determine based on physical appearances alone.

Attractiveness and beauty are more complicated ideas than they might seem at first, although specific characteristics and traits are more favorable than others when it comes to courting and selecting a mate, whether it be for a short-term relationship or something longer. People crave stability and familiarity in their partners and are attracted to these traits because they make them feel the most secure and comfortable. Levels of fertility, physical health, and personality traits can sometimes appear through physical features, including skin tone, bone structure, and coloration. People carry around both conscious and unconscious bias in their selection of potential mates with the ultimate goal of finding someone to better ensure their survival as well as the survival and health of their offspring. Maintaining good physical health is also essential for living a productive and fulfilling life. Health problems can be a significant impedance to achieving your personal goals, and they can leave you feeling exhausted and frustrated. Being fit and active are the cornerstones of a healthy body and mind, but with the modern stresses and demands of the family and workplace, achieving an acceptable level of physical fitness can seem nearly impossible.

Labels are Dangerous

People with disabilities and handicaps often face inexorable challenges toward their pursuit of physical health and wellness due to the limitations imposed by their bodies and minds. Before the passage of the American Disabilities Act (ADA)[55] in 1990, people with disabilities experienced a lack of protection from discrimination across multiple areas in life including jobs, transportation, schools, and both public and private venues for events and activities. Even with the passage of the ADA and recently instituted accommodations for people with disabilities, persistent stereotypes, and stigmas about people with disabilities can still make life challenging. The definition of *disability*, according to the Merriam-Webster dictionary, is "a physical, mental, cognitive, or developmental condition that impairs, interferes with, or limits a person's ability to engage in certain tasks or actions or participate in typical daily activities and interactions."[56] This definition is also substantiated, for legal purposes, by the ADA. People with diagnosed disabilities are protected by the ADA so that they can have the same opportunities in life as those without them.

Despite the legal protections offered by the ADA, the term *disability* can conjure up negative connotations and encourage insensitive people to make disparaging remarks and comments that are hurtful and discouraging toward others. Some insecure people feel threatened by anyone who they view is substantially different from them or that they feel uncomfortable around, and they will act out towards others because of these feelings. Stories of people with disabilities who are bullied or harassed are surprisingly plentiful.[57] A former insurance salesman in the UK claims that he experienced discrimination for having a condition that made his kneecaps spontaneously dislocate, causing him to miss time from work frequently. Instead of being supportive and accommodating, his employer subjected him to ridicule for his disability, with two of his co-workers taking his expensive walking stick and pretending to play golf with it.

Other times, it is the person experiencing the disability that is hard on themselves. Author Karla Culbertson,[58] who requires a wheelchair to get around because of her disability, spends a lot of her time feeling like an undue burden and responsibility on others from whom she needs assistance. She also feels unattractive because of her difficulty in attracting a mate. She said, "As a matter of fact, in my online dating experiences, I have had people tell me I was beautiful, yet when I told them I am disabled, I never heard from them again."[59] It is difficult to imagine the stress, anxiety, and depression people like Karla and the insurance salesman face because of the rudeness of others. It is challenging enough for them to understand and come to terms with their limitations. People do not generally realize the long-lasting effect a few cruel words or actions can have on others, or if they do, they are just too indifferent to care.

Being labeled as someone with a disability carries an endemic stigma with it. The word *disability* automatically implies that there is something different about the afflicted. Modifying labels to something more neutral can temporarily provide a sense of solace, but ultimately the fact that a name is needed reminds them of their problem. Even so, it may be necessary to change labels as required to appropriate specific legal resources or to establish a sense of civil sensitivity and inclusiveness. Putting in the effort both individually and socially to ensure that individuals with a disability feel valued and cared about are vital to their overall productivity and sense of well-being.

Another obstacle people with disabilities encounter is that they often cannot participate or enjoy activities that others take for granted. For instance, a quadriplegic individual may wish to go windsurfing, but not be able to because of his condition. In some cases, accommodations may become available that allow them to pursue their desires, but that is not always the case, which can be incredibly disappointing, but there is still hope that an accommodation will be made available in the future, allowing them to experience their dream. By focusing on supportive people and doing activities that bring them joy, some individuals can successfully overcome the challenges of their disability and choose not to allow themselves to be defined or limited by it. As Stephen Hawking famously was quoted, "My advice to other disabled people would be, concentrate on things your disability doesn't prevent you doing well, and don't regret the things it interferes with. Don't be disabled in spirit, as well as physically."[60] Hawking's point is to avoid feelings of exclusion and isolation by focusing attention on participating in activities and events that are inclusive of their abilities. Diss the "dis" in disability to feel enabled and joyful and realize that everyone, regardless of background, has limitations inherent to both their biology, personality, and socioeconomic status.

Mental health is another area in which people experience many prejudices, feelings of isolation, and other personal and professional struggles. Defining mental health is also not as easy as it sounds. What exactly does it mean to be of sound mind and spirit? The standard of reference for most psychologists, psychiatrists, and mental health professionals is the Diagnostic and Statistical Manual of Mental Disorders (DSM). This manual was created in 1952[61] by the American Psychiatric Association and has been through six iterations since its inception. The overall goal of the DSM is to aid clinicians and researchers in the identification, diagnosis, and treatment of mental illness and disorders.

Each successive iteration of the DSM considers the most current and widely accepted research findings of mental disorders and attempts to streamline, condense, or clarify information in line with clinical practice. For instance, the DSM 5[62] consolidated autism disorder, Asperger's syndrome, and pervasive developmental disorder into autism spectrum disorder. DSM 5 also considers the most recent findings in neuroimaging, genetics, and cultural and gender research.[63] Mental health research and analysis had come a very long way from just a century ago when psychiatric practices primarily happened in insane asylums, and there was little to no consideration, sensitivity, or awareness of mental health disorders including anxiety, depression, substance abuse, schizophrenia, or any other number of conditions.

Presently there are numerous pharmacological and behavioral therapies available for a wide range of conditions. The goal behind these therapies is to help an afflicted individual learn coping skills and make lifestyle changes to better deal with their health (e.g., cognitive-behavioral therapy) or to take prescribed medications to help balance out specific neurotransmitter levels in the brain to reduce or suppress psychiatric symptoms. Despite all the recent advances in psychiatric research and therapy, there is still a lot of social stigma and a widespread lack of awareness and support for individuals suffering from mental health issues. Many health insurance companies offer minimal (if at all) psychological, and psychiatric services and those that do are often too unaffordable for the general population. Often, those who need therapy the most are the most vulnerable and the ones who cannot afford it. Mental health awareness is a global problem with inadequate solutions.

According to *The State of Mental Health in America* 2018 annual report,[64] eighteen percent, or forty-three million Americans, have some mental health condition. Of these people, nearly half of them has a co-existing substance abuse disorder, and close to ten million of them experience suicidal thoughts or ideation. This report also cites that over half of American adults with a mental illness did not receive treatment and worse, there is a severe shortage of mental health providers nationwide, making this country ill-equipped to handle the growing need for mental health access and care.

It is easy to examine this report and feel like not enough is being done to address mental health care needs. While there is a lot of truth to that argument, you also have to keep in mind that almost all advances in the field of psychology and psychiatry have been very recent and only started blossoming in the latter half of the previous century. This country has come a long way from the horrors of the Salem Witch trials to defining and treating epilepsy as a neurological disorder. Despite this perspective, mental health has never been in a more promising place than it is now.

Advancements in Mental Health Awareness

There is remarkable work happening in the fields of cognitive science, artificial intelligence, machine learning, and neurology. Each of these disciplines interacts with one another, and many potential applications and therapies developed for both psychological and psychiatric purposes. Pharmacological and cognitive-behavioral treatments for mental health disorders may one day be augmented or even replaced by the technological advancements in artificial intelligence. One modern example of the use of artificial intelligence in therapy is the use of virtual reality simulations in the treatment of panic and phobic disorders. According to psychologist Albert Rizzo, "Right now, the biggest use of virtual reality in clinical settings is probably in the area of exposure therapy and that is probably because the technology is well-matched to the needs of the clinical application. We see with exposure therapy the goal really is about helping a patient, whether it's due to a simple phobia or PTSD, to engage, to confront and to process difficult, traumatic memories."[65] In this practice, the therapist guides the patient through the phobia process, gradually utilizing a combination of traditional psychotherapy and virtual reality guidance.

For instance, say a patient comes to therapy complaining about a phobia of spiders, a common fear. Suppose that this fear is debilitating and that they are on high alert during their waking hours and cannot sleep at night due to the pervasive nature of the fear. The therapist might begin therapy by taking a detailed account of the phobia and try to understand its origins. From there, the therapist might initiate exposure therapy and ask the patient to imagine the spiders. The idea is to gradually expose the patient to their fear more and more until they get used to it, and it no longer holds a chokehold on their life.

A simulation of reality containing virtual spiders offers a more provocative treatment than afforded by traditional exposure therapy. In virtual reality therapy, the therapist might ask the patient to wear a VR headset, and they will introduce the patient to real images of spiders while counseling them through their fears. This type of therapy can be very useful in training the patient not to react with excessive alarm to spiders anymore. These counseling sessions always contain a combination of virtual reality and cognitive-behavioral therapy. In this way, virtual reality serves as a safe adjunct to the rationalization and processing of the phobia. This type of treatment has also been used effectively to aid in the treatment of certain forms of PTSD, pain management, and even ADHD.

There is no doubt that there will be significant advancements in mental health research and treatment in the coming decades. Many of these novel treatments will be so exciting and creative that they will very likely completely revolutionize the fields of psychology and psychiatry even more dramatically than ever before. According to researcher Zaharia Mihai Horia, "Two distinct levels of IT use in psychotherapy have already been identified, especially from the patient treatment point of view. Within the first layer, we encounter the common tools developed to increase the efficiency and performance of the therapist. Within the second level, we have the complex systems that help both the patient and the therapist during the treatment."[66] Virtual reality simulation exposure therapy is just one recent example of the intersection of artificial intelligence with psychotherapy.

In the future, machine learning and artificial intelligence may play an even more pivotal role in psychotherapy. The classical model of psychotherapy utilizes existing categories of classification from the DSM 5 to help aid in the diagnosis and treatment of complex disorders, but the DSM 5 is imperfect in scope and needs to undergo periodic revisions to be as current as possible. Robust artificial intelligence programs could work, in conjunction with human subjects, to develop machine learning algorithms that accurately model human cognition and simultaneously can mine through scores of data to assist the therapist in diagnosing and treating mental health disorders. Machine learning could even redefine traditional views of psychiatric disorders and provide more precise neurobiological models for their definition and treatment concomitant with the existing social and cultural norms of the patient.

Even with all these pending technological advances and the improved quality of life they might bring with them, there is still the fundamental issue of what constitutes a mental disorder in the first place. Forming a proper diagnosis of a patient can be challenging, considering the limited number of diagnostic options contained in the DSM. According to author David Adam, "But even as walls between conditions were being cemented in the profession's manual, they were breaking down in the clinic. As psychiatrists well know, most patients turn up with a mix of symptoms and so are frequently diagnosed with several disorders, or co-morbidities."[67] Some improvements were made in the DSM 5 to reclassify certain disorders as being on a broad spectrum, most notably autism spectrum disorder and a schizophrenia spectrum disorder.[68] These edits, along with other broad reclassifications of certain disorders, make the DSM 5 the most trusted manual in psychiatry and psychotherapy.

The movement from categorical to spectrum diagnoses is a bold and modern shift for the fields of psychology and psychiatry because it represents a dramatic shift away from trying to place a person into distinct categories with complicated co-morbidities when the first type is not a perfect match, which it often is not. People are complex, and disorders may present themselves in a variety of ways, so it is essential to always look at the larger picture when making a clinical diagnosis. For example, the criteria for bipolar disorder and depressive disorders were substantially modified in DSM 5 to fit clinical presentations and characteristics of these disorders more realistically.[69]

It is also important to note that some mental health disorders are temporary, while others are chronic. It is entirely typical and expected for an individual grieving the loss of a loved one to experience symptoms of depression. The DSM 5 recently removed the two-month waiting period for people going through depression associated with grief to obtain proper diagnosis and treatment, which represents another positive change in the manual that will enable people who are depressed, irrespective of the reason, to receive appropriate care and treatment. Even with people experiencing chronic mental health conditions, there is considerable variation in their expression. Some people have more severe ongoing cases, and others encounter relapses separated by periods of remission. Specific environmental triggers, life circumstances, or even advancing age can also worsen mental health conditions. Therapy must be adaptable to the individual with the awareness that there might be a distinct period of trial-and-error with new medications and treatment.

Certain personality traits can make it more challenging to assist someone with a mental health condition. People who are incredibly stubborn and defiant are much harder to help than those who are naturally more open-minded and agreeable. You cannot help someone who does not want help no matter how hard you try to convince them that it is in their best interest to seek treatment. Furthermore, labeling mental health conditions as "disorders" may promote a negative connotation to something that the afflicted individual does not consider always to be a problem. There are countless anecdotes of creative people suffering from a variety of mood disorders. The famous artist Vincent Van Gogh, who committed suicide at 37 years old, suffered from severe manic-depressive episodes and was remarkably the most productive in the last few years of his troubled life. Martin Luther also suffered from bipolar disorder and produced some of his best work during his manic states, offering rigorous defenses to his *Ninety-five Theses*, which is commonly thought to have propelled the Protestant Reformation.[70]

The Link Between Mental Illness And Creativity

Although the link between mood disorders and creativity is well-established, there have been a surprisingly small number of rigorous academic studies done on the validity of that relationship, so it is crucial to define the concept and practice of creativity broadly.

According to psychiatrist Nancy C. Andreasen, "Although there are some differences between those currently pursuing research on creativity, a definition that most would embrace is one that emphasizes that creativity is the ability to produce something that is novel and also useful or beautiful in a very general sense."[71] There is also a need to clearly define what is meant by "mental illness" and what would constitute an acceptable control group and experimental group, which is not as easy as it sounds.

Back in 1974, one of the earliest known empirical studies was conducted to examine the relationship between creativity and mental illness. Subjects consisted of 15 writers from the University of Iowa Writers' Workshop and a control group comprised of people of equivalent age, gender, and educational achievement. A structured interview was used to evaluate the subjects, and the DSM 3 was used to make clinical diagnoses. The researchers found that 80% of the participants had a mood disorder with 30% of them having either bipolar 1 or 2 disorder, which was a significantly different rate of mental illness than that of the control subjects. Researchers also discovered higher rates of alcohol abuse in the participants than in the control group.

Two more similar studies occurred in the decades following the Iowa writers' workshop study.[72] One of them was a study done in 1989, examining the rate at which highly accomplished British writers and artists had received treatment for a mental health issue. Nearly half of the sample subjects had undergone treatment for a mood disorder, with some of them receiving psychotherapy and others receiving medication (or both) to treat their mental health issues. Another study in 1994 rigorously compared participants in the national Women Writers' Conference, held annually at the University of Kentucky, with controls from members of other women's clubs throughout the state who were matched by age and level of educational attainment. These researchers also discovered a high correlation between the presence of mental health conditions and written creative expression. One common theme that ran through all three studies was a high prevalence of bipolar disorder 1 and 2 in highly creative people.[73] One thing to keep in mind is that both the data and scope of research in these studies are limited, as they primarily focused on writers and not on other types of creators including inventors, scientists, or performing artists. Broader research needs to be done to draw any meaningful conclusions about the link between creativity and mental health disorders.

Another researcher, Christa L. Taylor, a graduate student in psychology at the University of Albany, performed a 2017 study that provided a systematic review and meta-analysis of the purported link between creativity and psychopathology.[74] In her research, she found that there was no clear link between the two and that previous research made several flawed assumptions in both their methodology and analysis. According to her, "Although depressive states have been suggested to provide opportunity for introspection, increased sensitivity, and 'greater depth and subtlety of feeling', which may be beneficial for creative expression, the diminished energy, interest, and cognitive ability that is characteristic of depression suggests that it is unlikely that creativity is enhanced during a depressive episode."[75] It is also not clear from the research whether mood disorders cause creativity or vice-versa.

While there is little empirical evidence to suggest a direct link between creativity and mood disorders, there is anecdotal evidence indicating a relationship between the severity of a mood disorder and the positive expression of creativity.[76] As mood disorders become more severe initially, levels of creativity are enhanced likely due to common neurological or genetic mechanisms underlying both the disorder and the creative expression. After mood disorders reach a critical level of severity, the adverse effects of the psychopathology inhibit creative expression, a finding that is consistent with anecdotal reports from individuals suffering from mental health disorders. For instance, Pulitzer Prize-winning poet Robert Lowell found that he was less creative during episodes of severe bipolar disorder compared to when he underwent treatment.[77]

There are conflicting reports about the link between pharmacological treatments of mood disorders and the effect on creativity. Some people, like Lowell, felt that they performed more efficiently on medication, and others thought that drugs blunted their creativity.

It may be the case that once a mood disorder has reached a critical level of severity, the symptoms become so impactful that they can, for instance, cause such major depression that the afflicted individual loses all drive and ambition and only with medical intervention can they function productively and coherently. Alternatively, the side effects of certain medications may be detrimental to creativity while simultaneously making the individual feel better. There is such considerable variation in the spectrum of mental health disorders and its associated treatment plan that no viable conclusion exists about the relationship between pharmacological therapy and perception of individual creativity levels.

In general, the presence of a mood disorder was not a predictor of whether someone was creative or not. Taylor's research did show that creative people with a mood disorder were creatively influenced in various ways by their mood disorder, especially in verbal and performance-based domains.[78] A higher incidence of mood disorders was found in creative people partly because heightened levels and practices of creativity have on a person's lifestyle and brain. According to Taylor, "Given that creativity in the arts often requires the channeling and expression of intense emotions artistic endeavors may lead to a dysregulation in mood, particularly when the mode of expression lacks a narrative (e.g., poetry). Difficulties characteristic of the creative lifestyle, including financial instability, immense competition, and stresses that accompany public recognition may also put individuals at risk for mental health issues, including mood disorder."[79]

There is possibly something to the pathophysiology of the creative process in the brain that leads to perhaps higher levels of introspection, reflection, and awareness that contributes to the systemic dysregulation often seen in mood disorders.[80] Whether or not creativity influences an already dysregulated mind, or it adds to its dysregulation is currently unknown, but the practice of creativity requires the individual to think and reason in novel ways that may be very taxing to the brain and mind. Creativity can be impulsive, unpredictable, and all-consuming. It can keep you up all night and present itself with a wide range of emotions all at once. It is no wonder that some of the most creative minds in history were also afflicted with treacherous mental health conditions. There is no set standard for what is considered "normal" creativity. This quality comes in many forms and varieties, but one thing is sure – without it, humanity would never have evolved to where it is today. Modern agriculture would not exist. Technological advances would never have happened. You would live in a world utterly devoid of art, poetry, and sculptures. Life would be very dull and mostly devoid of any meaning or value.

Understanding Intelligence

Everyone expresses their intelligence differently, and some people are more adept at a particular way of thinking than others. In 1983, American developmental psychologist Dr. Howard Gardner published a book detailing nine distinct types of intelligence, referred to as the "Multiple Intelligences" (MI) theory.[81] Gardner believed that knowledge occurs across a broad spectrum of abilities and skills and that there is no single type of intelligence that should be valued over any of the others. Naturalist intelligence[82] allows people to discriminate among natural artifacts in the world, including plants, animals, geological formations, clouds, and human-made artifacts and objects. Someone with a high level of this type of intelligence might be an accomplished chef or an avid gardener. Being able to cook delicious meals requires the ability to select ingredients that appear fresh and are flavorful. Having a keen fashion sense might also be a result of naturalist intelligence, as it gives you the ability to discriminate amongst different types of makeup, clothing, shoes, and other material things. This type of knowledge might also be useful for interior decorating, as it requires you to know what types of furniture and other objects go best with other ones. You will be able to discern high-quality items from lower quality ones by examining and feeling them.

Musical intelligence[83] enables people to discern amongst different sounds, rhythms, and tones. People with elevated levels of this type of knowledge hear and understand sounds that others might not even notice. They are often found humming tunes to themselves or strumming away at their guitar to relax. They are often aware of the deep connection between music and emotional expression and may utilize their music as a powerful form of self-expression. Logical-mathematical intelligence[84] presents itself as the ability to qualify and quantify logical relationships among different quantities. People with this type of knowledge utilize abstract and symbolic thought, along with inductive and deductive reasoning, to identify intricate algebraic and geometric patterns, make quantitative predictions from data, and model information from the social and physical sciences. Forensic researchers, investigators, and scientists may also use this type of intelligence to solve complex logical puzzles and draw meaningful and rational conclusions about their cases or experiments. Computer scientists and programmers also rely on this intelligence to solve complex problems in their field.

Existential intelligence[85] is the ability to think clearly about and make sound decisions about "big picture" issues such as running a company, coaching a professional sports team, or leading a religious organization. People who exhibit this type of intelligence are often both profoundly philosophical while at the same time highly socially aware and meaningfully connected to others around them. They think about helping others to define purpose in their lives and often place their ideas in the context of the human life cycle of birth and death. People with interpersonal intelligence can sympathize, empathize, understand, and relate to others based on responses to both verbal and non-verbal communication. They can thoughtfully and carefully consider multiple perspectives on a situation without rushing to judgment on any of them. They excel at organizing groups of people together and making sure that everyone feels valued and supported. They are emotionally stable and able to remain calm and collected, even in the most challenging circumstances or around unstable people. People with this type of intelligence excel at diffusing conflict and offering intuitive and useful resolutions.

Bodily-kinesthetic intelligence[86] focuses on the individual possessing an intricate mind-body relationship, sense of coordination, and well-defined muscle memory. Highly accomplished athletes, surgeons, and contractors often rely on this type of intelligence to excel at what they do. People with this type of knowledge have a deep awareness of how their body connects to the world around them and are also in touch with their physical condition. They are sure-footed, flexible, durable, and have remarkable endurance. They know how to properly fuel, hydrate, and rest their body to achieve optimal performance.

People with linguistic intelligence[87] are quite adept at using language to explain and express themselves. They can craft compelling stories, speeches, and plays that evoke both visceral and reflective emotional responses, all with the power of words. Linguistic intelligence is similar to musical knowledge, as both of them rely on sensory artifacts to evoke psychological reactions from people. Linguistic intelligence can also be used by technical writers to clearly explain otherwise complicated scientific processes or how to use or repair technological devices. People with high levels of linguistic intelligence are also avid readers and digest written information easily. They are also skilled at speaking clearly and thoughtfully so that people can easily understand them.

People with intrapersonal intelligence[88] are usually reflective, analytical, and highly aware of their true inner nature. They are self-motivated, and a higher sense of purpose often guides their personal decisions. Their internal monologue guides them, and they are highly aware of their own emotions, feelings, and opinions. Although they may not be expressive and tend to be more introverted, they can be highly sensitive and empathetic towards others. Spatial intelligence[89] consists of the ability to think and reason visually in three dimensions. Artists, pilots, and architects are among the people who demonstrate this type of knowledge. Spatially intelligent people can psychologically manipulate objects and visualize the results. They are keenly sensitive to visual patterns and shapes and can model them accurately in drawings, diagrams, and simulations.

Gardner's nine-dimensional model of intelligence has received much criticism since its publication. For one, his characterization of intelligence into these static categories is highly subjective and arbitrary. Other researchers could quickly come up with different types of intelligence or re-characterize Gardner's categories. Another criticism is that Gardner confuses the concept of knowledge with aptitude or ability. He also erroneously assumes that each type of intelligence arises from a different and distinct part of the brain. Unfortunately, there are no empirical validations of Gardner's MI theory. One of his main reasons for developing MI theory was to counteract the traditional construct of intelligence as being measured via the Wechsler intelligence quotient (IQ),[90] which he felt to be self-limiting and narrowly focused. His research, however flawed it may be in its methodology and findings, at least offers up a non-traditional and profoundly insightful view of intelligence as consisting of more than just the two dimensions of logical-mathematical and linguistic abilities measured in standard IQ tests.

Lynn Waterhouse further states that cognitive psychology and neuroscience research do not support the MI theory. According to her, "The majority of recent cognitive psychology, cognitive neuroscience, and evolutionary psychology research programs on human mental abilities have focused on three core explanatory paradigms for human cognition...general intelligence, multiple information processing systems, and adapted cognition models."[91] These models demonstrate a more general and holistic view of intelligence instead of categorizing it into arbitrary and static categories as the MI theory does.

The general intelligence model for intelligence, abbreviated as "g" theory,[92] theorizes that intelligence is related to the individual's working memory, overall brain volume, certain hereditary factors, and frontal lobe brain activity. An individual's IQ score best identifies this model of intelligence. The ability to store, manipulate, process, and recall information in a limited amount of time are primarily functions of working memory in the frontal lobes. Larger brains and elevated levels of grey matter were both closely associated with higher IQ levels.[93] Greater levels of frontal lobe activity, as measured by an fMRI machine, were also closely associated with higher verbal IQ levels.[94] Higher quantities of cortical neurons with elevated electrical conduction levels across neural networks define elevated levels of general intelligence.[95]

About two decades following the publication of his MI theory, Gardner added in two new categorizations of intelligence – the "mental searchlight" and "laser intelligence." He correlated high IQ scores with "mental searchlight" intelligence, believing that people who possessed this type of knowledge were able to sift through massive amounts of information efficiently and productively. "Laser intelligence" is associated with an ability to create tools and paradigms that are significant contributions to society (for better or for worse).[96] Gardner also theorized that there was a "Central Intelligences Agency"[97] that emerged from multiple intelligences working together.

According to Waterhouse, "Evidence has suggested that g represents working memory, and working memory is the core frontal lobe executive function, therefore, g is likely to be the same entity as Gardner's 'Central Intelligences Agency,' which he defined as the frontal lobe executive function."[98] Gardner unintentionally validates "g" theory through his explanations of information storage and processing even though ironically he intended to discredit it. Intelligence is more in the overall information processing efficiency than the specific forms of expression outlined by Gardner.

Multiple Information Processing Systems (MIPS)[99] is a body of research that demonstrates that seemingly distinct types of information processing can occur across the same neural pathways. MI theory claims that specific types of information processing occur exclusively in one area of the brain, but MIPS contradicts that claim. Cognitive neuroscience research has suggested that the neural pathways involved in object identification and location represent different variations of the same overall neural network. Further research demonstrated connections between the areas for music perceptual skills and nonverbal reasoning, emotional expression and logical reasoning, and other complex behaviors including walking, gesturing, speaking, and reading comprehension. Complex skills such as reading and mathematical thinking, involve highly integrated non-specific skills such as long-term memory, working memory, and attention. The theory is that genetics are primarily responsible for the form and function of these neural pathways through what Waterhouse refers to as "generalist genes."[100]

Other research has suggested that there are two distinct, yet interconnected, neural decision-making systems which Waterhouse refers to as the "intuitive intelligence" system and the second one as the "deliberative intelligence" system.[101] The intuitive intelligence system is associated with rapid and effortless decision-making. This system improves with practice and is related to an individual's judgments and preferences. The deliberative intelligence system is responsible for slow, deliberate, and thoughtful decision-making. This system is thought to have the ability to monitor, modify, or override the decisions of the deliberative system. These two systems are believed to interact for one purpose only – to make decisions, unlike Gardner's MI in which each type of intelligence is responsible for a set of specific tasks. According to Waterhouse, "Neither [of these systems] is theorized to create, compose, appreciate, or perform."[102] In summary, MIPS uses individual processors to operate on multiple contents, whereas MI uses a multipurpose processor to work on a single substance.

Adapted cognition theory[103] suggests that specific neural networks have evolved in humans to deal with social or cognitive problems. One example of such a network is the mirror neuron system[104] which activates when you interact with or observe another person. These neurons are involved in mimicking the behavior of others' movements, gestures, and actions, which in turns enables you to understand better and interpret emotions and body language. Mirror neurons are also involved in learning complex behaviors from other people.

Neural networks that deal with social cheating detection are present in humans and even primates and microorganisms. As Waterhouse explains, "Cheating bacteria do not make the beneficial extracellular compounds that their noncheating neighbors do. Insect queens engage in social cheating when they steal workers from other colonies to tend their own larvae. Birds engage in social cheating when they deposit their eggs in other nests thus avoiding the effort of raising their own chicks."[105] Cheating in humans takes on many forms, including infidelity, theft, plagiarism, and taking credit for others' work. Humans have adapted to become quite skilled at detecting cheating behavior, perhaps as a survival tool.

Adapted cognition such as mirroring behavior or cheating detection is likely a result of evolutionary changes in the brain that occurred in response to specific recurring environmental problems. Neural networks restructure and develop that are most advantageous to the survival of the human species. The plasticity of the brain is, therefore, a useful evolutionary characteristic that allows for neurological changes in response to the changing challenges and demands of the surrounding environment.

MI theory enthusiasts might point out that adapted cognition models are themselves artifacts of the brain and therefore specific types of intelligence, but this is not the case. Mirror neurons operate across a wide range of brain regions, allowing individuals to mimic behaviors based on gesturing, facial movements, tool usage, and other forms of body language and expression.[106] The variety of brain regions mirror neurons operate across is therefore much broader in scope than the narrow, more specific regions of MI theory. Mirroring behavior is also not a complex expression of intelligence like the models posed by MI, but a tool used for learning adaptive responses and strategies from others.

Social cheating detection neural networks[107] hypothetically also function over broad regions of the brain and are too general to fit neatly into any one of Gardner's multiple intelligences. Plus, the only function of the social cheating network is to determine if someone is cheating, something narrower than any of Gardner's categories. The systems for social cheating detection likely evolved from a need to make sure that individuals had equitable access to limited resources. MI theory presumes that the nine categories of intelligence grew to deal with generalized content instead of naturally arising through the complicated "trial and error" processes of biological evolution. If intelligence is presumed to occur as creative and innovative solutions to social, environmental, and intellectual problems, then MI demonstrates a general lack of evidence to support how the categories of intelligence developed in the first place.

In a similar spirit to Gardner, Daniel Goleman proposed an emotional intelligence (EI) theory based on four general domains: self-awareness, self-management, social awareness, and relationship management.[108] Goleman was one of the pioneers of EI theory, which posited a distinct type of intelligence that he claimed was a predictor of future professional and personal success. Goleman believed that excelling in these emotional dimensions was a predictor of future leadership success. One of his goals was to promote the use of EI in education, business, and leadership training. Other researchers also developed tools for describing and measuring emotional intelligence including the Mayer-Salovey-Caruso-Emotional Intelligence Test (MSCEIT),[109] the BarOn Emotional Quotient Inventory (EQ-I),[110] the Schutte self-report EI test (SSEIT),[111] and the Brain Resource Inventory for Emotional Intelligence Test.[112]

The MSCEIT was the main inspiration behind Goleman's work on EI. One of the main concepts of this theory was that some people reasoned more effectively than others with emotions, and for others, their thinking became enhanced by emotions. Like the IQ test, the MSCEIT critically examines and evaluates the participant's Emotional intelligence quotient (EIQ) through a battery of different questions. These questions covered a range of emotional topics and concepts including accurately identifying emotions through facial gestures, selecting appropriate moods for different social situations, understanding how emotions transition from one to another, and how to best manage emotions in a particular case. Participants take the test and then receive an MSCEIT score, which is viewed similarly to the standard IQ score. Specific guidelines of interpretation developed for different ranges of scores, ranging from "consider development" to "consider improvement."

Baron EQ-I was created to help people learn more about their emotional and social functioning and utilize this information to make informed professional and personal decisions. As Bar-On explains, "Total EQ describes the broadest area of skills looking at overall emotional and social functioning. The composite scales break Total EQ into the [five] domains of Intrapersonal, Interpersonal, Stress Management, Adaptability, and General Mood. The

15 subscales then provide very focused information about specific skills within each of those domains."[113] Researchers provided the EQ-I participants with a report that made both specific and general recommendations based on both their total EQ score and scores across the various subdomains.

Dr. Nicola Schutte created the SSEIT in 1998 to measure general EI using the four subscales of emotion perception, utilizing emotions, managing self-relevant emotions, and managing others' feelings. Inspired by the MSCEIT and EQ-I models of emotional intelligence, the SSEIT uses a 33-item self-report containing a five-point scale ranging from a score of 1 (strongly agree) to 5 (strongly disagree). One of the goals of the SSEIT was to break away from the way previous models of EI made implicit or explicit connections with the "big five" personality dimensions of neuroticism, extraversion, agreeableness, conscientiousness, and openness to experience. According to Schutte, test results were not highly correlated to any of the "big five" dimensions except for openness to experience.[114] She also claimed that her test measured skills differing from pure cognitive ability, such as that demonstrated by the scholastic aptitude test (SAT).

Schutte further argued that the SSEIT might be a useful tool for "theoretical research [involving] exploring the nature of emotional intelligence, including the determinants of emotional intelligence, the effects of emotional intelligence, and whether emotional intelligence can be enhanced."[115] She goes on to mention that the scale might be a useful tool for individuals seeking self-exploration of their emotional nature or for those people who self-identify as having personal issues with emotional skills such as impulse control. One of the main findings of her study into EI was that higher emotional intelligence scores correlated highly with first-year college grades.[116] She used these results to argue that the SSEIT can help identify underprepared college students and get them on the right track to succeed in college by preparing them with the emotional skills and abilities they need to cope with the emotional challenges of this new and challenging academic environment. She did, however, caution that companies or other prestigious organizations should not use her test as part of their hiring or selection criteria.

A more recent self-report measure of EI is called the Brain Resource Inventory for Emotional Intelligence Factors (BRIEF). The goal of the BRIEF was to form different factors of EI, ranging from the internal to the external. The inner emotional capacity factor measured vital components that are involved in skills such as empathy and intuition – the ability to perceive and recognize emotion in yourself and others. The external emotional capacity factor measured an individual's ability to form and maintain social relationships and interpersonal relationships. The self-concept factor is involved in an individual's perceptions of themselves, including the ability to be self-critical and develop self-confidence.

Researchers Andrew Haddon Kemp et al. conducted a research study whose goal was to correlate scores on the BRIEF with factors including gender, age, personality, cognitive intelligence, and resting-state electroencephalography (EEG). Researchers recruited nearly six hundred subjects for this study. They took a holistic online exam consisting of demographic information, the BRIEF, and a personality test involving the "big five" personality dimensions. They also participated in a separate review for cognitive ability, and researchers recorded resting-state EEG recordings while the subjects had their eyes open and closed.

The researchers found that female subjects had a higher EI than their male counterparts.[117] They hypothesized based on this data that females may have higher levels of emotional functioning than men and therefore be more likely to experience mood disorders, including clinical depression. Females are thought to be more "cognitively [vulnerable]"[118] than men because of heightened neurological activity in the brain's emotional regions, and they may be more susceptible to feelings of low self-esteem because of a tendency to ruminate over their thoughts and decisions. The researchers also determined that EI is highly dependent on personality traits and less so by cognitive abilities.[119] Openness and extraversion were the two strongest predictors for total BRIEF scores.[120] Other qualities, including conscientiousness and neuroticism, were also associated with EI factors.[121] Lastly, the researchers concluded that particular frontal lobe EEG activity (raised theta waves and raised beta waves) were correlated with higher EI whereas raised theta and lowered beta waves were associated with lower EI and hence some degree of social impairment relative to their higher EQ counterparts.[122]

Contrary to popular belief and the variety of heavily researched EI concepts, there is not much scientific basis to validate the existence of a unitary EI. Waterhouse explained in her research on MI theory that there is no evidence that EI exists as a traditional construct in the brain and there is insubstantial evidence linking it with information processing or other higher-level functions and interactions between people and their social environment. According to her, researchers have shown that "there were too many conflicting EI constructs, that EI was not successfully differentiated from personality constructs and general intelligence, and that there was no validation of the claim that EI was critical for real-world success."[123]

There are too many different and conflicting constructs of EI, which has led to considerable confusion among researchers. Another point of contention is that while some researchers (such as the BRIEF ones) claim that there is a strong association of EI with general intelligence (IQ) and personality factors, there is little evidence to reveal a distinction among EI, intelligence, and personality. Furthermore, there is no validation for the claim that EI is a predictor of personal or professional success. Waterhouse mentions that while it is unlikely that there exists a unitary EI, there is a growing body of research supporting that emotional and social skills work in concert with general cognitive function. As she states, "Basic social attachment in all mammals depends on a system of the hormones oxytocin, vasotocin, and vasopressin operating in brain-body circuits."[124] Just as is the case with the mirror neuron system, human brains have evolved complex circuitry to process emotional information, including having empathy, recognizing facial expressions and body language, and communicating with social cues.

The other dimension to emotional processing is through language. The left-hemisphere neocortex (including Broca's area and Wernicke's area) and the basal ganglia tissues are among the brain regions responsible for language processing. Being able to process, describe, and express emotions require finely-tuned synchronicity among these different brain regions. Additional research suggests that personality plays a significant contributing role in an individual's emotional temperament.[125] These are the "big five" personality aspects, including warmth, conscientiousness, sociability, neuroticism, and openness. People express emotions differently, and their personality plays a prominent role in how they come across to others and deal with emotional issues. Someone extroverted might be more outwardly expressive with their emotions, preferring to talk about them to a close friend or family member. Somebody who is introverted, however, might turn to journal writing or playing music to express their emotions. The bottom line is that there is no standard way in which to express or handle emotions, and while some ways of dealing with emotions are indeed healthier than others, coming up with an emotional set standard that quantifies emotional intelligence seems both counterproductive and counterintuitive considering how subjective and variable most feelings can be.

A truly comprehensive theory of EI should consider both the neurological and psychosocial aspects of emotional cognition in the brain in addition to the other characteristic nuances of emotion found across many of the existing theories of EI. In the meantime, people should approach the concept of EI with great caution, and the discrimination should be discouraged amongst individual abilities based on their scores on different tests that have no solid scientific or factual foundation. A common belief about general intelligence is that faster processing speed is associated with higher levels of intelligence. Increase the rate at which an individual processes information, and you will notice an overall increase in their knowledge. While scientific studies have suggested a correlation between processing speed and general knowledge, there is little evidence to support a causal relationship between the two.

To further examine if there was a causal link between processing speed and general intelligence, researchers Anna Lena Schubert et al. conducted a scientific analysis using nicotine to determine if an increase in mental processing speed equated to better performance on information processing tests.[126] They recruited a group of occasional smokers under the assumption that nicotine administration would result in a decrease in reaction time and would positively affect their results in a general intelligence test. The results of this study were surprising and contradicted the notion that there is a positive correlation between higher mental processing speed and general intelligence levels. Transdermal nicotine decreased the reaction times of participants in the Sternberg memory scanning test, but it did not improve their overall performance compared to the control group.[127] Just because someone processes information more quickly than someone else does not automatically make them more intelligent.

It is possible, however, that long-term intense use of stimulants such as nicotine may structurally alter specific pathways in the brain, such as the microstructure of white matter, responsible for information processing and particular cognitive abilities. This hypothesis is currently untested, so longitudinal studies would have to be carried out to validate it, but if it is true, it could have serious implications for potential pharmacological treatments for specific learning disabilities. Another possibility is that an individual's ability to pay attention for sustained periods may influence both their information processing speeds and general intelligence. People who experience significant lapses in concentration demonstrate slower reaction times and in turn, may perform more poorly on intelligence tests. People who can focus clearly on tasks for sustained periods might be more likely to perform better on these tests, but there is no scientific consensus on this theory. The ability to focus without interruption is advantageous towards learning, but it should not be considered the defining feature of an intelligent person.

Embrace Your Individuality

When it comes to the ways that people define themselves, there are no standard ways to do it. Everyone has a unique set of physical characteristics, mental abilities, and personality traits. People change both mentally and physically over time as they mature from children into adults and then into senior citizens. Some of these changes are quite subtle, and others are more dramatic. There are no such things as normal intelligence, normal mental health, normal physical health, or a normal personality. Conforming to the ideals, vision, and characteristics of a specific group might provide you with a sense of normalcy within that group, but it will likely come at the expense of your individuality. That is not to imply that all conformity is terrible because sometimes it is in your benefit to fit in, but only temporarily. Problems arise when coerced, threatened, or otherwise pressured to conform for fear of retaliation or retribution. Everyone, including you, is a masterpiece of genetic and environmental variability. To not honor that at the expense of conforming to some social standard or group is to strip yourself of your uniqueness.

There is no need to strive to be normal nor to try to encourage normality onto others. When was the last time you heard of someone who achieved personal greatness or made an extraordinary discovery referred to as a remarkably average person? Even in a seemingly homogeneous social group, there is usually great diversity among its members. The differences among people are what make socializing fun and exciting. Everybody comes into this world with their own unique set of strengths and challenges. Even identical twins often have remarkable differences in their personalities. To try to conform is to compare yourself against some imagined or real standard or stereotype. There is nothing wrong with admiring or imitating people who inspire you so long as you do not blindly follow their ways without first considering yourself. Keep in mind that others respect you too. The best relationships are the ones in which people can be themselves without fear of judgment or rejection. It is even better if you can have that sort of relationship with yourself.

It is also normal to experience doubts, anxiety, and stress in your life. It is normal to struggle some days and feel anger, sadness, or loneliness. Pain and suffering are a normal part of everyone's life, and it can be discouraging to experience them in the face of others' triumph and joy. People can also make you feel bad when they project their insecurities onto you. Being around people who have negative vibes or who gossip can be toxic to your health and personal development. Most people struggle with finding balance in their lives, and this challenge is a normal part of life. Some people are prone to addictive behavior, and others experience low self-esteem. Some are narcissistic or unreasonable, and others are pushovers or too accommodating. Striving for something in between two extremes is the key to productivity and happiness. It takes resilience and effort to achieve moderation, but the journey is worthwhile. People who are too selfish, for instance, often miss out on social opportunities and invitations because people might not want to be around them as much. Being too selfless, on the other hand, can cause people to take advantage of them and not value their contributions.

If you are to strive for anything in life, strive toward moderation. Accept that there are aspects and traits that you cannot change, but focus on the ones that you can. Even the most seemingly minute changes can make the most considerable impacts later on. These changes can seem uncomfortable or even painful at first, but they will build resilience and courage. If you are someone who does not challenge yourself, then it might be a good idea to try doing something novel and exciting. If you have the opposite issue and are always challenging yourself, then maybe it is an excellent time to step back for a moment and relax.

What is normal for one person might not be for another. What is normal in one situation might not be appropriate in a different context. The way you live your life, the thoughts and decisions you make, and the people you associate with are all important pieces of you. In between the beginning and the end of your life are your choices, possessions, circumstances, and relationships. These are the pieces of you that compose the puzzle of your life. These are all unique to you. There never has been and never will be anyone who has ever lived their life the way you have. Every moment you are here is an important one, and this life is your abnormal treasure.

Chapter 6 – No Decisions

"In philosophy, they talk a lot about humans being actual organic machines, and the idea of free will is something that we've made up. We actually don't have free will. We're acting according to our programming as organic mechanisms."[1]

— Joel Kinnaman

The Power of the Unconscious Mind

Your ability to think for yourself is what led you to pick up this book. Something about it grabbed your attention – maybe it was the title, a review you read online about it, or a recommendation from a friend. Either way, the choice to read this book was *your* decision, and nobody else coerced you to do it. There is no way you are sitting here reading this book because you were destined to do so. There is no way at all. Everything you do requires some thought to put it into action. You can consciously choose whether you want to eat that bologna sandwich you packed yourself for lunch or discard it and opt for the tastier pizza in the restaurant down the street. You can wake up one morning and decide to go to the beach because it is hot outside and you want to cool off.

Each decision leads to another choice. Once you decide to go to the beach, you need to think about what to wear and what to pack. After you do that, then it is time to plan out how you will get there. Maybe you will ride together with a group of friends or perhaps you will opt to go alone instead. Every single moment of your life, you must make choices, even with the most straightforward and mundane tasks. If you are sitting on the couch and get hungry, you have to make the decision to get off the couch and go to the kitchen to find something to eat. The imagination can also play a role in this decision-making, as you may visualize and plan for what you want to eat long before you ever leave the couch.

Decisions from others can also impact you, and sometimes in a significant way. If someone cuts you off while you are driving, it forces you to make an instantaneous decision on what to do in response. The best course of action might be to hit on the brakes and slow down or perhaps a better option is to swerve into the next lane over if space is available. Sometimes you make the wrong decision in a situation, and that turns it into a mistake or accident. It can be a frustrating moment and result in feelings of anxiety and disappointment. Some of these mistakes happen instantaneously, and others are more meticulously planned out, only to regretted later. For instance, a person who committed a crime of passion and ended up in prison might end up regretting their choices, but only after the fact. Some people seem to make the same mistakes repeatedly and appear to never learn from them.

For all the decisions you and others make every day, there certainly has to be some control over them, right? It turns out that this may not be the case at all. According to prominent psychology professor Ezequiel Morella, "[Consciousness] is not only less purposeful and 'all-knowing' than expected, but also contributes only one function (albeit an essential function) to a wide range of processes, much as how the Internet plays the same critical role for a varied group of events."[2] Morella's theory is known as the "Passive frame theory,"[3] and it implies that the unconscious mind calculates all actions and plans for the person and then executes them through the conscious mind. The unconscious mind acts as a sort of data processor that uses the conscious mind as a sort of middleman to put thoughts into action. The conscious mind is concerned only with the events of the present moment and does not act on its own accord. The unconscious mind provides you with a sense that you are really in control of your thoughts and actions when, in fact, you might not be.

The passive frame theory might seem utterly counter-intuitive at first, but it makes more sense the more you think about it. Every moment there is an unbelievable amount of information entering your thoughts – indeed more than you can handle. Something must filter through all of that data, decide what is relevant and what is not, and somehow piece together a narrative from it all that fits within your survival framework. The description you receive from your unconscious mind becomes your conscious experience, and the decisions you make are the results of finely-tuned information processing that is delivered to your conscious mind to actuate in the physical world. The conscious mind is not the majestic and ethereal entity that it initially seems to be, but it is the unconscious mind that should elicit those deep and mysterious feelings. In this framework, you can even consider the conscious mind to be an essential extension of the unconscious mind.

One of the most ubiquitous experiences people have is the "gut feeling" where something inside your gut informs you of what your best action should be in each circumstance. It turns out there are neurons in your stomach and there are several meaningful connections between the digestive and nervous systems. Dr. Louann Brizendine believes that the insula, which is the neural center for the feelings of empathy and self-awareness, is connected to the vagus nerve and is involved in the regulation of stomach and intestinal contractions as well as the functioning of other organs.[4] She contends that it is through these neurobiological connections that people experience powerful, intuitive feelings that correspond with gut involvement.

Whether or not to trust a gut feeling is not always an easy call to make. The digestive system is a sort of primitive brain and has been around a lot longer than its cerebral counterpart. Gut feelings are excellent at alerting you to dangerous situations and people. If you are around a stranger and they give you a funny feeling that you should not trust them, it is usually best to listen to your gut and proceed with caution. Other times gut feelings may not be as helpful, especially when it comes to addictive behaviors. An alcoholic might get a gut feeling that they need another drink, or a compulsive gambler might get a gut feeling that they should go out and spend a small fortune on lottery tickets. A daredevil might get a gut feeling to dive off a cliff into a lake but end up injuring themselves on the way down due to a mistimed jump. The utility of the gut feeling has its limitations.

Sometimes it is in your best interest to take time out to think through your decisions. Metacognition is an excellent tool for deciphering the meaning behind the feelings you get and deciding what is the best course of action to take in any given situation. Competitive sports rely heavily on instinct and intuitive muscle memory to play efficiently, but there are times where deeper reflection and analysis are warranted. In playing a slower-paced game such as chess or poker, it is in your best interest to think through your moves. The best chess players can anticipate several steps ahead of their opponent, and they are also quite adept at visualizing different scenarios, along with their pros and cons. Being too impulsive in a strategy game like chess or poker could lead to a quick loss. Of course, there is always the random element of luck which can influence the outcome, for the better or the worst, of even the most well-timed moves.

The most successful people know how to navigate between their gut intuition and critical thinking skills. Every situation requires a different combination of these, and it is only through experience that someone can learn to determine the right balance for different circumstances. Sometimes you must rely predominantly on your gut instincts to protect yourself in a potentially dangerous or harmful situation, and other times, you need to use more abstract reasoning skills for planning and to strategize out your actions. To what extent the conscious mind plays a role in the decision-making process is not precisely clear, but there are many factors at work throughout the brain and body with any decision, which may make you wonder just how much control you have over your own life. When you make a decision, what exactly is involved in that process?

Philosophers often like to discuss decision-making ideologies in binary terms. If a person truly has free will, then they are free to go about their lives as they please and do whatever they want. They alone are responsible for the choices they make and must also accept whatever consequences come their way. Alternatively, if an individual's life is entirely determined by fate or by some other force of nature, then no decisions are made deliberately. They would have no control over their own lives, and everything that happens would be because of some predetermined order of events.

Decision-making does not necessarily need to be a binary process. How people make choices could involve a combination of free will and fatalism. It is also not easy to define what is meant by "free will" anyway. Do you need to be completely aware of the decisions being made by your brain to feel a sense of ownership over them? The answer to this question is entirely subjective, as some people might think that any unconscious motivation that they are not aware of is fatalistic and others might think that all thoughts are necessarily part of the same process and it does not matter where they originate before they become actions.

The conscious mind is never the only part of the nervous system involved in decision-making. All thoughts must pass through various neurological and experiential filters along the way before they can become active. Even the decision to move your limbs requires careful planning and coordination with both your central and peripheral nervous system. If any of those systems fail, you will most likely not be able to move whatever part of your body you were trying to move. The conscious mind acts as part of an ongoing feedback loop with its unconscious counterparts. Decisions only happen when there is consensus throughout the nervous system. Sometimes actions get suppressed when there is a gut instinct that they might not be beneficial to act out. Other times the higher brain takes over and prevents a tempting gut instinct from actuating. There are numerous error-checking mechanisms and controls located throughout the brain and especially in the prefrontal cortex that can enable people to make genuinely sound decisions.

Your surrounding environment can heavily influence your thoughts. Environmental cues can trigger individual emotional and physiological responses that elicit specific reactions from you. In this sense, you are reacting to your situation, and your answer, in turn, influences the surrounding environment in a continuous feedback loop. You do not have much control over what happens to you in any given situation, and the decisions you make depend entirely on your circumstances. For instance, you cannot decide to go sky-diving from the bottom of a cave, nor can you use a stepladder to climb to the moon. No paradoxes or impossibilities are allowed.

Some of the decisions you make are semi-autonomous, including walking a certain way or breathing with a certain rhythm, and others are more deliberate such as exploring rock formations and mining for minerals. If you have a wandering mind, it is possible you might think about making decisions that have nothing to do with your current location or circumstances, but most of the choices will be directly related to your surrounding environment. The same principle also applies to social interactions. You cannot always control who you interact with, but every social exchange involves both verbal and non-verbal communication and action. If you are social-izing with a threatening individual, your instinct might cause you to recoil in defense. Your adrenaline levels will surge, and you might be on high alert. Some of the feelings you experience in this situation are a direct reaction to the perceived threat, and your nervous system acts out of instinct, producing the sensation that you are in a potentially dangerous scenario.

Environmental triggers demand your attention. A loud siren blaring outside your house will be very difficult to ignore whereas you might not even notice the faint buzzing noises of nearby flies. Other times, it is challenging to overlook something. For example, if you are trying to study, and a baby starts crying hysterically in the background, there is nothing that will prevent you from hearing the cries of the baby and reacting to it. Distractions like these are often annoying and very difficult to tune out. Even when you feel like you are making a conscious decision, it may still be the case that you are reacting to some internal or external impulse. For instance, you might decide to plan a family vacation to Disneyland one day. That decision might feel impulsive and spur-of-the-moment, but maybe you have been feeling overwhelmed at work and are in desperate need of a getaway. The reason why you chose Disneyland might have to do with some previous experience you had at the park when you were a child, or perhaps you noticed an advertisement for it. You cannot think of something like a Disneyland vacation without prior knowledge about the park, and you also cannot plan a trip without something there to compel you to do so.

Every action is a reaction to another action. Even the thoughts you have are reactions to other ideas or triggers in the environment. You are like a leaf blowing through the wind landing on a wall for a moment and then being blown out into the lake. Whatever comes next will be a direct result of what happened before. This rule of causality underlies every decision you will ever make. In this sense, how you define "free will" depends on how much liberty you are willing to give to your decision-making processes. No matter how independent a thought you feel that you may have, there was a trigger for it somewhere either in your internal or external environment. Sometimes patterns of thinking can seem random and disorganized, which can be the result of anxiety in response to a stressful situation or a reaction to certain stimulants. Racing thoughts can have many causes, and not all of them are identifiable, but to the person experiencing them, they can be tough to stop. Some people also experience thought disorders where they cannot control the types of thoughts that intrude into their minds.

Some decisions are quick, and others require a great deal of planning and forethought. The speed at which a decision happens is also dependent on the personality of the person as well as the circumstances of the moment. One person could decide to purchase a brand-new car impulsively while another might wait a few months and negotiate the best offer. For the impulsive person, it might be the case that they just noticed a brand-new vehicle that they wanted. The less spontaneous person might not have any significant issues with their current car and takes their time to make an educated decision about purchasing a new one.

In countries with abundant food and resources, people do not need to worry about feeding their families, and the threats to their survival are minimal, which provides time for personal enlightenment, education, and creativity. Children play in parks, and there are plenty of leisure opportunities. A lack of challenges to survival, however, can also bring about mischievous and reckless behavior as bored individuals have to find a way to expend their extra energy. History shows that good times cannot last forever, and unpredictable disasters are an ever-present threat. Sudden disease outbreaks, natural disasters, and wars pose an immediate threat to the safety and security of the civilized world. In these times, resources may become suddenly scarce and not easily accessible. These dire conditions may persist as an acute or chronic problem, but the presence of these questionable circumstances force people to make difficult decisions that they might otherwise not even consider.

Difficult times can, in the most extreme circumstances, bring out the primitive nature in people. In the movie *Alive*,[5] some members of an Uruguayan rugby team survive a plane crash in the remote Andes Mountains. They must survive in the snow with limited resources and nobody searching for them after an initial search team declared them dead. After running out of their limited food rations and experiencing several more deaths of their team members and family, the survivors are forced to make a difficult decision – eat the remains of the deceased or face certain death. In any other situation, doing something this cannibalistic would be unthinkable, but due to the unique position the survivors were facing, they had with no other choice. Fortunately, a few of the team members were somehow able to hike their way out of the mountains over 12 days and summon assistance for their stranded comrades. A total of 16 people survived out of the 45 original passengers.

When extreme hunger strikes and there is no food available anywhere, this can cause people to make decisions that they would have never thought possible. The survival instinct takes over and can cause people to seek out a means of sustenance no matter the cost. This instinct can conflict with rational thought and morality, as most people will do whatever they have to do to survive, and higher-order brain regions cannot function well without food for long.

Genetic Memories

Genetic memories are another major factor that might play into decision-making. Although there is currently no scientific evidence that memories are directly handed down through your ancestors, there is evidence that certain traits and behaviors may have a genetic basis to them. Descendants of Holocaust survivors were discovered by researchers Adam Klosin et al. to have lower levels of cortisol in their blood, thus making them predisposed to higher levels of stress and anxiety than those with normal levels of the hormone. To refer to the lowered cortisol blood levels as a "memory" would be a misnomer, but the results of this study descendants show that dramatic experiences of ancestors can alter DNA in such a way that the effects of those experiences are indirectly passed down over generations.

Genetic variations may influence personality traits and affect the way people make decisions. Elevated or depressed hormone and neurotransmitter levels in some areas of the brain can lead people to be impulsive or cautious in their choices. If an impactful experience that happened to one of your ancestors made its way through the bloodline to you, then there is an excellent chance that you will have inherited the effects of that experience without necessarily realizing it. Some decisions you make may be the by-product of these inherited genetic changes. The Holocaust study demonstrates that the lives of your ancestors can influence specific behaviors, but it does not provide a causal link between the memories of your ancestors and your daily life. It only provides a relationship between what they experienced and how those experiences shaped their genetics in such a way to influence the development of your personality and traits.

A study by researchers Adam Klosin et al. showed that a particular species of roundworm was genetically engineered to carry a gene that caused them to glow under ultraviolet light.[6] The glow was initially very faint in a cold environment but brightened dramatically in a warm climate. Interestingly, the worms retained this brighter glow when they returned to the more chilled environment, a result that suggests that the worm developed memory about the luminescence from the warm atmosphere.[7] Remarkably this glowing gene was transmitted through 14 successive generations of roundworms, indicating some basis for genetic memory. According to study co-author Tanya Vavouri, "Worms are very short-lived, so perhaps they are transmitting memories of past conditions to help their descendants predict what their environment might be like in the future."[8] In roundworms, the past experiences of their ancestors very likely were encoded into their genetic memory so that they exhibited the same fluorescing behaviors without any prior training.

More research needs to be conducted on the possibility of genetic memories transferring down through successive generations, but it would be interesting to uncover the potential links between the experiences of your ancestors and your current thoughts and behavioral patterns. You share a substantial percentage of their genetic material, and it is possible that you also share some of their traits and habits too. Addictive behavioral patterns and mental health issues run in families and it is also not uncommon to discover that a child is interested in the same activities as their parents or grandparents either. It is unlikely that specific memories transfer over to children, but until more research is done, you will never know for certain.

Déjà Vu

Real genetic memories in people would imply that you were able to experience or, at the very least, detect the actual memories of one of your ancestors. People have often detected that they have been somewhere before or done something that they know that they have not done. This phenomenon is commonly referred to as "déjà vu" and refers to a gut feeling of familiarity where there should otherwise be no such feeling. Déjà vu has resulted in some people believing in the idea of past lives and reincarnation. They think that they are experiencing a sense of familiarity, and since there are no actual memories of being there, then it must be because of their existence in a past life or they are experiencing the genetic memories of one of their ancestors.

People sometimes also believe that these experiences are a result of some karma inherited from the deeds and misdeeds of a past life. They will use this experience to guide their decisions in the future so that they may have a better life now. If they suffer, it will be for a commendable reason to extoll the sins of the past, and if they rejoice, it is because of some ancient virtue. Although these beliefs are not easily falsifiable, there may be a less ethereal explanation to the experience of déjà vu. Researchers Akira O'Connor et al. conducted a study on subjects in which they were able to successfully trigger the sensation of déjà vu in a laboratory setting by telling each participant a list of related words, but not revealing the word that relates all the other words together.[9] For instance, they might say something like, "Homework, books, teachers, desks, classrooms, library," but they would not say the keyword that links all these other words together – school. The subjects were then immediately asked if they heard the keyword, and they all admitted that they did not.

The researchers ran fMRI scans on the subjects and asked them if they heard a word that started with the letter "s." The participants said that they had not. Then they asked participants if they noticed the keyword, and the subjects commented that they had not, but the word still felt familiar to them. What was especially interesting was that during the déjà vu experience the memory centers of the brain, including the hippocampus, were not active during the scan. Instead, the frontal areas of the brain were active, suggesting that the decision-making regions of the brain were the most active during the déjà vu experience.[10]

The researchers concluded from the study that the frontal regions of the brain act as an error-checking mechanism for the validity of memories. If a false memory is suspected, these regions attempt to resolve that issue, and that is very likely how the experience of déjà vu plays itself out. Déjà vu is a sign that the memory systems of the brain are intact and are functioning correctly. Frequent déjà vu experiences are a good sign that your memory is working well.[11] The error-checking involved in memory validation happens autonomously, and the only conscious awareness you experience is the feeling of déjà vu, which is yet another example where an unconscious process executes higher-level cognitive resources without the need for any conscious decision-making.

Sleep, Dreaming, and Metacognition

Another area where you have very little conscious control over your experiences happen when you are asleep. Certain regions in the brain ordinarily active during wakefulness become less responsive, and other areas become more productive. Some scientists believe that sleep serves an essential purpose for the regulation of energy. Body temperature and energy metabolism are reduced during sleep, thereby allowing for people to have greater access to energy stores during periods of wakefulness when conscious willpower and effort are required to carry out daily routines and activities. Not getting enough sleep can result in poor work performance, decreased energy levels, and a depressed mood.

Besides the lack of productivity imposed by sleep deprivation, other theories say that sleep also plays a vital role in the repair and rejuvenation of physical and cognitive functions. During a person's waking hours, there is a certain amount of stress placed on the immune system, musculoskeletal system, and mind. Neurons heartily produce adenosine during wakefulness, and it accumulates in a person's brain throughout the day.[12] Caffeine can temporarily block the action of this hormone, but when enough of it is present, tiredness sets in and a person feels sleepy. During sleep, the body clears itself of adenosine and promotes alertness upon awakening. Muscle growth, tissue repair, protein synthesis, and growth hormone release and occur during sleep and allow the body to repair and rejuvenate itself. The idea that your brain expels waste products that need to be cleared out daily during sleep is a popular one among researchers.[13]

Perhaps the most curious stage of sleep is REM (rapid eye movement) sleep, in which brain wave activity is the most similar to active wakefulness, which is the stage where most dreams occur. Infants, children, and teenagers spend a lot of their time asleep in this state, and it may be that this stage is closely correlated with brain plasticity and influencing memory, problem-solving, and other cognitive processes and skills. People who are sleep deprived, or deprived explicitly of REM sleep, tend to experience difficulty concentrating, forming new memories, and learning new things. These cognitive deficits are especially noticeable in children and adolescents[14] and lack of adequate REM sleep can mimic the effects of ADHD.[15]

You cannot make any decisions about when you fall asleep or the type of dreams you will experience on a given night, but there is a strange phenomenon that many people experience called lucid dreaming, which is a bizarre type of dream state where you are dreaming, but are somehow aware of it, and you may try to influence the content and outcomes of your dreams during that period of alertness. Researchers Elisa Filevich et al. discovered that there was a strong correlation between high levels of lucid dreaming and metacognition,[16] the ability to monitor thoughts. The scientists had participants undergo brain imaging scans while participating in a thought monitoring activity. They divided the participants up into two groups, each corresponding to either high or low levels of self-reported dream lucidity. Participants were asked to delineate thoughts that entered their head during the study into two categories – externally or internally oriented. Externally oriented thoughts were those that were directly related to the external environment, including the noise from the scanner or the visual surroundings. Internally oriented thoughts were not related to the external environment but involved mental tasks, memories of past events, or planning.

Fascinatingly, the brains of people with high and low levels of dream lucidity were functionally different. Participants who experienced high levels of lucidity in their dreams were found to have a higher concentration of grey matter volume in the frontopolar cortex than those who reported a lower level of lucid dreaming. Brain scans confirmed more elevated levels of activity in this cortex during moments of internally oriented thoughts leading researchers to suggest a direct correlation between high levels of thought monitoring and a higher frequency of lucid dreaming.[17] Filevich et al. mention that the frontopolar cortex is larger in humans that other primates[18] and that metacognitive ability is likely exclusive to humans.[19] The clinical characteristics of metacognitive insight during pathological conditions including psychosis is remarkably similar to that performed during dreams, suggesting a similar underlying neurological mechanism.[20]

Metacognition is simply fascinating. The ability to think about thoughts seems almost contradictory on the surface, but it is a skill that can be quite beneficial at times, although it can also be a nuisance during periods of high anxiety. According to Nancy Chick of Vanderbilt University, "Metacognition is, put simply, thinking about one's thinking. More precisely, it refers to the processes used the plan, monitor, and assess one's understanding and performance."[21] What is most interesting about metacognition is the brain's ability to layer cognitive processes in such a way that one thought process monitors another one. In doing so, you can impose a higher level of self-awareness upon yourself and use that to improve the techniques you use to learn new skills and make better decisions. The ability to be reflective and mindful of your learning process can lead to significantly enhanced problem-solving skills and emotional coping strategies.

While learning how to monitor your thoughts and plan for future action are both useful skills, too much rumination can be a sign of anxiety, obsessive-compulsive disorder (OCD), or depression. People who frequently analyze their thoughts are prone to planning and calculating out the potential consequences of their actions. They exercise caution in everything they do but might worry themselves sometimes over inconsequential actions. Although anxiety is something that everyone experiences, some people experience it often leading them to live in a constant state of fear and worry. People who have this problem have little control over how they feel, and the sensations that come along with an anxiety disorder can lead to overly cautious and avoidant behavior. For instance, individuals with social anxiety tend to avoid crowds and might avoid social functions if they cannot move past their fears.

What these experiences show is that mentality can have a significant impact on decision-making. People who are prone to addictive behavior might have a harder time turning down an invitation to drink than someone who has anxiety about alcohol. Your mental state and certain predispositions can have a profound influence on the type of decisions that you make. Overcoming the effects of these types of feelings can be challenging and require significant lifestyle changes, cognitive-behavioral therapy, and other interventions. Someone suffering from an anxiety disorder might benefit from learning and practicing relaxation techniques, joining a gym and working out, or meditating and doing yoga. They can slowly retrain their brains to becomes less reactive to non-harmful stimuli and learn coping skills for dealing with intrusive thoughts and other distractions.

The Problem of Indecisiveness

The quality of being indecisive is another trait that some people struggle with daily. You are asked to decide on something, possibly important or possibly trivial, and you cannot make up your mind. This experience can be very frustrating and lead to feelings of helplessness and disappointment. In the worst case, the inability to decide can cause someone else to make that decision for you, and it is not always going to be in your best interest. It turns out that there is a neurological basis for indecisiveness, and it predominantly has to do with the intensity of the information processing across different regions of the brain. Researchers Rafael Plania et al. experimented with volunteer subjects using transcranial alternating current stimulation, a non-invasive brain stimulation method to either intensify or reduce information flow between the prefrontal cortex and parietal cortex.[22] These subjects had to make preference-based or perceptual (sensory) decisions about food while being stimulated, although they were not aware of the stimulation during the experiment.

Researchers found that when they reduced the information flow between the two cortices, subjects were more indecisive and had difficulty making preference-based decisions.[23] On the other hand, perceptual-based decision making was unaffected by fluctuations in brain stimulation.[24] Increased brain stimulation did not appear to have any significant effect on either type of decision-making.[25] The study concluded that there needed to be a certain threshold of information processing for people to more easily make preferential decisions about whether they like something or not. According to Plania et al., "Our modelling results show that disruption of fronto-parietal coherence resulted in lowered precision of value-based food choices. In other words, on any given trial, participants' choices became more inconsistent with their preferences as stated before the experiment, but the average preference across trials remained stable."[26] Despite subjects' initial preferences, depression of cortical activity in the pathways between the two cortices caused them to be indecisive and not make decisions based on sound reasoning or judgment.[27]

Value-based indecisiveness, such as that induced in the study, demonstrate the delicate nature of the intensity of information processing in the brain. People who chronically have problems making these types of decisions may have impaired cortical processing intensity in these regions.[28] It is entirely possible that in the future, there will be medical interventions and therapies that could assist people in becoming more decisive. Perhaps there will be implantable stimulator devices that could help amplify signal processing between the two brain regions to enable better information flow and hence more effective decision-making processes. Indecisiveness, while troublesome, does typically result in some decision either made by the individual or by someone else even if the decision is to do nothing at all or something completely different than what they were initially mulling over. There are also times when people are not making any decisions at all and are just letting their mind wander. It turns out that, according to researchers Daniel Gilbert and Matthew Killingsworth, the average mind wanders about 46.9% of the time.[29] "Mind-wandering" occurs when a person does not focus on anything in particular, but instead, they allow their thoughts to drift aimlessly.

The researchers also found that people who let their minds wander more often were typically unhappier than those who did not engage in mind-wandering as often.[30] Being actively involved in activities such as dancing, hiking, working, engaging in conversation, or even meditating were all associated with much higher levels of happiness than doing nothing at all. Too much ruminating over the past or worrying about the future typically leads to negative and depressing thoughts. Being mentally present and engaging in regular mindful activities are some of the keys to escaping the traps of anxiety, stress, and depression.

Mindfulness

According to author David Rock, the difficulty in discussing mindfulness with people in corporations and other institutions is that "these people tend to spend little time thinking about themselves and other people, but a lot of time thinking about strategy, data, and systems. As a result, the circuits involved in thinking about oneself and other people, the medial frontal cortex, tend to be not too well developed."[31] Highly intelligent and capable people may be very skilled at navigating complex systems and coming up with solutions to enhance company profit margins, but they may experience difficulties understanding the complex personal struggles and characters of the people who work for the company, including themselves.

Researchers Norman Farb et al. discovered that people have two fundamentally distinct ways of perceiving the world – the default "narrative" network and the direct experience network.[32] The prefrontal cortex and specific memory regions in the hippocampus interact when there is not much activity in your immediate surroundings, activating the default network.[33] Think of this network as the slightly powered down state your computer enters after a brief period of inactivity. The default network activates when nothing else of significance is going on, and it is responsible for self-directed thoughts and introversion. If you are relaxing by the pool on a hot summer day, you might find yourself focusing on what errands you need to run when you return home later in the afternoon. This network is also involved in planning, daydreaming, and ruminating.

While the default network is active, you will not be able to immerse yourself in the sights, sounds, and smells of the surrounding environment. Thoughts occur about how much time you have left to be at the pool or how late it is getting, and that might get you to start worrying about all of the things you have to do. It is as if your ability to experience your environment is overridden by thinking and introversion to the point where you are barely present at all. According to David Rock, "When you experience the world using this narrative network, you take in information from the outside world, process it through a filter of what everything means, and add your interpretations. Sitting on the dock with your narrative circuit active, a cool breeze isn't a cool breeze, it's a sign that summer will be over soon, which starts you thinking about where to go skiing, and whether your ski suit needs a dry clean."[34] Instead of experiencing the breeze, you are too immersed in analyzing it and using the incoming sensory data to calculate the types of decisions you will soon need to make, which can be a very frustrating experience, making it difficult to relax and enjoy the moment.

Sometimes it is outright dangerous or inappropriate to engage the default network. For instance, if you are in the kitchen cooking, and you have several pots on the stove all going at once, and then you start daydreaming about wishing you were in Hawaii, you might accidentally burn yourself when you grab the blazing hot cast iron skillet by the handle rather than using your oven gloves to touch it. The problem is the default network is easily activated, and people with short attention spans may find themselves drifting in and out of it even in moments where finely-tuned attention matters the most. Thoughts about yourself and other people also activate the default network. This network is responsible for forming the narrative of your personal life and the roles and issues of all of the people involved in it. In this way, the default network is instrumental in piecing together your entire history and turning it into a story with a definite past, which allows you to make predictions and inferences toward the future. This network can, therefore, be a handy planning tool for making sound interpersonal decisions.

The other network, the direct experience network, is characterized by activation of the insula (perception of bodily sensations) and the anterior cingulate gyrus (region for switching your focus of attention).[35] When this network is activated, your focus is mainly on the feelings generated by incoming sensory data. You fully experience your environment and everything in it. You can feel the coldness of the glass of water in your hands, and you can smell the fragrances of the flowers blooming in your garden. As David Rock explains, "[In the direct experience network] you perceive more information about events occurring around you, as well as more accurate information about these events…you also become less imprisoned by the past, your habits, expectations or assumptions, and more able to respond to events as they unfold."[36] This network is where people have fun and genuinely enjoy themselves. It is also the network where people feel love, grief, amusement, and all of the myriad emotions of the human experience.

Becoming mindful of the difference between these two distinct networks resulted in people becoming able to differentiate between the two in any given moment and also switch from one to the other. There is an inverse relationship between the two networks so that when one is active, the other is dormant. People who can master the art of mindfulness can switch between the two mindsets at any given time effortlessly. If they catch themselves in a moment of anxiety about something, they can decide to focus on their surrounding environment by switching off the default network and transitioning into the direct experience network. David Rock sums this ability up in his article very succinctly. He says, "If you're on the jetty in the breeze and you're someone with a good level or mindfulness, you are more likely to notice that you're missing a lovely day worrying about tonight's dinner, and focus your attention onto the warm sun instead."[37] This ability to switch from one mode of cognition to another is a refined skill that comes more naturally to some people than others, but nearly everyone is capable of learning about and practicing mindfulness.

It is essential to strike a finely-tuned balance between the two distinct mindsets and to be keenly aware of how to optimize each mindset to your direct benefit. Whether you are making decisions about plans that are important or you are merely making a decision to let go and relax in an extraordinary moment, it is important to feel in control of your mindset. While you have a limited amount of control over the circumstances and events of your life, you can learn to control how you react to them. Sometimes you need to switch your mind off and fully immerse yourself into something with your bodily sensations and other times you need to flip that switch back on when you need to focus and plan. Do not make any decisions that would ever jeopardize your long-term happiness and health.

You are the main character in the story of your life, and you get to determine some of the memories to make along the way. The journey might be tense and stressful at times, but nothing lasts forever, including hard times. Everything has a way of balancing itself out over time and finding its way back to the center, which is where you are. Stay centered and learn to balance the pain with joy, grief with delight, and anger with love. Decide what kind of life you want to live, imagine it, and then make it happen. Your unconscious mind will guide you to the places you need to visit, the people you need to interact with along the way, and the skills you need to master before you can experience your dreams. You already know everything you need to know before you are even aware of it. Just trust in the power of your unconscious mind to guide you there. It will always take you to exactly where you need to be.

Chapter 7 – No Identity

"I ain't what I ought to be, I ain't what I'm going to be, but I ain't what I was."[1]

— Author Unknown

Early Childhood Identity Development

Your identity sets you apart from others and brings you together with your friends, family, colleagues, and religious and social groups. Some parts of your identity revolve around personal preferences, including your sexual orientation, clothing preferences, or taste in music and movies. Other parts of it are more concerned with your physical appearance, racial heritage, and socioeconomic status. There are countless categories and subcategories of identity, but the one thing they all have in common is that they help to define you. Some of these traits and characteristics are static, while others can change over brief or more extended periods. A proper examination of identity should consider early childhood development and adolescence, which are both periods filled with many milestones and individual physical and psychological changes. The field of developmental psychology contains several prominent historical figures including Jean Piaget, Lev Vygotsky, and Erik H. Erikson, and each of their theories is quite broad but offers a reasonable starting point for an informed discussion on identity development.

Jean Piaget, a Swiss biologist, and psychologist who became interested in the cognitive development and educational abilities of children developed a theory known as *genetic epistemology*[2] to explain their behavior and limitations via distinct stages of development. The four stages are the sensorimotor stage, preoperational stage, concrete operational stage, and formal operational stage.[3] Piaget believed that these stages were the same for everyone, regardless of socioeconomic, sociocultural, or psychiatric background. He often referred to children as "little scientists,"[4] with the idea being that as children learn about the world around them, they assimilate that knowledge and in turn develop their ideas and concepts. Piaget did not believe that children were less intelligent than adults, but just that they thought differently than them. As children progress through the different stages of development, their thinking becomes less action-oriented and more concentrated on developing sophisticated mental operations and conceptual processes. He believed that there were significant qualitative and quantitative differences in the ways older and younger children reasoned.

The earliest stage of cognitive development in children is the *sensorimotor stage* and occurs between the ages of birth and two years old. This stage involves knowledge acquisition strictly through the five senses. Fundamental actions including sucking, grasping, looking, and listening are how children at this age make sense out of the world around them.[5] Children at this age absorb new information and sensory data like a sponge, quickly assimilating it and putting it into action, and this is the stage where they learn first how to crawl and then walk. They also acquire the necessary language skills and learn how to communicate with their parents. Children also develop *object permanence*,[6] which is a critical developmental milestone where they realize that objects which disappear outside of their immediate visual field still exist. Object permanence is a prerequisite skill to developing mental representations for things, such as children attaching words or labels to them. They also become aware that they exist separately from their parents, which allows them to form their most fundamental concept of identity.

The *preoperational stage*[7] is the next stage of development and is associated with children ages 2 to 7 years old. Although they already have the fundamentals of language and object representation, children at this age develop more sophisticated oral and written language skills, progressing from verbally articulating more coherent and complete thoughts to writing legible sentences down on paper. Children at this stage still think and reason in very concrete terms and struggle to adopt alternative perspectives or empathize with others. They also generally struggle with logical reasoning skills and may have difficulty with conceptual and operational equality. For instance, consider someone cutting a piece of play-dough in half from a can, and pressing out the other half to make it appear more massive than the other one. Then if they offer the child to choose to take one of the pieces, the child would most likely take the larger one without ever realizing that the two pieces were the same size.

The *concrete operational stage*[8] occurs between ages 7 and 12, in which children develop a sense of empathy and improved logical reasoning skills. They are better able to understand the feelings of other people and begin to realize that others may think differently than they do. Although they still operate in mostly concrete terms, they are better equipped to deal with fundamental logical problems, including representational equality. For instance, children this age would likely understand that two glasses of different shapes and sizes could contain the same volume of liquid. Despite a significant enhancement in logical reasoning skills, children in this stage may still struggle with abstract or hypothetical reasoning.

The fourth and final stage in Piaget's theory is the fo*rmal operational stage*,[9] which occurs from age 12 on up. During this stage, abstract reasoning and formal mental operations become more developed, and the individual can construct and justify theories about social, philosophical, and scientific subjects. Teenagers learn how to approach problems from multiple perspectives and how to use deductive reasoning to form generalizations from given information. One of the significant intellectual developments is the ability to make quantitative and qualitative predictions about the world using existing knowledge, data, and data trends, which is also when people learn to think outside the box and mentally form and articulate abstract ideas and concepts.

To more accurately explain how each of his stages functioned psychologically, Piaget introduced some important terms into his theory of child development, including *schemas*, *assimilation*, *accommodation*, and *equilibration*.[10] He defined schemas as categories of knowledge collected to for children to make sense of the world around them. Schemas are dynamic and flexible and can change according to new experiences. For instance, a child who has a black cat as a pet at home might assume that all cats are black, but as soon as she sees a brown cat somewhere else, she would correct her schema to now include the idea that not all cats are colored the same way.

The process of assimilation involves processing information into an existing schema. Consider a child who sees another cat while they are out at the park. The method of mentally identifying and labeling the animal a "cat" involves placing the animal observed into an existing schema. Likewise, the process of accommodation consists of modifying current schemas to more appropriately fit incoming sensory data, such as a child adjusting to the idea that all cats are not black. Accommodation is also the process by which new schemas occur when a child sees completely novel objects, information, and experiences. The delicate balance between the ongoing processes of assimilation and accommodation is equilibration, where children modify their behavior in response to new knowledge about certain things while maintaining existing schemas for stable information. One of Piaget's major ideas concerning knowledge is that it is not a static entity, but instead is a dynamic and fluid process subject to continuous change as the child matures in their psychological development. Furthermore, the acquisition of new knowledge is not a passive process, but children are actively involved in obtaining new knowledge through social interactions, real and imaginary play, and other interactions with the world.

Lev Vygotsky was a Soviet psychologist who contended that an individual's psychological development was firmly rooted in social interactions.[11] He believed that there were two primary methods, not necessarily at the exclusion of each other, by which children learned concepts – through their personal lives and at school. He referred to knowledge gained at school as *academic concepts*[12] that are both systematic and scientific. This knowledge is brought to children through their experiences in the classroom and taught to them by their teacher or out of their textbooks.

Vygotsky used the term *everyday concepts*[13] to refer to knowledge obtained through social interactions with peers and adults. He believed in a top-bottom approach in which children explored and absorbed new ideas through social interaction, which then filtered its way into their brains for further reflection and development. Through meaningful social interactions in the outer world, children gradually assimilate learned characteristics and traits into their personality. Vygotsky strongly believed that social interactions laid the blueprint for individual personalities. Academic concepts further influence these everyday concepts to modify their expression. In this way, theoretical and everyday concepts blend synergistically.

Unlike his predecessor Piaget, Vygotsky did not place much emphasis on the development of identity through intrinsic factors and individual skill acquisition. He coined the *zone of proximal development* (ZPD)[14] as consisting of the interaction between adults and peers in meaningful ways such that it directly facilitated the education of children. Vygotsky strongly believed that learning was only possible in a profoundly social environment and that it was necessary to facilitate regular interactions with teachers and other adult figures to activate essential developmental tools and processes within the children's minds. He also believed that certain psychological functions, including memory, cognition, and attention, were socially distributed within a community of learners. Vygotsky believed that the ZPD was the foundation behind formal learning within the classroom. The most effective instruction occurs in actively engaged learning environments with plenty of social activities and frequent interactions.

The Russian-Soviet psychologist Piotr Galperin[15] brought new light to the ZPD to highlight specific instructional strategies and techniques that could be adapted within a Vygotskian framework and used in the classroom to facilitate socialized learning processes. Galperin's approach was to both empirically and rigorously study the specific concepts and skills that students needed to learn and the process they must learn them with for the knowledge to develop into mature mental actions. Although he acknowledged that multiple pathways could be used to arrive at the same critical junction in the teaching-learning process, there were specific developmental milestones that needed to occur before a child achieved conceptual mastery.

According to researchers Jacques Haenan et al., "Within the framework of activity theory, actions are conceived as conscious attempts to change objects according to some intended result."[16] Galperin's actions involve using concepts with increasing levels of abstraction. For instance, one such idea might be gardening, which is a pretty broad term that could describe a multitude of actions including planting seeds in fertile soil, measuring and interpreting certain chemical levels in detailed soil analysis, or drawing up blueprints for a vegetable garden. To account for these distinct progressive possibilities, Galperin defined four categories of action based on different levels of abstraction.[17] These levels share some similarities to Piaget's stages of cognitive development despite them being conceptualized exclusively in a socialized learning environment.

The first level of action is the *materialized level*, which is the level at which activities are performed directly with the assistance of material objects or representations. For instance, children may model necessary counting skills using blocks or draw out figures on a whiteboard to model the arithmetic of fractions. The second level of action, the *perceptual* level, is characterized by children using mental representations of material objects to perform actions. If their parents ask them to clean their room, for example, the child may first visualize where she is going to put away all her toys and clothes before doing it. This type of action requires a more sophisticated level of thinking than that of the materialized level because children must possess an intrinsic understanding of the physical objects in the room.

The third level of action is the *verbal level*. At this level, the child uses the tools of language, speaking out loud to communicate ideas about material objects and their properties. Being able to verbalize concepts requires the ability to carry mental images or representations of the described items. The fourth level of action is the *mental level*, which is when children exclusively use their minds to manipulate mental imagery and solve problems.

Galperin believed that mastery of each of these levels of action along with the ability to function through all of them in different situations was of paramount importance to carry out meaningful mental activities. To pass through all the levels of action, the student must *generalize*[18] an action's properties so that she becomes aware of which features of the objects involved in it are essential and which ones are irrelevant in a learning task or situation. Students can improve their generalizations by experiencing and manipulating objects in a variety of different contexts. For instance, in counting the total number of fruits in a basket, students must be aware that the texture and taste of the fruit are irrelevant. If the same basket of fruit, however, were presented to them with the task being to identify the fruit by taste and texture while being blindfolded, then those previously irrelevant properties would suddenly become quite significant.

As students progress through the four levels of action, their efficiency improves, and the steps are *abbreviated*.[19] When first asked to distinguish and count different types of fruit in a basket, children might pull the fruit out of the basket, one by one, and count out loud until they have the correct amount. They might also have difficulty identifying the fruit and may need to manipulate the fruit to help them to identify them correctly. As they improve at this task and pass through the four levels of action, they get to a point where they can look at the fruit and quickly identify them. The time spent doing the task will decrease remarkably, as previous operations used to carry it out are abbreviated, leading to the eventual mastery of the action.

Piaget and Vygotsky's models for learning and intellectual development in children arise from different, but not irreconcilable, approaches. There are similarities in the theories of action offered by Galperin and the four stages of learning outlined by Piaget, but at the heart of each philosophy lies a fundamental difference – the importance of the individual. Contemporary interpretations of Piaget's theory of learning assert that their movement shapes the child's identity through four distinct and progressive stages of individual development. His approach appears somewhat rigid in that children must progress through rigorously defined stages in set age intervals. There also seems to be a lack of emphasis on social interaction in children's identity development. Vygotsky overemphasizes social interaction to the point where it becomes a prerequisite for learning anything deeply. He asserts that it is only through meaningful social experiences that children can increase and strengthen their cognitive capabilities and skills. Vygotsky's theory of learning may seem more holistic in scope than Piaget's, but it leaves out the possibility of discrete cognitive milestones that are defined by a child's age. His ideas might not be plausible for children raised in specific environments or cultures where frequent social interaction is uncommon.

Early Childhood Development Professor Rheta DeVries disagrees with contemporary interpretations of Piaget and Vygotsky that present a battle between individual versus social factors in learning. She considers it a myth that Piaget's sole focus was on the child as a "little scientist" and that he did not consider social factors as necessary in childhood development.[20] The problem is that most people only focus on his theories of intellectual development, but do not contemplate his vast breadth of work on the psychosocial factors involved in child development. What they do not know is that Piaget did not rigorously assess social influences on children during his research concerning their logical reasoning abilities, but that he did develop separate social theories. According to DeVries, "Piaget's social theory focuses on the relation between the individual and the social in socio-moral, affective and personality, and intellectual development, on the identity of intellectual operations and social co-operations, and on the role of norms (rules)."[21]

In his sociomoral theory of child development, Piaget described two types of adult-child relationships that he believed influenced children's personality development. The first type is referred to as *heteronomous morality*,[22] in which a child does not regulate her behavior, but instinct or unconscious obedience to others regulate it. Piaget viewed this type of morality as being one where the adult uses their authority in covert or aggressive ways to control the child's behavior. Adults may use tactics including manipulation, sarcasm, bribery, aggression, verbal or physical abuse, or other harsh tactics to coerce their child into obeying them. This obedience offers one-way respect from child to parent and encourages the child to behave in an overly submissive way toward others. They are not likely to engage in independent thoughts and are susceptible to blindly following the whims, desires, and orders of perceived authority figures. As the child matures into an adult, they may become rebellious and defiant, only following rules when they are being monitored or just refusing to comply with any orders at all. Such individuals may never understand the deep meaning behind moral imperatives or other types of morality and may only possess a superficial understanding of social behavior, feeling more comfortable being controlled by others. Piaget viewed heteronomous social development as being detrimental to an individual's personal and intellectual values, as this type of coercion only serves to make them more dependent on others and less capable of thinking for themselves.

The second type of adult-child relationship described by Piaget is *autonomous morality*,[23] where the child is encouraged to develop their own automatic and meaningful moral principles. This type of morality happens out of a mutually respectful and cooperative relationship with an adult authority figure. If the adult can restrain their authority while maintaining a healthy level of respect, it encourages the child to feel comfortable to think for themselves and develop personal convictions that are in the best interests of everyone. Piaget intentionally hyphenated the word "co-operation" to emphasize the root meaning of the word. According to DeVries, "Co-operating means striving to attain a common goal while coordinating one's own feelings and perspective with a consciousness of another's feelings and perspective."[24]

Co-operation develops out of feelings of mutual respect and admiration between individuals. It also establishes the foundation for trust and empathy in interpersonal relationships, allowing people to experience authentic and meaningful bonds with each other. Autonomous morality is rooted in a firmly defined sense of personal identity and a healthy balance between caring for yourself and taking care of others. Co-operation fosters people to view each other as equals and discourages judgmental attitudes. It is essential also to note that Piaget is not implying that children should be equals to adults, but that enough boundaries should exist so that they sense psychological equality in the relationship. Children with autonomous morality are comfortable sharing their ideas and opinions with adults without fear of punishment. They also respect and have a healthy fear for the moral authority of adults, but not to the point where they feel discouraged or threatened.

Piaget asserts that there are limitations to how much control adults can exert over children, with the process becoming more challenging as they grow older and mature into young adults.[25] Following the commands of their parents is the child's first exposure to forming moral rules, but if they develop autonomous morality, they will gradually come to understand these rules as being necessary and beneficial toward productive relationships with other adults and peers. They can also create new regulations and adapt existing ones to novel situations. Children who have a heteronomous morality, however, will have difficulty integrating their social experiences with their authoritarian adult interactions. They will have trouble understanding the perspectives of others and incorporating themselves into a diverse and dynamic social atmosphere. They can be easily influenced and coerced by others because of their inability to reason independently about their moral values. This subservient attitude may pose significant issues for children as they mature into adults, as their identity can easily change by peer pressure, criminal enterprises, or the unpredictable whims of an authoritarian figure. People with heteronomous morality will do whatever they need to do to gain the approval of others.

According to DeVries, "As a child acts and reacts in more or less stable ways in similar situations with a variety of people, personality becomes more consolidated and can be observed in consistent patterns."[26] Piaget believed that children construct social schemes in a similar way to how they develop schemes in the physical world.[27] The child's interpretation of social patterns and interactions shapes these schemes that are used to make sense out of social situations.

Their personality emerges from a multitude of social interactions in a variety of contexts over time, eventually stabilizing so that the child might identify as shy, ambitious, overly sensitive, or aggressive.

Some of Piaget's ideas about children's identity development are not that different from Vygotsky's.[28] Piaget asserted that social reciprocity was at the very core of personality development. He thought of social reciprocity as a type of mutual validation of feelings and other engagements that occurs during social interaction. Furthermore, this social development exists within the child's intellectual development. Piaget also believed that children must be capable of representational thoughts before they have the mental tools necessary to form schemes centered around feelings and values. A child at this stage of intellectual development would be capable of experiencing feelings of love and affection for another individual even after they have left the room, an idea similar to the concept of object permanence in the physical world.

Being able to coordinate different social perspectives and co-operate with others requires the use of each of the four levels of Piaget's intellectual development. He also emphasized that a necessary step for children to develop their personality is to liberate themselves from the desires and whims of others. This experience comes about from a stable relationship with an adult in which there is mutual respect.[29] Co-operation with others is a necessary foundation for a stable personality because it involves frequent interactions, including those involving comparison, opposition, and joint adjustment. This co-operation is an essential skill for developing children to foster productive and fulfilling interpersonal relationships, as heteronomous ones stagnate and can be harmful to both the individual and their associated social groups.

Piaget believed strongly that social life was prerequisite to healthy individual development.[30] He argued that the quest for human knowledge arises primarily out of interacting with the opposing ideas of other people, which causes people to doubt them and try to verify their beliefs or to seek out their truths. The act of socializing is what motivates people to learn new things and obtain knowledge.

Piaget even went as far as to claim that without socialization, learning new skills would be nearly impossible.[31] According to him, every behavior pattern consists of cognitive elements and the structure of pre-operations or operations, the emotional aspects of individual values, and the verbal, visual, or body language in which the previous two components express themselves. He also believed that every equilibrated social exchange consisted of a common language and perspective, agreement with social propositions, and reciprocity involving mutual respect and validation between partners.

As an illustration of Piaget's idea of social equilibration, consider two children, Sam and Joe, playing together at school. Sam asks Joe if he can be his basketball coach, and Joe agrees by responding, "Alright." This statement represents a transformation in their relationship because Joe validated and demonstrated an interest in Sam's idea. Joe must decenter himself to take Sam's perspective and accept his suggestion. In accepting this agreement, Joe feels obligated to act toward Sam as though he is his coach and he has an imaginary action embedded in his mind about Sam being his coach at a future date. This belief sets up the possibility of Joe conserving this agreement and establishing, in the words of DeVries, "the future potential (or virtual action) for respecting this role consistently (with non-contradiction) in future play."

Joe's current sense of obligation is conserved for future expression because he will not contradict himself, as this feeling will be the same then as it is now. He is ready to execute his obligation toward Sam at any moment, which in turn provides Sam with a certain kind of credit that he can use to get Joe to act the part of being coached by him. Sam is also similarly obligated to expect of himself what he expects from Joe. Sam has to take on the part of the coach to make the interaction equal. Now suppose that Joe proposes an idea for Sam to be his soccer coach. Since Joe accepted Sam as his basketball coach, Sam will likely feel obligated to accept this offer because if he were to reject it, chances are Joe would think that he was acting unfairly toward him. They will have the most fun if they can share in the experience of coaching each other, albeit with different sports. It is essential to keep in mind that at this point in their relationship, all their implicit agreements exist based on virtual actions, which are mental representations of future ones.

These implicit agreements and mutual obligations lay the foundation for a series of real actions between the two children. For example, Sam might pick up a nearby basketball and say, "Let's learn how to shoot free throws right now – what do you say?" This statement represents conservation of their original agreement and elaborates on it with this new idea. Then Joe might respond by picking up his soccer ball and saying, "Yeah, let's do that, and then I will show you how to dribble a soccer ball." This statement by Joe represents an attempt to get Sam to act on the value he initially presented with the play idea. As DeVries mentions, "The *correspondences* between the actions and ideas of...two children *comprise* a sequence or *grouping of coordinated actions* in which each child *takes the others'* perspective and coordinates it with his own."[32] Successful play between children, therefore, represents an equilibrated and ongoing exchange of co-operations where both kids feel obligated to mentally refer to a past agreement to bring propositions of new ideas and elaborations to existing ones to light.

Feelings of reciprocity and mutual respect lead to stable, ongoing, and productive exchanges between partners. In the case of Sam and Joe, if they continue to be sensitive and understanding toward each other's perspective, it can lead to a stable equilibrium in their relationship and ensure future positive experiences between them. They can expand their skills together to include more than just basketball or soccer coaching, as they grow and mature together in their friendship. It is vitally important that children do not contradict their implicit agreements in their exchanges; otherwise, there might be a perceived disequilibrium in their relationship. Too many of these contradictions can be detrimental to the health of friendship and lead to conflict or hurt feelings.

Piaget recognized that it takes time for children to develop the necessary cognitive operational skills to form equilibrium in their relationships with others. He also acknowledged that there are times when one partner might become dissatisfied or disinterested in the current obligation and may propose a modification to it or a new proposition altogether. The changes to desires and interests happen because their conservations did not evolve from moral or legal principles, but are held together by spontaneous desires and mutual feelings of excitement and curiosity. It is normal and expected for children to experience fleeting passions, and Piaget characterized this pre-operational behavior as *regulations*,[33] which may achieve transient states of equilibria but do not represent co-operations.

Nevertheless, these pre-operational efforts to co-operate with other children typically evolve into more stable social operations as they mature in age. Piaget believed that operations and co-operations occurred around ages 7-8 and later progressed into more profound and meaningful relationships alongside the stage of formal operations between the ages of 11-12 years. According to DeVries, "The development of moral feelings is a particular type of the construction of affective schemas. Moral actions, according to Piaget, are disinterested. That is, these are not motivated by utilitarian personal interest or success."[34] Two individuals who act out of moral reciprocity do so out of mutual respect for their feelings and perspectives.[35] They can substitute their point of view with a mental representation, or schema, of the other person's point of view. The result is a stable equilibrium in their relationship, leading to productive and enjoyable times together.

Piaget viewed the concrete-operational period as the one where children develop semi-normative feelings that serve as the foundation for the future development of moral norms.[36] These feelings can be generalized to any situation and are long-lasting and are autonomous, meaning that they are not present out of mere obligation or because of an external rule. Piaget viewed norms as essential to the conservation of moral values, the essence of a civilized society.[37] He also believed that educational systems ought to focus on helping children develop autonomous moral values so that they might not become thoroughly entrenched in the heteronomous values of their authority figures.

In summary, Piaget's social theory emphasizes the importance of individual autonomy and equilibrated relationships in children developing a healthy identity. Too much heteronomy in interpersonal relationships is counterproductive to the development of a stable self-image because it leads individuals to doubt themselves and blindly trust others who may not have their best interests at heart. Children develop their moral and social values through successive social interactions and as they progress through the stages of cognitive development. As they mature, children learn to solidify their moral values while being able to identify from the perspective of others and recognize the value in co-operating with them. Their identity forms through social norms handed down by generations and personal values developed through interactions with authority figures and peer groups.

Comprehensive Identity Development Theories

German-American psychologist Erik Erikson offered his theory about identity development that is well-balanced in terms of focusing on both intellectual and social developmental milestones.[38] He described identity development in people as occurring in eight distinct stages. The first stage is known as *trust vs. mistrust*[39] and embodies an associated sense of well-being and confidence in self and others, or a distrust, that is typically developed during the first year of life. This stage is not considered to be an entirely conscious one, as babies operate mostly on instinct and are still developing their memories and basic senses.

Babies less than one-year-old rely mostly on their mouth to sense and explore the world around them. They are utterly dependent on their parents for food and must use their mouths to take it in. Erikson hypothesizes that the oral stage of development precipitates the baby trusting in each of their other developing senses as they gradually mature into toddlers.[40] Some parents feel that they should coddle their babies as much as possible, reinforcing maternal and paternal dependency and comfort, while other cultures try to encourage their babies to kick around, cry, and make demands for food, promoting independence. Cultural norms and the goals of society generally determine the type of parenting recommended to help nurture the developing baby into what they think is the best path to survival and success. As Erikson says, "There is some intrinsic wisdom, some unconscious planning and much superstition in the seemingly arbitrary varieties of child training: what is 'good for the child,' what *may* happen to him, depends on what he is supposed to become and where."[41]

A type of mutual regulation between the parents and child develops, in which the baby learns what she needs to do to get her parents' attention, be it a desire for food, nurturing, getting a dirty diaper changed, or general engagement. Thus the baby forms a mutual identity with their parents being utterly dependent on them for her survival. When these mutually regulatory behaviors do not function as expected, the baby must find other ways to try to control the situation. Sometimes this takes the form of crying to the point of exhaustion, sucking her thumb, or wriggling around restlessly. These behaviors, in turn, elicit a reaction from the parents, who may change their routines in frustration and do whatever it takes to calm their baby. They may alternatively elect to ignore the baby's demands, depending on the circumstances, and let their baby exhaust herself to sleep.

There are psychoanalytic theories that how the parents respond to the baby's pleas for help may serve as a model for their future psychosocial development, with babies whose requests for support are ignored being more likely to be distrusting of the world and other people, including family members. Likewise, there are alternative methods to soothe an irritated baby, including being held, rocked back and forth, swaddled, or otherwise comforted in a non-oral manner. These actions demonstrate to the baby that their parents can be trusted to respond to their needs, even if it is not necessarily specific to their desires at the time.[42]

The second stage of development is *autonomy vs. shame/doubt*.[43] This stage is most closely associated with toddlers between the ages of one and three years old, where they desire to form independence from their parents and build self-esteem to aid in their future survival and happiness. An example of a child building autonomy would be when they are trying to make their bed after getting up in the morning or perhaps attempting to brush their teeth by refusing their parents' help. Despite most likely not being able to perform these tasks adequately, allowing them to try can raise their levels of self-confidence.

Parents who try to interfere with their toddler's desire for autonomy by chastising them or otherwise preventing them from acting independently in these situations may inadvertently encourage feelings of self-doubt or shame in their young children. They may grow older and continue to doubt their ability to perform tasks or make decisions independently, and this hesitation may lead to them being taken advantage of or becoming less capable of taking care of themselves. They may develop low self-esteem and not believe in their capabilities to navigate the world around them, leading to feelings of depression and alienation.[44]

Erikson's third stage of development is referred to as *initiative vs. guilt*[45] and is associated with children between the ages of three and six years old. Parents who encourage their children to explore their social and physical world through developing friendships and playing with toys within an assertive, but flexible set of boundaries, set their kids up for developing self-confidence and a sense of personal responsibility. A child's sense of identity at this stage depends mainly on how supportive their parents are toward their desire to explore and interact with their world. Parents who are overly controlling or express too much criticism toward their children may cause them to become anxious and insecure. Children raised in a loving and supportive environment will be more likely to develop a sense of purpose, which can lead them to discover new hobbies, activities, and learning experiences.

The fourth stage of development, *industry vs. inferiority*,[46] occurs between ages 6-12 and is characterized by children feeling accomplished and taking pride in their work and abilities. They may become heavily involved in academic, extracurricular, and other recreational activities while simultaneously becoming young ambassadors and leaders in their school and community. Children who feel inadequate when they compare themselves to their peers may become socially withdrawn and develop an inferiority complex about themselves, believing that they are incapable of meaningfully participating in social activities and events. They may doubt themselves, and this low self-esteem can carry itself over into adulthood in the absence of some active intervention. This unhealthy attitude can develop out of experiencing neglect or criticism from their family members or not having an adequate emotional support system. Frequent bullying at school or home may further perpetuate this unhealthy view of themselves.

Between ages 12-18, teenagers enter the fifth stage of development referred to as *identity vs. identity diffusion*[47], which is one of the most critical stages of an individual's life. Adolescence is a time where hormones are running high, with teenagers going through a multitude of physical and emotional changes, and there is an increased demand on them for their time and resources as some of them enter the workforce while simultaneously going through school. Adolescents with a strong sense of purpose will set reasonable goals for themselves and work hard to attain them. They will spend time experimenting in different social groups to figure out which ones suit them best and make them feel included. They focus on developing supportive friendships and meaningful relationships that will help guide them into adulthood. Typically, adolescents who develop these healthy habits and traits have a well-developed sense of personal identity and can successfully navigate personal and professional challenges that come their way without losing control. They often can use these challenges to further strengthen their identity, social skills, and personal development.

Growing up in an unstable household can be detrimental toward an adolescent forming a secure personal identity. They might become especially susceptible to addictive behaviors and other self-destructive habits which prevent them from realizing their full potential. Instability in the household does not necessarily imply abuse, neglect, or violence are taking place, although adolescents growing up in those kinds of homes will certainly be more likely to experience developmental issues. Adolescents who were raised in environments where there is too much micromanagement of their schedules and too little freedom given to them to do what they want to do can also suffer consequences. Furthermore, growing up in poverty and missing out on valuable opportunities for personal growth because of socioeconomic circumstances can also hinder stable identity development.

While it is normal and expected for adolescents to explore different personal and social identities as they go through their teenage years, they should be able to develop and maintain a core set of beliefs and values that guide them through social situations and personal challenges. Adolescents who come from dysfunctional or overbearing environments may become apathetic or overly anxious, and these behaviors can stay with them into adulthood, where they may continue to struggle to find themselves. They might not know what they stand for or what they value and may be subject to influences from the unpredictable intentions of other people who might not always act in their best interest.

Erikson's sixth stage of identity development is known as *intimacy and distantiation vs. self-absorption*[48] and occurs between the ages of 20-40. This stage is primarily concerned with the development of stable relationships with other people – be it with friends, family, or co-workers. People who developed stable identities in their adolescent years often desire to further develop and share their skills and personal resources with others, which is a healthy foundation for both interpersonal and professional relationships. These are the years where people typically complete their higher education or technical training, start families and have children, and begin their careers.

Individuals who developed unstable identities during their adolescence may continue to struggle to form stable relationships and friendships and might end up feeling socially isolated and alone. They may not be able to emotionally bond with others because of a lack of self-confidence or a fear of intimacy. The good news is there are many opportunities for young adults to develop the tools and confidence needed to form successful relationships, and sometimes all it takes is some trial-and-error. Sometimes people have to go through a series of unstable relationships before they discover what it is they are looking for in others and first and foremost, who they are to themselves.

From age 40 to approximately 65, individuals in middle adulthood are in the seventh stage of development, *generativity vs. stagnation*.[49] This stage marks the age group where people become leaders in their field and make significant contributions to the world, be it through raising a family, participating in philanthropic endeavors, or advancing in their careers. People may serve as volunteers in their community and might also become personal or professional mentors to those around them. A healthy goal is to prepare the next generation for the responsibilities and challenges of adulthood. Individuals within this age group often find themselves taking care of children and aging parents, so it can be challenging to find a proper balance between donating their time to others and making time for themselves. Individuals with secure personal identity and a firm sense of purpose are more likely to navigate this productive yet demanding period in their life confidently, and they will leave behind a memorable legacy that may inspire others along the way.

On the other hand, individuals who fold under the pressures of middle adulthood and get stuck in the same old boring and tired routine may feel like they are stuck in place and powerless to change their circumstances. This problem may be especially present if they feel locked down by longstanding personal or professional commitments and relationships. These feelings may cause them to become socially or mentally withdrawn and lead to depression and hopelessness. They may consequently take little interest in developing new hobbies, skills, or engaging in activities centered around improving themselves.

The eighth and final stage of Erikson's identity development is *integrity vs. despair and disgust*[50] and refers to the period of life after your mid-60s, which is the period known as late adulthood, a time of reflection on past accomplishments, relationships, and the legacy of a long and storied life. If they have grandchildren or great-grandchildren, they will spend quality time with them and share tales of their childhood or highlights of their adulthood. They generally feel proud of what they have accomplished in their lives and believe they made genuine and meaningful contributions to the world. They have also fostered many healthy relationships, and likely have many people in their life, relatives and close friends, who are happy to help take care of them as they age.

People who enter this final stage of life feeling unaccomplished or that they wasted their lives on fruitless endeavors may feel greatly disappointed in themselves and live in regret, thinking about what should have or could have been different if they lived their lives more productively. They may feel bitter, depressed, and angry with themselves and others, and will likely be unable to accept responsibility for their unhappy life. Their misery will only serve to further isolate them from others, who may not want to be around them because of their negative attitude. In their old age, they may have to take care of themselves entirely or end up spending their final days alone and away from family. Persistent negativity will cause them to continue to pass up moments of joy and laughter in favor of feeling sorry for themselves and feeling like a failure.

While Erikson's theories of psychological identity are well-accepted by some, they have also faced substantial criticism from others. Researchers Gwendolyn T. Sorrell and Marilyn J. Montgomery assert that Erickson's theories oversimplify identity development as being unilateral and patriarchal, leaving out consideration for different ethnic groups and other marginalized groups.[51] Erikson's theories share many of the same pitfalls as other universal theories of identity, including Vygotsky's and Piaget's, oversimplifying something more complex and individually nuanced than it might initially seem.

Sorrell and Montgomery explain that "These theories of ethnocentric foundationalism, naive realism, presumed universal-ism, and rampant individualism, all of which have constrained our consideration of contextual and historical influences on develop-ment [have] repressed recognition of the particularness of experience and knowledge within unprivileged groups."[52] These researchers argue that privileged European or American men wrote most of the universal theories, and did not accurately consider or reflect the much more diverse and pliable nature of identity development across different cultures, socioeconomic groups, and genders.[53]

They also call into question the utility of Erikson's grand theory of psychosocial identity, feeling that it initially stemmed from a desire to understand himself. Most of his ideas existed in the framework of a mostly White middle-class capitalistic society, hardly representative of the diverse socio-cultural variations found not only in America and Europe but in other non-westernized countries too. The researchers worry that his theories are too biased and nuanced to be of value toward understanding identity in a multicultural context, let alone addressing the variation in identity development between men and women. According to them, "[A generalized identity] theory's developmental principles must be viewed from a perspective that acknowledges the uniqueness of life experiences associated with broad social categories of gender, class, and culture as well as the particularity of individual experience."[54] It is important to note that the researchers do not intend to invalidate the work of Erickson or other similar researchers but to point out their limitations and offer solutions for broadening their work.

Standpoint epistemology is a framework in which social and natural relationships define a variable identity that is subject to change within a changing socio-cultural environment.[55] Sorrell and Montgomery define a "standpoint" as a "local and lived reality," or an individual perspective that exists in the context of their direct surroundings.[56] Different individuals within a social group may have different understandings and views on social relations and social structure, depending on their background and position within the social group.

Sorrell and Montgomery use the critical feminist standpoint[57] to illustrate how a particular perspective can explain relationships within a society that would be challenging to understand from an Ericksonian point of view. They offer a deeply personal window into what it means to identify as a woman in a patriarchal culture, something that their privileged male counterparts could not possibly experience. The feminist perspective can also open opportunities for novel research and dialogue concerning the role of gender in identity development,[58] as well as identify portions of Erickson's theory that are relevant to it.

One of the distinguishing characteristics of Erickson's theory is how it views identity development as a dynamic lifelong process involving social relationships. He saw this process taking place from birth until death, unlike many of his contemporaries, who were more focused on childhood and adolescent developmental processes. Erickson was primarily concerned with how individuals unconsciously and consciously define themselves as unique and distinct within the greater social context.[59] This activity is decidedly modern and one that people from ancient civilizations would be unlikely to ponder, as there was less emphasis on the role of the individual back then and people did not have the breadth of opportunities available today.[60] The historical concept of identity was prescriptive, as people were called upon to fulfill specific roles in their community. Only recently did identity become descriptive, allowing people to search within themselves to find a personal sense of meaning and purpose. This idea of a self-prescribed identity is also in line with feminist theories, but it is still essential to consider the historical context.

As Sorrell and Montgomery explain, "Most theories of human behavior and development have historically sought to explain all behavior and development as outcomes of antecedent causes and consequently have tended to exclude the concept of the self as actor and agent from serious scientific study."[61] They call attention to numerous explanations from behavioral geneticists and biologists who believe that the processes of evolution and reproductive success underlie human development with the idea of individual identity regarded as a mere afterthought. Behaviorism takes these ideas even further, prescribing that all behavior is the result of immediate reactions to nearby events and circumstances. In each of these theories, there is no need for the concept of individual identity. People serve to promulgate the survival of the human species, and their behaviors occur through simple cause-and-effect reactions to local environmental and social stimuli.

Some post-modern philosophers believe that human actions are unintentional and are the direct result of involuntary reactions to circumstances or interactions with other people or within a specific environment.[62] They use this argument to invalidate the concepts of personal identity and self-development because they consider human choices and actions determined by random chance. This perspective naturally assumes that humans act deterministically where every action exists as a reaction to another one. Other post-modern philosophers are less radical but still challenge the notion of a unified autonomous self.[63] They believe that there exist multiple selves or a fragmented self where different parts of it correspond to different actions and responses to events or circumstances.

Some feminist researchers have also been reluctant to acknowledge the existence of a singular self because of their beliefs about the "exquisite human contextuality of life."[64] By recognizing the inherent diversity of human experience and recognizing differences in factors such as gender, race, and ethnicity, these researchers exercise caution in producing a one-size-fits-all approach to identity. Androcentric theories, such as those proposed by Piaget, Vygotsky, and Erickson, place males at the center of their discussion and hence offer an incomplete approach regarding the nature of experiences of women and other marginalized social groups. A feminist standpoint offers to supplement these theories with perspectives and ideas relevant to the social groups omitted from the original arguments.

One of the critical issues in the study of identity is the methodology used to define it. Classical studies occurred from a collection of direct observations without much scientific rigor, but some modern approaches suffer from similar issues. For instance, researcher James Marcia modified Erickson's theory to more accurately reflect the developmental processes of adolescents by coming up with four statuses of identity development.[65] This four-stage process involves the adolescent progressing through a series of decisions, conflicts, and finally resolution concerning their identity. In going through this process, they determine their sexual orientation, moral values, and ideals, and set vocational goals. Marcia used a series of interviews with teenagers to validate the ideas in her study. Other researchers adopted Marcia's revisions to Erickson's identity theory and continued to revise it to be more inclusive and representative of the diverse nature of people, including women and minority groups.

Despite the vast improvements to Erickson's original identity theory, there are still researchers who criticize the approach of these theories as being too general and abstract. Some researchers, including Dan McAdams et al.,[66] believed that identity development theories should focus instead on being more individualized. They argued for the use of narrative approaches[67] to preserve the uniqueness and distinctiveness of the individual instead of averaging out certain traits and placing them in broad categories or stages. For their study, they used a sample of 40 highly generative and 30 less generative adults with similar backgrounds to analyze differences in which the two groups constructed personal identities.

The researchers hypothesized that highly generative adults would demonstrate the ability to reconstruct their past and use it within a stable personal framework to anticipate their future. They used the analogy of a protagonist to describe how a highly generative individual would likely approach new situations with optimism, a steadfast sense of morality and values, the ability to transform challenging or problematic situations into positive outcomes, and a dedication to the service of others. They refer to the life story of Mahatma Gandhi[68] as a prototypical example of a highly generative adult – someone who was secure in his personal beliefs and values and lived a humble and productive life.

Three categories of generativity were used to recruit and screen potential subjects, including professional-volunteer status, scores on a 20-question generativity test, and scores on another test that measured the degree of daily generativity for subjects. For the first category, researchers recruited a group of exemplary teachers highly involved in the local community who regularly participated in volunteer work. They also solicited another group of individuals who were not currently involved in any educational or volunteer activities. From the people recruited in the first category, a second category was developed to further screen subjects by using their responses to the Loyola Generativity Scale (LGS),[69] which was a self-reported subjective assessment scale based on individual feelings of how purposeful and meaningful their lives are at present, including reflections on past experiences and projections of future events. For instance, one of the questions on the LGS asked subjects to assess, on a four-point scale, how significant they feel their life's contributions will be once they pass away.

The third category contained potential subjects' responses to the Generative Behavioral Checklist (GBC),[70] which is an inventory of 40 generative behaviors and ten non-generative behaviors. Participants were asked to respond with a frequency count as to how often they participated in various activities, including things like attending a community meeting or teaching a child how to read. Individuals were chosen to participate in the study based on similar demographic backgrounds and either high or low scores on the two generativity tests.

For the study, participants were also asked to complete a life story interview,[71] in which the researchers asked the subjects to envision their life story as a book and to divide it into eight distinct chapters. They were also asked to provide detailed descriptions of eight scenes from their book. These experiences were meant to be high or low points in the person's life, vivid childhood memories, or other significantly impactful experiences. They were also asked to provide future insights into their story and describe what they anticipated might be future goals and outcomes of their life as well as how they would affect others. Then the interviewer asks the subject to recount the four most meaningful people in their lives and if there is someone who stands out as a personal role model or inspiration. Researchers referred to this life story as the *commitment story*[72] because of how the stories revolved around subjects' nature and breadth of commitment to positive and fulfilling life experience.

Participants were then asked to provide details about two areas of personal or professional conflict. Finally, they were inventoried on their religious, political, and philosophical values and asked to reflect on the entire interview and identify significant themes or messages in their life story. The researchers coded the interview transcripts based on the following five categories of generativity: "experience of an early blessing or advantage, early sensitivity to the suffering of others, steadfast commitment over time to a clear and detailed personal ideology, redemptive affective sequences in which bad events become good outcomes, and the pursuit of future goals aimed at benefiting others or society as a whole."[73] One additional coding scheme was developed to measure the overall emotional tone of the narrative. These coding schemes were all developed through a trial set of life story interviews involving ten test subjects who did not take part in the official study.

The first major theme, *early advantage*,[74] was used to examine generative features of the participant's childhood, including their degree of secure attachment to parents and family, feelings of being cared for and possibly favored, experiences of having a particular advantage compared to others, and their level of philanthropic involvement in their local community. The first sub-theme of early advantage was *family blessing*,[75] which assessed the degree to which participants experienced their childhood with an atmosphere of caring, nurturing, and support to provide them with an overall sense of well-being. They used a score of 1 for the presence of any of these type of factors, and 0 in their absence.

The second sub-theme of early advantage focused exclusively on *childhood attachments*[76] to family members, friends, and religious or community groups. The coders assigned a score to this category based on the nature of the attachment to six different people from each of these three categories. Anxious-ambivalent or avoidant attachment, where there is significant anxiety about the security of the relationship, resulted in a score of 0. Responses that were ambiguous, unclear, or empty were assigned a score of 1. Coders gave a rating of 2 for answers that demonstrated a secure attachment to the individual or group, characterized by feelings of trust, confidence, and closeness. The total attachment score was the sum of the six ratings providing an overall attachment rating from 0 (least secure) to 12 (most secure).

The third sub-theme of early advantage, *helpers versus enemies*,[77] was concerned with whether the subject portrayed others in their story as benevolent or adversarial. They defined helpers as nonrelatives who expressed some positive impact on the participant through assisting, encouraging, or otherwise aiding them in a meaningful way. Enemies were characters who deceived, threatened, or otherwise harmed the participant and discouraged or disallowed them toward achieving their personal goals. Coders read through the stories and calculated two ratios, one for helpers and the other for enemies, based on the total number of them divided by the number of typed lines of the life story interview.

The second major theme they coded was *suffering of others*,[78] a measurement of empathy and emotional sensitivity to the plight of other people as expressed through their written reconstructions of past events. Coders read through the life chapters, earliest memory, and significant childhood memory sections to discover elements of the participant's life that were indicative of acts of empathy and understanding toward others, be they elderly, handicapped, economically disadvantaged, or otherwise in need of assistance. Coders used a score of 0 for participants who demonstrated no evidence of empathy or empathic acts and gave a score of 1 for minimal evidence or awareness of others with special needs. They used a score of 0 for a detailed description of an encounter with an individual or group of people with special needs that demonstrated evidence of sensitivity and empathy.

Moral steadfastness[79] was the third primary theme coders used to measure generativity. They focused on aspects of the participants' last two sections of their life story interview that showed evidence of a life lived with clear moral convictions and certainty about their ideologies. Coders assessed the depth, clarity, and continuity of these ethical and personal values using a four-point scale. *Depth* was the overall strength and certainty of the individual's moral convictions and the extent to which they lived their life as a direct reflection of these values. *Clarity* was how clear and well-defined the participant's expressed ideology was. *Continuity* was as a measurement of how well a participant's current beliefs and doctrines were connected to their past actions, regardless of whether their values changed over time. If a change happened, then the participant was expected to justify it and explain how it positively affected them in the present. For each quality, coders assigned a value ranging from 0 to 3, with a score of 0 given out for deficient qualities of moral steadfastness and a score of 3 given for steadfast ones.

The fourth major theme was *redemption (versus contamination) sequences*,[80] which reflected how well subjects transformed negative experiences into positive outcomes and perspectives. Highly generative individuals are more likely to reflect on adverse events and life experiences in such a way that they felt these situations served as meaningful precursors to positive ones. Non-generative people were apt to find no correlation or pattern to the sequences of negative or positive events. The coders defined *redemption sequences* as narrative events whereby adverse events are turned around into positive ones or positive outlooks toward future ones. They described *contamination sequences* as the opposite of these, in which the participants cast a shadow of negativity onto good events, thus transforming them into bad ones. Coders scored narratives across three dimensions for both redemptive and contamination sequences. Participants earned 1 point for turning a bad experience into a good one and an extra point if they expressed a conscious effort to make that change. Coders also used the same scheme to evaluate how participants responded to a turning point scene. They also derived the third ratio from tallying up the total number of explicitly redemptive scenes in their narrative and dividing by the total number of typed lines in the life story interview. Coders used an identical coding scheme for contamination events which they also scored across the same four dimensions.

The fifth major theme was *prosocial goals for the future*,[81] which examined the future chapters section of the life story interview. The three dimensions scored on a four-point scale included self, family, and society. For the domain of *self*, coders analyzed participants' personal, professional, and leisure time and for the domain of *family*, they examined close relationships, including those between spouses, siblings, and other relatives. The domain of *society* was concerned with an individual's goals that were intended to benefit large groups of people, including schools, churches, or other societal institutions. The idea here was to see how much the participants valued and planned for socialization as part of their future. A score of 0 reflected no goals in the area, and a score of 1 indicated goals that were not clearly described or were otherwise vague. A score of 2 meant there was the presence of one well-articulated goal, and a score of 3 indicated the presence of two or more of these goals in one of the three areas.

The coders also analyzed the overall tone of the story,[82] scoring all eight scenes from the personal narrative based on whether participants exuded positive or negative emotions. Two expressions of joy and happiness in a scene earned one point while their absence along with four illustrations of negative emotions including stress, anger, shame, sadness, anxiety, and fear resulted in no points awarded for that scene. The coders then provided a summative score for each of the three life chapter interview sections: childhood, adolescence, and adulthood. Coders assigned a score between 1 and 5, where a score of 1 meant a wholly negative and pessimistic story and a score of 5 indicated an entirely positive and optimistic one. These three scores were then summed together to provide a rating for an index of overall affective positivity.

Based on a rigorous analysis of the study results, the researchers were able to confirm their hypothesis that people who developed a positive and optimistic attitude as children and felt supported by their family, friends, and community groups (having an early advantage) led benevolent and productive lives even in the face of significant adversity or misfortune. They also demonstrated evidence of being committed later in life to distinct moral values and a calling of service to others. McAdams et al. caution that, "This prototypical story of commitment is not a Panglossian tale of mindless cheer, nor a conventional fairy tale in which everyone lives happily ever after in the end."[83] Highly generative adults do not typically use emotive language that is distinct from their lower generative counterparts, nor do they indicate more secure relationships during their childhood experiences. What truly set the two groups apart is simply a matter of attitude. Highly generative adults recanted personal narratives in which unfortunate events served as precursors toward good ones. This phenomenon occurred consistently, even though both groups experienced the same types of negative life experiences. Less generative adults were apt to describe negative life experiences as directly following from good ones. They did not believe that the good times would last for long and that bad times were quietly lurking around the corner.

Although specific methods and expressions of generativity may vary, the results demonstrated that most highly generative adults derived their attitude from a lifetime of feeling committed to a higher calling and empathy to the suffering of others. Their steadfast commitment to their moral ideals and behavior enables them to raise their children in a stable and loving environment or to contribute to significant advancements to their community and society.[84]

McAdams et al. cited an example from their study of Diana,[85] a daughter of a Methodist minister, who scored very high on criteria for high levels of generativity. Her deep religious convictions guided her outlook on life, as she believed certain events, including her brother's untimely passing, served a purpose in her life, eventually leading to her marrying her high school sweetheart. As a teacher, she always tried to make significant contributions to her school and the overall betterment of the educational system. Even though hardship and difficult circumstances continually tested her religious faith, she never let her doubts overcome her beliefs.

There are, of course, certain limitations to these narrative studies. For one, they did not address whether low generative adults could transform into highly generative adults and vice-versa. If such transformations are possible, it would have remarkable consequences for individual development, as less generative adults could learn through therapy and instruction how to change their overall attitude to one of increasing optimism about the future. There is also ambiguity as to what constitutes generativity and how stable this concept is considering the variability of human experience. Furthermore, this study cannot be regarded as exhaustive, considering the limited sample size of its participants and controversial methods of interview, coding, and analysis. There is also an issue with the fact that these stories were provided verbally to interviewers, and there are few ways to verify individual personal anecdotes and stories for accuracy.

Despite the apparent limitations, the personal narrative study does lay the groundwork for alternative theories of identity, based on stories instead of strictly being grounded in philosophical or cultural ideologies. The authors argue that the healthiest approach to understanding individual identities lies in a delicate compromise between the classical methods of Piaget, Vygotsky, Erickson, and other traditional researchers with the modern personal narrative methods of identity analysis. This shared approach is known as *psychosocial constructivism*[86] and is the way an individual constructs their identity using their own story in the broader context of their culture.

The authors caution that these identities are not meant to define a person, but instead to discover certain ephemeral qualities such as a life story that helps to define certain characteristics about an individual. As McAdams et al. explain, "A main goal of the current story was to identify a certain kind of story, a story of commitment that seemed to support adult generativity, but not a certain kind of person per se."[87] The researchers were not attempting to categorize people or even identify their research as conclusive about adult generativity. The commitment story was just one idea of how to qualitatively measure this quality, but there may be other equal or more reliable means to do so. Generativity is only one of many individual attributes, and countless others could exist in similar ways by taking a dynamic approach between personal narrative and sociocultural norms and experiences.

Identity as a Physiological and Psychological Construct

While there are seemingly countless approaches to identity, one fundamental question that remains is what role biology and physiology play in identity construction. Memories are of paramount importance to your character. Short-term and long-term memories overlay each other throughout your entire life, helping you to remember who you are. When you look in the mirror, you can identify yourself mainly in part due to your memories of how you ought to appear. Your memories also give your life a sense of continuity, which becomes an integral part of your identity as you age.

Author Todd E. Feinberg defines the self as "A unity in consciousness and perception that persists in time."[88] His idea is similar to the narrative self, in that identity varies temporally based on internal and external factors that change over time. Of interest to him was how the presence of certain neurological conditions affected the individual perception of identity. The understanding of the self is highly sensitive to pathological changes such as those brought about by psychophysiological instabilities. Both transient or permanent neurological changes can manifest themselves through noticeable inward and outward alterations to the self.

A prominent neuroscientist, Jill Bolte Taylor, experienced this phenomenon firsthand one morning while she was having a stroke in the left hemisphere of her brain. As she put it, "For those of you who understand computers, our right hemisphere functions like a parallel processor while our left hemisphere functions like a serial processor...Because they process information differently, each hemisphere thinks about different things, they care about different things, and dare I say, they have very different personalities."[89] Taylor said that she felt like a newborn child while she was experiencing her stroke and kept switching in and out of that blissful state as her left hemisphere phased in and out of functionality. With her left hemisphere offline, she could not even tell where the boundaries of her body were. She went on to say, "And I lost my balance and I'm propped up against the wall. And I look down at my arm and I realize that I can no longer define the boundaries of my body. I can't define where I begin and where I end. Because the atoms and the molecules of my arm blended with the atoms and molecules of the wall. And all I could detect was this energy."[90]

In the time that her left hemisphere was malfunctioning, she felt a sense of blissfulness and peace. Her internal monologue, or inner voice, was utterly silent. She felt as though she were one with the world around her, and it felt great. Every time her left hemisphere would come back online, she would obtain brief bursts of clarity. In these moments, she sensed the urgency of her condition and struggled to get help. Fortunately for her, she survived the stroke and lived to tell about it. Complete recovery of her language abilities took about eight years of tirelessly hard work and dedication.

What her experience reveals is that the reality both around you and within your own body are dependent on the proper functioning of both hemispheres of her brain. Without a functioning brain, the world can become a very grainy and pixelated place, and you can also lose all sense of identity, language, communication abilities, and boundaries. When individual neurological faculties break down, you can regress into an infantile state instantly. Even the portion of the brain responsible for alerting you when something is wrong can also malfunction leading you to feel blissful and peaceful even in moments of sheer danger.

Another lesson from Taylor's experience is that your identity may be more complicated than it seems. She describes the two hemispheres of the brain as almost having their distinct personalities and characteristics. The right side of the brain is lofty, emotionally expressive, and focused on the big picture, whereas the left side of the brain is more task-oriented and focused on details. The right side of the brain is artistic and ethereal, and the left side is scientific and literal. How these two different halves coalesce to form a singular identity is quite mysterious and marvelous.

Taylor's ability to recall and analyze her experiences during the stroke is nothing short of remarkable. The consequences the stroke caused to her perception of both her physical and psychological sense of self were profound. Fortunately, these effects were transient, and the experience did not alter her identity, although it opened her mind to new perspectives and experiences. She made a complete, if not miraculous, recovery from the stroke and used the experience to educate people about stroke recognition and prevention, the neurological construction of the self, and the many lessons she learned from her stroke and subsequent recovery.

As illustrated in the case of Taylor, there is certainly a grey area when it comes to the distinction between the ideas of the self and personal identity. Disorders of the self happen through a confluence of neurological and psychological factors which can complicate an individual's perception of their social relationships and physical environment. The personality effects of these conditions can be reversible (if only temporarily) and do not typically impact an individual's core social or moral values or sense of who they are. Although uncommon, major confabulations can exist that can temporarily or permanently distort the individual's sense of who they are. Most of the time, the individual maintains a firm understanding of who they are and what they stand for, even in the face of persistent delusions. Furthermore, many of these delusions are transient, and the effects on the individual's memories are often temporary in these situations. Taylor's experience with her left-hemisphere stroke represented a transient disorder of the self, but not of her identity.

Feinberg was fascinated with stories such as those described by Taylor and created his own three types of perturbations and disorders of the self, each with its relational anecdotes. The first identity disorder involves issues with the *bodily self*, where individuals lack sufficient awareness or cognizance about their physical limitations or abilities. In these disorders, the patient may be unaware of the nature of their physical condition and act accordingly.

The term *anosognosia* is "a lack of knowledge of the existence of disease"[91] and this condition is often present in individuals with left hemiplegia, or total paralysis of the left side of the body, typically the result of a stroke or acute lesion in the right hemisphere of the brain. Feinberg illustrates this condition by referring to a patient of his, AP,[92] who experienced a stroke in the temporoparietal region of his brain and encountered full paralysis of the left side of his body. Despite his compromised physical condition and his acknowledgment that he suffered a stroke, AP denied that there was anything wrong with his left arm and leg. He even believed that he could walk out of the hospital on his own will if he wanted to.

Some patients with anosognosia acknowledge their defect when it is directly pointed out to them, but others do not. Feinberg mentions the case of patient PM,[93] a woman who developed acute left hemiplegia following a massive stroke. She denied that there was anything wrong with her, even in the presence of direct evidence to the contrary. She was confused after falling over a coffee table and argued with the researcher that there was anything wrong with her, complaining that people are always accusing her of being weak when nothing is wrong. When confronted with the reality that she could not touch her right arm to her nose, she claimed this did not happen because she did not want to look comedic. With other requests, she claimed she would not participate because she does not like being ordered around. It seemed that no matter what the circumstances were, she had an excuse for her non-cooperation at the ready. PM was in total denial about her health condition and delusional about the reasons for her inability to move her arm.

One interesting finding that was before her stroke, PM demonstrated a pattern of persistently stubborn and private behavior. She avoided seeing doctors for her health issues and went out of her way to keep a previous hospital visit a secret from most of her friends and family. While it indeed could be speculated that these characteristics were precursory to her current attitude after suffering a stroke, Feinburg mentions that there is often a multitude of factors at work that could be responsible for this phenomenon including confusion, the loss of a sense of position in the paralyzed limb, and hemispatial neglect. Nonetheless, the patient's personality before significant injury plays a vital role in how they will likely respond afterward.

The condition of denying ownership of a part of the body is known as *asomatognosia*[94] and occurs most frequently in patients with damage to the non-dominant side of the body. The most typical response to people with this condition is confusion or ignorance over the identity of the affected limb. This response is understandable considering that there is often a complete loss of sensation there, but it is sometimes reversible if the patient is made aware that this is indeed their limb.

Somatoparaphrenia[95] occurs when the patient is in extreme denial of the personal ownership of their limb that they experience delusional thoughts about it, claiming that it belongs to a friend or family member and adamantly denying that it could be their own. Sometimes they will even employ metaphorical language to their limb, depersonalizing it and turning it into something else entirely. Often these metaphors relate to death, likely due to the perceived uselessness of the appendage. Feinburg mentions two patients who referred to their paralyzed hands as "the Devil's hand" and "a pet rock" respectively.[96] Another paralyzed patient of his claimed that his arm belonged to his deceased brother and one other patient referred to her paralyzed arm as being her dead husband's. It is as though psychological emotions projected onto the lifeless arm as a sort of eulogy to the deceased. Patients even go so far as sometimes to name their paralyzed limbs and interact with it as though it were a separate individual.

Feinberg's second type of disorder involves problems with the *relational self*,[97] whereby the affected individual experiences significant issues identifying the people, places, and objects around them. He identifies two common types of delusional misidentification syndromes (DMS)[98] that involve problems with the relational self. One common such disorder is known as Capgras syndrome, which is a disorder in which an individual believes that an imposter or double have replaced another person. Another condition, *Fregoli syndrome*, is marked by the individual thinking that a stranger is a familiar person in disguise. Feinberg believes that Capgras syndrome represents an "under-personalized response" and Fregoli syndrome is indicative of an "over-personalized response" to seeing someone, whether supposedly familiar or not, respectively. Although both of these DMS happen in a variety of neurological impairments, including traumatic brain injuries, they also occur in patients with Alzheimer's disease, a progressive disorder marked by significant memory loss.

To illustrate the inner workings of Capgras syndrome, Feinberg used the example of an elderly lady with Alzheimer's disease who frequently mistook her sister for another person and interestingly, this was the only misidentification she made. It is typically the case that people with this impairment misidentify their primary caregiver, the individual that they rely on the most. People have also been observed misidentifying inanimate objects such as doors, keys, light switches, or clothing, where they believe someone came in their house and stole all their belongings and then replaced them with unfamiliar ones. They often defiantly act when presented with conflicting opinions or evidence against their delusional thoughts and stubbornly persist in their beliefs about altered or moved material possessions.

People experiencing the ill effects of Fregoli syndrome will commonly believe that they are in familiar surroundings or around familiar people despite being in a completely new place surrounded by strangers. Feinberg noticed that the confabulations usually stem from a mixture of the patient's memories before the injury or syndrome and current events in the patient's life. One of his patients, OE, sustained a traumatic brain injury in mid-life and experienced severe memory deficits, causing him to incorrectly identify the ages of his children and making him mix details of his previous workplace environment with his current rehabilitation center where he was living.

Other types of DMS include variations where the individual believes they have relationships with imaginary people, who may take the form of a fictitious person, a misidentified individual, or an anthropomorphized inanimate object. They can even believe that their mirror reflection represents an entirely different person from themselves. Sometimes the afflicted individual believes that the delusions are persecutory and they may fear the worst. Feinberg recounts the story of a woman likely in the early stages of dementia who imagined that she had a double who was following her all around the house, which would only appear in mirrors.

At other times, the individual harbors paranoid beliefs that an evil invader is living in their house and even though they cannot visually or otherwise detect this person, they rationalize that they must be living craftily in some hidden crevice or room in their house, out of sight but still very much a threat. One of Feinberg's patients with right-hemisphere brain damage from a stroke believed that a diabolical force inhabited his body.[99] The shocking part was that this patient was completely lucid and coherent, but he could not shake the feeling of being intimately associated with an evil internal force. There was nothing he could do to convince himself otherwise, even if it did not make much sense at the time.

Not all patients experience paranoid delusions, and there are currently no reliable pathological markers to reveal the type of misconceptions they are likely to have. Feinberg illustrates this point by mentioning the case of a group of Alzheimer's patients with right-parietal, temporal, or frontal hemisphere dysfunction[100] who developed personal relationships with stuffed animals. One woman even went as far as to treat her teddy bear as a child, treating it as her traveling companion and offering it an allowance. Another woman believed that her deceased husband was still living through a collection of toys and dolls that she would leave in her living room. She reasoned that he was always present and watching television with her. While it is reasonable to point out that many of these patients share similar neurological profiles, according to Feinberg, "There appears to be an interaction between neurological, neuropsychological, and socioemotional variables in the creation of the full-blown syndrome."[101]

Feinberg recounted the story of a man who believed that his inner monologue was, in fact, the voice of someone else, or occasionally, a collective montage of voices. Other patients claim to have relationships with relatives who may or may not have existed. A common theme amongst all these patients is delusional thoughts that appear to be coping mechanisms for past grief, trauma, or loss. Some individuals, who suffer major neurological disorders, project their suffering and deficits onto others, either real or imaginary, while simultaneously minimizing their struggles and acting as though they live with little to no disability. They may be in denial about their condition and imagining that their disorder inflicts others in their family or social circle may be a survival mechanism in the face of an otherwise harsh and unforgiving disease.

Feinberg cites the famous case of a man who suffered massive bilateral damage to his frontal lobes from a ruptured aneurysm,[102] and despite him experiencing remarkable neurological deficits across the board, he was in complete denial about his condition and reasoned that he was in the hospital on a humanitarian mission. Although this man lost his wife to complications related to her severely compromised health, he expressed the most grief over an imaginary adopted child that he thought he had with his former wife. This man claimed that this child had problems that nobody understood. He also provided conflicting information about the nature of this child, but the common theme in his story involved the child being a victim of unfortunate circumstances beyond his control.

The third type of disorder defined by Feinberg are disorders of the *narrative self*,[103] whereby individuals confabulate false or distorted stories about their personal experiences. Patients may unwittingly engage in this practice due to neurological deficits involving extensive memory damage. One prominent theory is that these false narratives may be metaphorically or symbolically representative of the patient's current life situation. By listening to patients recount stories about their past life, clinicians could experience a window into their current affairs and relationships.

Feinberg recants a tale told by one of his colleagues about a young Air Force officer who experienced a terrible car accident while stationed in Korea. He suffered a significant degree of physical and neurological impairment, including difficulties with reading, writing, and speaking. When the officer described the incident to the researcher, there was no mention of the accident but instead represented a fictitious story about himself involving a court marshal and communist issues. In the story, he provided vital details that alluded to his present life struggles, all the while referencing a fictional past.

Some of these narrative delusions can be quite dramatic. For instance, one individual who suffered a ruptured arteriovenous malformation[104] and ended up in a wheelchair tells a different story when pressed about what happened to him despite being repeatedly reminded about the exact cause of his impediments. He insists that he is sleepwalking as a direct result of a massive explosion that destroyed his mind. His narrative is a tale of contradictions and confusion about his waking state, but it appears to be a specific type of metaphorical rationalization about his current state of mind and affairs.

You do not need to have a neurological or psychological condition to experience a dissociative episode. If you have ever caught yourself daydreaming or become so immersed in an activity that you temporarily forgot about everything else, then you have experienced one. Most clinicians would not go as far to even called these mental states dissociative because they are always transient and part of a typical everyday experience. The practice of sensory gating[105] is inherently a dissociative activity as the brain systematically tunes out irrelevant sensory data such as the shifting of gears in an automatic transmission while driving. In this sense, a certain amount of mental dissociation is quite helpful, allowing you to focus on what is essential while ignoring irrelevancies in your environment. Similarly, the practice of daydreaming or imagining things will enable people to conjure up ideas for the future, plan for important events, or envision new ideas.

Dissociation can become a significant problem when psychological or neurological factors cause temporary or permanent unstable effects on an individual's identity. Dissociative identity disorder (DID), psychogenic amnesia, and other fugue states arising from neurological or psychiatric disorders are among the conditions associated with identity loss or transformation. Feinberg refers to these as *disorders of the personal identity and global sense of self.*[106] As he explains, "In the context of clinical pathology, the DSM-IV-TR defines dissociation as 'a disruption in the usually integrated functions of consciousness, memory, identity, or perception of the environment.' The disturbance may be sudden or gradual, transient or chronic."[107] This type of dissociation is more severe than disorders of the self because the afflicted individual experiences detachment from their former selves and identities and may quite literally become a different person altogether from who they were before the incident.

Feinberg presents the case of RD,[108] an elderly patient suffering from the early stages of dementia, to illustrate the effects of DID on an individual's identity. When RD looked in the mirror, she became bewildered by her reflection, fearing that it harbored malevolent intentions toward her and posed threats of violence and hostility. She was so afraid of this mirror image that she even became aggressive toward it and attacked it on several occasions. The reflection was still the same individual, but her interpretation of it was as a person with a completely different identity.

Another patient, AR,[109] who suffered a series of debilitating strokes, reported feelings of déjà vu following experiences that he never had. This issue caused a lot of problems for him socially and in his relationships, as he erroneously claimed that he already saw a movie, or insisted he already paid the freeway toll at the toll booth even though this was not the case. Everything felt familiar even when it was not. When his family members would try to correct him, he became defensive, and also went as far as accusing his wife that she was developing a memory disorder. In both the cases of RD and AR, their DID was caused by an underlying neurological pathology and was irreversible, so the effects on their personality were permanent. They can never return to the same person that they were before. Their identities have fundamentally changed.

The Hard Problem of Consciousness

While it is straightforward to discuss the effects of brain pathology on disorders of the self and identity, a precise definition of the self is a much more complicated issue. Doing so invokes the *hard problem of consciousness*, as there are brain states that are not directly reducible to objective neurological functions. For this reason, many philosophers have argued against the objective existence of a self and attribute the idea as more fantasy than science. To address this issue, Feinberg introduces philosopher John Searle's concept of *ontological subjectivity*, which claims that "conscious states have features that are irreducibly first-person which cannot simply be reduced to the nervous system."[110] Searle firmly believed that certain aspects of consciousness were not reducible to observable physiological phenomena.

Feinberg disagrees with Searle's proposal that conscious experience must be separated from the nervous system and proposes an alternative theory, the *Neural Hierarchy Theory of Consciousness* (NHTC),[111] to explain the phenomenon of experiencing a conscious self. Within this theory, Feinberg addresses three specific problems arising from thinking of consciousness as a unified concept in the face of a brain with a multitude of working parts. He refers to these as the problems of *mental unity*, *qualia*, and *intentionality*.

The concept of *mental unity*[112] is the difference between the unified sense of self as a single entity versus the parts of the brain in different regions. Feinberg argues that there are many reasons to believe in a unified self, chief among those that certain disturbances to the brain cause the sensation of unification to become unhinged.

In other words, there are scientific and medical methods by which this unified feeling can disintegrate, and this sensation would only be possible with an initially integrated self. The problem lies in the hypothesis that because the brain contains so many distinct and dynamic parts that disruptions to the connections between them would undoubtedly disrupt the overall sense of self.

Feinberg cites a famous case of a patient of German neurologist Kurt Goldstein who felt that her left hand had a mind of its own, a condition referred to as *alien hand syndrome*.[113] According to the patient, her hand would behave erratically, tearing up the bedsheets and hitting her. She had to admonish her hand frequently to get it to behave appropriately. Patients who have *split-brain syndrome*[114] from having their corpus callosum severed to treat specific chronic neurological syndromes often experience alien hand syndrome as a direct consequence of the separation of the hemispheres. They may completely lose coordination of their hands or may have difficulty getting one of their hands to cooperate, finding that it appears to have a mind of its own, sometimes a very naughty and rebellious one.

In split-brain patients, sensory stimuli that would usually integrate across the two hemispheres dissociates and only operates on one side or the other. Such disintegration can be especially troubling when it comes to vision, as the right hemisphere processes sensory data perceived by the left eye, so when the crossover of information processing does not occur, the patient might not even be aware of data in their visual field. Individuals experiencing hemineglect may perceive the two halves of their face as belonging to two separate individuals, one of them possibly not being referred to as belonging to themselves.

Feinberg asserts that even with the severe neurological and psychiatric disruptions that occur with split-brain patients, their identity remains more or less intact. Even though some of their brain functions are less integrated than before, they are still likely to perceive the world as a single person and not as multiple people all living within the same body. Despite missing the corpus callosum, there are still numerous inter-hemispheric connections that provide meaningful feedback from one hemisphere to the other. What makes the brain remarkably unique compared to other organs in the body is the absence of a physical hierarchy to its parts. There is a top-down hierarchy for most human organs where the function at a higher level happens via actions at a lower level of organization, but the brain does not always follow this pattern of organization. The heart, for instance, is composed of chambers, which are supplied blood via a system of valves and arteries. Skin is similarly composed of networks of specialized cells.

There are parts of the brain that are adjacent to, or even within each other that serve entirely different functions than other parts. Just because brain regions are hierarchical does not mean that they are necessarily dependent on each other for proper functioning. Even though brain regions may nest within one-another, their functions can differ significantly. Additionally, the brain interconnects so well that areas in the distal part of the brain can communicate with frontal regions. It is also highly dynamic and malleable and can adapt to injuries and deficiencies by rewiring itself. The compartmentalization and diversification of neural processes are not experienced separately but blend beautifully into a unitary experience of consciousness. This arrangement of brain regions is remarkable in the way it allows for such diversity of neurological operations in such small spaces.

The concept of *qualia*[115] refers to the subjective experience of mental states, which is the idea behind why yellow conjures different emotions than purple or why something red makes you feel different than something blue. The five senses are inherently a part of human experience, and they do not exist independently in nature. There is no sense of taste or smell in the jungle any more than there is a sense of vision in the ocean. Many people believe that due to the subjective nature of these experiences, that qualia do not exist, but Feinberg cautions against this assertion by explaining that, "There is no mandatory relationship between the particular wavelengths of light in the world and certain ontologically subjective experiences... But there is a mandatory relationship in our world between certain neural pathways in the brain and certain conscious experiences."[116] Any human sensation is unique to the neural networks and pathways behind it. There are defined neuro-chemical reactions that are behind every subjective experience, including things like pain, thirst, hunger, and love.

Qualia are the direct result and product of specific neuronal reactions in the brain, unique to the individual experiencing them. How the brain constructs itself determines how it responds to environmental and internal stimuli. For instance, the auditory cortex cannot provide a physical sense of balance just as the cerebellum cannot perceive loudness. Conscious experience comes down to a finely tuned set of neural activity in and across specific regions in the brain. All internal observations and experiences, including subjective consciousness, are processes and are not tangible items in the world.

Although you can sympathize and relate to someone else's feelings or experiences, you cannot directly experience them yourself. For instance, the subjective experience of red to someone in a rival street gang might evoke visceral emotions, whereas that same color exposed to a wedding planner might make them think of love and romance. The physical properties of red, or the wavelength of the light, is the same in either case but the subjective experiences with it are entirely different. While some of the activity in the neural pathways of each person would be similar at first as they process red, their overall brain activity would diverge once the basic properties of the color are processed. Their subjective qualia would be distinct even though they arose from the same primary visual stimulus.

The concept of *intentionality*[117] is the way the brain's mental states are about or refer to material objects, events, and relationships in the world. Intentionality only refers to purposeful actions done by the individual and does not reflect automatic or reflexive responses such as involuntary pupil dilation or muscle twitches. Activity in the brain always refers to something external and is never directly about the brain itself. When someone experiences physical pain, it is felt somewhere on the body, but never directly inside the brain where the electrochemical signals originate. The pain signals refer outward from the brain to the affected limb. During experiments consisting of electrodes placed into the brain, subjective experiences are always felt either outside or inside the body but are never felt directly in the brain.

Furthermore, the experience of external objects and feelings always exist in direct relation to the observer. For instance, while taking a brisk nature walk all the sights, sounds, and smells are experienced in direct relationship to the individual. Two people could be present in the same location at the same moment, but their experiences and observations would certainly differ because of their respective physical positions and unique brain chemistry. There is also a specific intentionality, or willfulness, that must be present for the individual to be conscious of the experience and derive meaning from it.

According to Feinberg, "A simple primitive reflex such as a pupil's constriction in response to a beam of light has no mental unity, requires no feeling, and displays no conscious meaning or purpose. But it is the higher self that achieves and experiences this wholeness of being, feels the warmth of the sun and the pain of the flame, and appreciates the underlying meaning of a Picasso."[118] The brain is organized hierarchically so that complicated intentional actions elicit a more significant neural response and feedback than simple reflexes. The meaningful conscious experience begins to unfold as more brain regions participate across the hierarchy of nested neural networks, and the separation between the external world and the self evolves.

Even fundamental self-awareness requires highly complex networks of neural activity spread within and across various brain regions. It is difficult to imagine that at some point during human evolution, people may not have been self-aware. It took time, a little bit of luck, and the right circumstances for identity to develop. The proliferation of language, arts, and science also led to further development and evolution of the brain and the flourishing of a more complicated human identity. Your identity, however, is immaterial, and there is no way to locate it anywhere in the mind or body. As Feinberg explains, "Consciousness is what the brain *does*."[119] If your brain were to be frozen and left structurally intact, consciousness would cease to exist the moment all neural functions stopped.

Neurons and cells within the body are not individually conscious, as every year, millions of these tiny objects die, and yet the individual self remains intact. It is the proper functioning of nested neural networks and structures within the brain that keeps the story of consciousness and the experience of *you* going until it ceases to function.

Your physical appearance also changes dramatically over time. At the time of conception, you are little more than a fused cell. You are then born into this world as a tiny baby, and within a few weeks of that, your appearance changes remarkably. Then you develop into a mature child, teenager, and then eventually a young adult. Throughout each of these stages, your physical appearance changes dramatically. Some physical features remain, but many more change and leave you looking completely different from earlier periods.

These physical changes occur continuously throughout your life. Changes can appear subtler in adulthood, but a careful inspection of photographs over decades reveals the distinct signatures of the aging process – fine lines, wrinkles, grey hairs, and liver spots. There is also no way to recover your exact physical appearance at any point in time. The elderly cannot suddenly receive a procedure that would restore them to their younger selves just the same as a teenager could not accelerate the aging process turning themselves into a much older individual.

At every moment, you are someone completely different than who you were before. Pieces of you fall away into the dust in the air, and new parts of you accumulate from the very same materials. Internally, changes occur progressively and sometimes frenetically. It takes several weeks to months to notice the effects of regular exercise and a healthy diet, but these gradual changes accumulate over time to reveal someone who looks quite different than they did before. An unfortunate accident can also change someone's appearance in the blink of an eye. Not all changes are beneficial or glamorous.

The idea that you are indeed an individual is illusory. Time changes you with each passing moment and makes you into someone completely different than who you were before. Your body is crawling with creatures from within and on the outside, hair is growing and falling off, and fluids are collected and secreted every day. You are no longer the same person you were at the beginning of this chapter as you are now. You cannot precisely locate your identity, yet there is a sense of continuity to it thanks to the complex and well-developed neural hierarchies in your brain that fuse the memories, personal values, and feelings that make you truly unique. Pieces of you swirl around in the air, collect in the soil, and sometimes end up on other people. As Virginia Woolf famously said, "I am made and remade continually. Different people draw different words from me."[120] There are things and people that will eventually become a part of you and parts of you that will ultimately become a part of something or someone else. Interacting with others changes you, sometimes in a very impactful way. People develop themselves through social interactions, relationships, and other meaningful experiences.

The most important aspect of identity is defining yourself, knowing what you stand for and believe, and acknowledging that there is much left to discover. Keeping an open mind about yourself and others ensures that you will be able to reach your highest potential and thrive. There are opportunities for personal growth everywhere, and there is something to learn from everyone, and there are always new opportunities to find new passions, explore different hobbies, and reinvent yourself. Your career, your appearance, or where you reside, do not define you. Your attitude first and foremost defines you. Everyone has a complicated life with ups and downs, difficult decisions, and challenges. No matter how perfect someone else's life may appear, you never know what struggles they are going through, and it is these struggles that link everyone together. Your identity is not like any other. There has never been anyone like you, and there never will be another. You are to be treasured and valued for the unique expressions and contributions you make to the world. You have no beginning and no end.

Figures

Figure 1 - The phenomenon of pareidolia, as illustrated in a tree trunk.

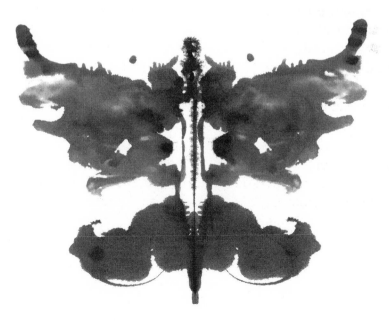

Figure 2 – Rorschach Inkblot image isolated on a white background.

Figure 3 - Example of rhythmic visual movements.

Figure 4 – Old Woman/Young Woman Illusion

Figure 5 – La Grenouillere, by Pierre-Auguste Renoir

Figure 6 – Bain à La Grenouillère, by Claude Monet

Figure 7 – These two models exhibit typical female and male facial features, which many people would likely find beautiful due to the averageness in their faces.

Appendix

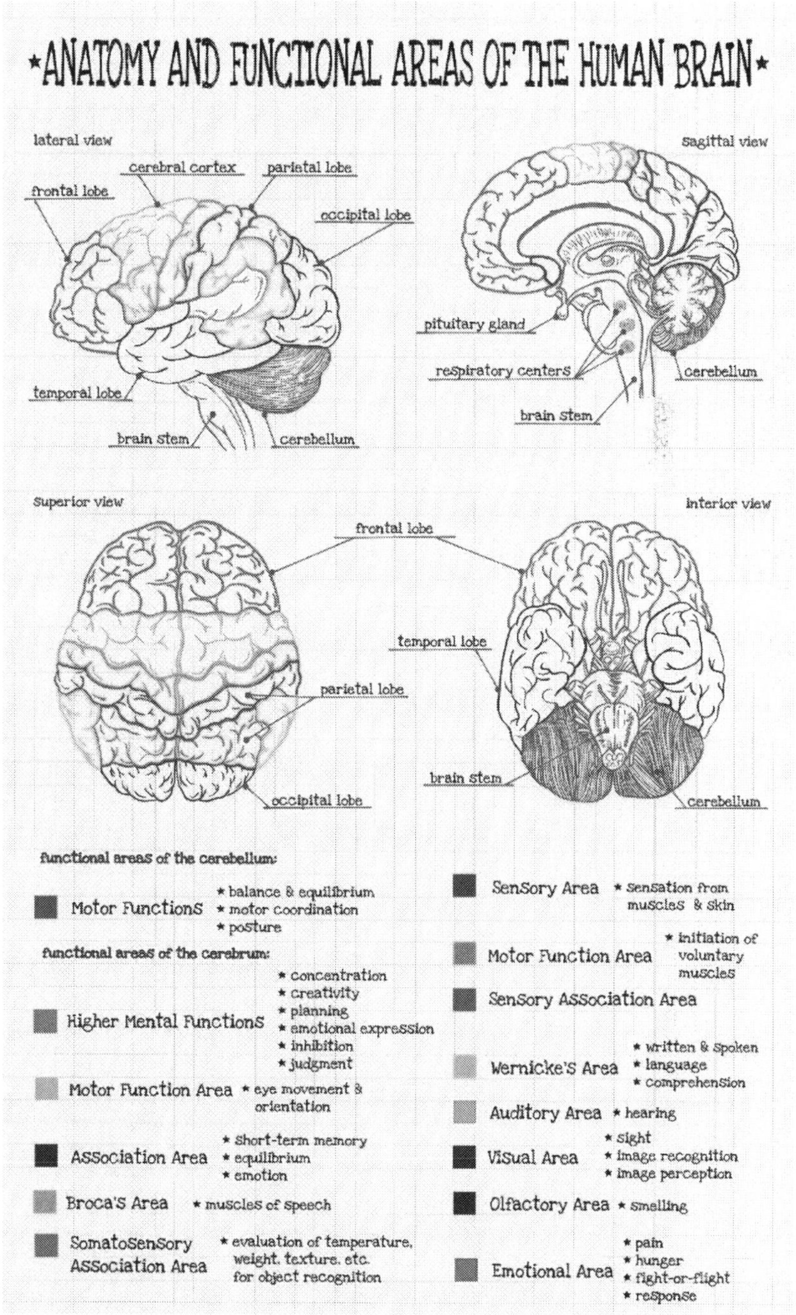

Figure 8 – Functional anatomy of human brain.

THE SYNAPSE

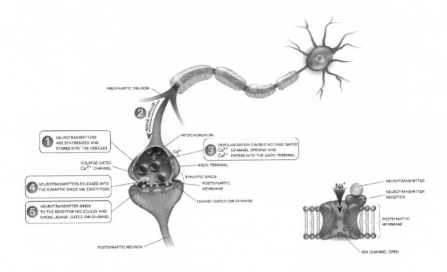

Figure 9 – Diagram of communication between two neurons.

Notes

For complete publication data on works cited below, see the references.

0. INTRODUCTION

[1] Steve Jobs, YouTube, November 19, 2011, accessed August 21, 2019, https://www.youtube.com/watch?v=UvEiSa6_EPA&fbclid=IwAR0Foxr7266U-jtzA1sD2ya8JlgHiM0QdE0qPCk6obli0g-SOGCi_fMgNl0E.

[1] *Dark*, prod. Baran Bo Odar, Jantje Friese, Quirin Berg, Max Wiedemann, and Justnya Müsch, perf. Louis Hofmann, Andreas Pietschmann, Daan Lennard Liebrenz, Lisa Vicari, Ludger Bökelmann, Julika Jenkins, Mark Waschke, Dark, December 1, 2017, accessed December 2017, https://www.netflix.com/title/80100172.

1. NO SPACE

[1] Damion Searls, "Can We Trust the Rorschach Test? | Damion Searls," *The Guardian*, February 21, 2017, accessed July 03, 2019, https://www.theguardian.com/science/2017/feb/21/rorschach-test-inkblots-history.

[2] James J. Dicarlo, Davide Zoccolan, and Nicole C. Rust, "How Does the Brain Solve Visual Object Recognition?" *Neuron* 73, no. 3 (2012): 415-434, doi:10.1016/j.neuron.2012.01.010.

[3] Ibid, 415.

[4] Ibid.

[5] Ibid, 416.

[6] Ibid, 418.

[7] Ibid, 420.

[8] N. J. Majaj et al., "Simple Learned Weighted Sums of Inferior Temporal Neuronal Firing Rates Accurately Predict Human Core Object Recognition Performance," *Journal of Neuroscience* 35, no. 39 (2015): 13402-13418, doi:10.1523/jneurosci.5181-14.2015.

[9] Ibid, 13416.

[10] Ibid, 13403.

[11] Ibid, 13404.

[12] Ibid, 13414.

[13] David Hume, The Natural History of Religion (Boston: MobileReference.com, 2010), Section 3 [2].

[14] Adam Waytz, John Cacioppo, and Nicholas Epley, "Who Sees Human?" *Perspectives on Psychological Science* 5, no. 3 (2010): 219-232, doi:10.1177/1745691610369336.

[15] A. S. Heberlein and R. Adolphs, "Impaired Spontaneous Anthropomorphizing despite Intact Perception and Social Knowledge," *Proceedings of the National Academy of Sciences* 101, no. 19 (2004): , doi:10.1073/pnas.0308220101.; F. Castelli, "Autism, Asperger Syndrome and Brain Mechanisms for the Attribution of Mental States to Animated Shapes," *Brain* 125, no. 8 (2002): , doi:10.1093/brain/awf189.

[16] Waytz et al., "Who Sees Human?," 221.

[17] Ibid, 223.

[18] Ibid, 228.

[19] Sinem Kuz et al., "Mirror Neurons and Human-robot Interaction in Assembly Cells," *Procedia Manufacturing* 3 (2015): 402-408, doi:10.1016/j.promfg.2015.07.187.

[20] Ibid, 407.

[21] Nicholas Day, "Humans at Birth Are Drawn to Faces, Regardless of Species," Lehighvalleylive.com, April 09, 2013, accessed July 04, 2019, https://www.lehighvalleylive.com/entertainment-general/2013/04/humans_at_birth_are_drawn_to_f.html.

[22] Ibid.

[23] Susana Martinez-Conde, "The Fascinating Science Behind Why We See 'Faces' In Objects," *Mental Floss*, May 01, 2018, , accessed July 04, 2019, http://mentalfloss.com/article/538524/science-behind-pareidolia.

[24] Ibid.

[25] Ibid.

[26] Jane Framingham, "Rorschach Inkblot Test," Psych Central, October 13, 2018, accessed July 04, 2019, https://psychcentral.com/lib/rorschach-inkblot-test/; R. P. Taylor et al., "Seeing Shapes in Seemingly Random Spatial Patterns: Fractal Analysis of Rorschach Inkblots," *Plos One* 12, no. 2 (2017): 1-17, doi:10.1371/journal.pone.0171289.

[27] Damion Searls, "Can We Trust the Rorschach Test?"

[28] Jane Framingham, "Rorschach"

[29] Patricia Oelze, "The Use Of The Rorschach Inkblot Test In Psychology," *Betterhelp*, February 24, 2018, accessed July 04, 2019, https://www.betterhelp.com/advice/psychologists/the-use-of-the-rorschach-inkblot-test-in-psychology/.

[30] Alison Abbott, "Fractal Secrets of Rorschach's Famed Ink Blots Revealed," *Nature News*, accessed July 04, 2019, https://www.nature.com/news/fractal-secrets-of-rorschach-s-famed-ink-blots-revealed-1.21473?error=cookies_not_supported&code=d86a3f5b-b5b7-4bd7-a9cc-0207df1aec27.

[31] R.P. Taylor et al., "Seeing Shapes," 12.

[32] Damion Searls, "Can We Trust the Rorschach Test?"

[33] Ibid.

[34] "Traffic Jam in Empty Space," *ScienceDaily*, January 18, 2017, accessed July 04, 2019, https://www.sciencedaily.com/releases/2017/01/170118132244.htm.

[35] Adam Blumenfeld, interview by author, January/February, 2019.

[36] Victoria Williamson, "The Music of Silence," *Music Psychology*, April 2, 2011, accessed July 04, 2019, http://musicpsychology.co.uk/the-music-of-silence/.

[37] Elizabeth Hellmuth Margulis, "Silences in Music Are Musical Not Silent: An Exploratory Study of Context Effects on the Experience of Musical Pauses," *Music Perception: An Interdisciplinary Journal* 24, no. 5 (2007): 485, doi:10.1525/mp.2007.24.5.485.

[38] Ibid.

[39] Ibid, 501.

[40] David J. M. Kraemer et al., "Sound of Silence Activates Auditory Cortex," *Nature* 434, no. 7030 (2005): 158, doi:10.1038/434158a.

[41] Ibid.

[42] Melanie Sard, "Reflected Words: Meaning and Silence in Language and Translation," DigitalCommons@Macalester College, 2005, 17, accessed July 04, 2019, http://digitalcommons.macalester.edu/philo/vol15/iss1/3.

[43] "10 of the Best Words in the World (that Don't Translate into English)," *The Guardian*, July 27, 2018, accessed July 04, 2019, https://www.theguardian.com/world/2018/jul/27/10-of-the-best-words-in-the-world-that-dont-translate-into-english.

[44] Michal Ephratt, "The Functions of Silence," *Journal of Pragmatics* 40, no. 11 (2008): 1909-1938, doi:10.1016/j.pragma.2008.03.009.

[45] Ibid, 1917.

[46] "What Are Your Miranda Rights?" Miranda Warning, accessed July 04, 2019, http://www.mirandawarning.org/whatareyourmirandarights.html.

[47] George W. Baltzell, "Constitution of the United States - We the People," Constitution for the United States - We the People, , accessed July 04, 2019, https://constitutionus.com/.

[48] Michal Ephratt, "The Function."

[49] Ibid.

[50] Clinton Nguyen, "Science Made This Chamber Silent, Your Mind Is What Makes It Terrifying," *Vice*, October 29, 2015, accessed July 04, 2019, https://www.vice.com/en_us/article/78kzez/science-made-this-chamber-silent-your-mind-is-what-makes-it-terrifying.

[51] Ibid.

[52] "Sensory Deprivation Tank: Effects and Health Benefits," *Healthline*, 2018, accessed July 04, 2019, https://www.healthline.com/health/sensory-deprivation-tank.

Paul Simon et al., writers, The Essential Simon & Garfunkel, CD.

2. NO POINT IN TIME

[1] T. S. Eliot, *Four Quartets* (San Diego, CA: Harcourt Brace Jovanovich, 1988).

[2] Rae Silver and William J. Schwartz, "The Suprachiasmatic Nucleus Is a Functionally Heterogeneous Timekeeping Organ," *Methods in Enzymology Circadian Rhythms*, 2005, 451-465, doi:10.1016/s0076-6879(05)93022-x.

[3] Ibid.

[4] Ibid, 454.

[5] Ibid.

[6] Ibid, 455.

[7] Rhailana Fontes et al., "Time Perception Mechanisms at Central Nervous System," *Neurology International* 8, no. 1 (2016): 14, doi:10.4081/ni.2016.5939.

[8] Ibid.

[9] Ibid, 15.

[10] Simon Grondin, "Timing and Time Perception: A Review of Recent Behavioral and Neuroscience Findings and Theoretical Directions," *Attention, Perception, & Psychophysics* 72, no. 3 (2010): 563, doi:10.3758/app.72.3.561.

[11] Ibid.

[12] L. Nyberg et al., "Consciousness of Subjective Time in the Brain," *Proceedings of the National Academy of Sciences* 107, no. 51 (2010): 22356, doi:10.1073/pnas.1016823108.

[13] Ibid.

[14] Ibid, 22357.

[15] Ibid, 22358.

[16] Marc Wittmann, "Moments in Time," Frontiers in Integrative *Neuroscience* 5 (October 18, 2011): 1, doi:10.3389/fnint.2011.00066.

[17] As cited in Edmund Husserl, "Vorlesungen Zur Phänomenologie Des Inneren Zeitbewußtseins," 2000, doi:10.1515/9783110916072.

[18] Marc Wittmann, "Moments," 2.

[19] Ibid, 3.

[20] Ibid, 1.

[21] *Americas Greatest Hits: History*, Warner Bros., 1983, CD.

[22] Marc Wittmann, "Moments," 4.

[23] Yi-Huang Su and Elvira Salazar-López, "Visual Timing of Structured Dance Movements Resembles Auditory Rhythm Perception," *Neural Plasticity* 2016 (2016): 1, doi:10.1155/2016/1678390.

[24] Ibid, 1-2.

[25] Ibid, 3.

[26] Ibid, 9.

[27] Ibid, 13-14.

[28] Jürgen Kornmeier and Michael Bach, "Ambiguous Figures – What Happens in the Brain When Perception Changes But Not the Stimulus," *Frontiers in Human Neuroscience* 6 (March 22, 2012): 1, doi:10.3389/fnhum.2012.00051.

[29] Ibid, 14.

[30] Marc Wittmann, "Moments," 4.

[31] As cited in Harald Atmanspacher and Thomas Filk, "Temporal Nonlocality in Bistable Perception," *Journal of Mathematical Psychology* 54 (2010): 314-321, doi:10.1063/1.4773119.; Harald Atmanspacher, Thomas Filk, and Hartmann Romer, "Quantum

[32] Zeno Features of Bistable Perception," *Biological Cybernetics* 90, no. 1 (2004): 33-40, doi:10.1007/s00422-003-0436-4.

[33] Marc Wittmann, "Moments." 3.

[34] Ibid, 5.

[35] Luke Masten, Short-Term Memory and Working Memory - Types of Memory - *The Human Memory*, 2019, accessed July 05, 2019, http://www.human-memory.net/types_short.html.

[35] Luke Masten, Long-Term Memory - Types of Memory - The *Human Memory*, 2019, accessed July 05, 2019, http://www.human-memory.net/types_long.html.

[36] Corinne O'Keefe Osborn, "Retrograde Amnesia: Causes, Symptoms, and Treatment," *Healthline*, accessed July 05, 2019, https://www.healthline.com/health/retrograde-amnesia.

[37] Oliver Sacks, *The Man Who Mistook His Wife for a Hat and Other Clinical Tales* (Washington: Produced in Braille for the Library of Congress, National Library Service for the Blind and Physically Handicapped by Clovernook Home and School for the Blind, 1987), 23.

[38] Ibid 29.

[39] Marc Wittman, "Moments," 5.

[40] Ibid, 2.

[41] Ibid, 6.

[42] Ibid, 3.

[43] Ali Shahabifar and Ataollah Movahedinia, "Comparing Time Perception among Morphine-Derived Drugs Addicts and Controls," *Addict Health* 8, no. 1 (January 5, 2016): 32-40.

[44] Ibid, 35.

[45] Ibid, 36-37.

[46] Ibid, 37.

[47] Steliana Yanakieva et al., "The Effects of Microdose LSD on Time Perception: A Randomised, Double-blind, Placebo-controlled Trial," *Psychopharmacology* 236, no. 4 (2018): 1159-1170, doi:10.1007/s00213-018-5119-x.

[48] As cited in D. E. Nichols, "Psychedelics," *Pharmacological Reviews* 68, no. 2 (2016): 264-355, doi:10.1124/pr.115.011478.

[49] Steliana Yanakieva et al., "The Effects of," 1161.

[50] Ibid, 1164.

[51] As cited in Aronson, "Influence of Lysergic Acid Diethylamide (LSD-25) on Subjective Time," *Archives of General Psychiatry 1*, no. 5 (1959): 469, doi:10.1001/archpsyc.1959.03590050037003.

[52] Steliana Yanakieva et al., "The Effects of," 1167.

[53] Cristián Oyanadel and Gualberto Buela-Casal, "Percepción Del Tiempo Y Salud: La Influencia Del Perfil Temporal Equilibrado(BTP) Y El Perfil Temporal Negativo (NTP) En La Salud Física Y Mental," *Revista Argentina De Clinica Psicologica* XXVI (2017): 99-107, doi:10.24205/03276716.2017.1034.

[54] As cited in VB Yarovitskii and VA Baturin, "Reproduction of the Minute Time Interval in Depression in Patients with Schizophrenia and Manicdepressive Psychosis," *Z Nevropatol Psikh* 91 (1991): 112-114.

[55] As cited in GN Nosachev, "Perception and Experience of Time with Depression in Manic-depressive Psychosis and Attack-like Schizophrenia by Patients," *Z Nevropatol Psikh.* 91 (1991): 114-117.

[56] Sandrine Gil and Sylvie Droit-Volet, "Time Perception, Depression and Sadness," Behavioural Processes 80, no. 2 (2009): 169-176, doi:10.1016/j.beproc.2008.11.012.

[57]Cristián Oyanadel and Gualberto Buela-Casal, "Percepción," 100.

[58] As cited in PG Zimbardo and JN Boyd, "Putting Time in Perspective: A Valid, Reliable Individual-differences Metric.," *Journal of Personal & Social Psychology* 77 (1999): 1271-1288.

[59] As cited in Philip G. Zimbardo, Richard M. Sword, and Rosemary K. M. Sword, The Time Cure: Overcoming PTSD with the New Psychology of Time Perspective Therapy (San Francisco: Jossey-Bass, 2012).

[60] Cristián Oyanadel and Gualberto Buela-Casal, *"Percepción,"* 106.

[61] Ibid, 102-105.

[62] Perrine M. Ruby, "Experimental Research on Dreaming: State of the Art and Neuropsychoanalytic Perspectives," *Frontiers in Psychology* 2 (2011): 3, doi:10.3389/fpsyg.2011.00286.

[63] Michael H. Herzog, Thomas Kammer, and Frank Scharnowski, "Time Slices: What Is the Duration of a Percept?" *PLOS Biology* 14, no. 4 (2016): 1-12, doi:10.1371/journal.pbio.1002433.

[64] Ibid, 6.

[65] Ibid, 2.

[66] As cited in Talis Bachmann, Endel Põder, and Iiris Luiga, "Illusory Reversal of Temporal Order: The Bias to Report a Dimmer Stimulus as the First," *Vision Research* 44, no. 3 (2004): 241-246, doi:10.1016/j.visres.2003.10.012.

[67] Michael H. Herzog, et al., "Time Slices," 2.

[68] As cited in F. Scharnowski et al., "Long-lasting Modulation of Feature Integration by Transcranial Magnetic Stimulation," *Journal of Vision* 9, no. 6 (2009):1-10, doi:10.1167/9.6.1.

[69] Michael H. Herzog, et al., "Time Slices," 2-3.

[70] Ibid.

[71] Ibid, 4-6.

[72] Ibid, 5

[73] Ibid, 4.

[74] Ibid.

[75] As cited in David Alais and John Cass, "Multisensory Perceptual Learning of Temporal Order: Audiovisual Learning Transfers to Vision but Not Audition," *PLoS ONE* 5, no. 6 (2010): 1-9, doi:10.1371/journal.pone.0011283.

[76] Michael H. Herzog, et al., "Time Slices," 6-7.

[77] Ibid, 5.

[78] Ibid, 7.

[79] A. Schlegel et al., "Network Structure and Dynamics of the Mental Workspace," *Proceedings of the National Academy of Sciences* 110, no. 40 (2013): 16277-16282, doi:10.1073/pnas.1311149110.

[80] Ibid, 16279.

[81] Ibid.

[82] Adam Zeman, Michaela Dewar, and Sergio Della Sala, "Lives without Imagery – Congenital Aphantasia," *Cortex* 73 (2015): 378-380 (1-18 in PDF), doi:10.1016/j.cortex.2015.05.019.

[83] Ibid, 2.

[84] James Gallagher, "Aphantasia: A Life without Mental Images," *BBC News*, August 26, 2015, accessed July 06, 2019, https://www.bbc.com/news/health-34039054.

[85] Adam Zeman et al., "Lives without Imagery," 4-5.

[86] Andrew Griffin, "You Might Not Be Able to Imagine Things, and Not Know It," *The Independent*, April 25, 2016, accessed July 06, 2019, https://www.independent.co.uk/news/science/aphantasia-software-engineer-blake-ross-writes-mind-blowing-post-about-being-unable-to-imagine-a7000216.html.

[87] Adam Zeman, "Extreme Imagination in Mind, Brain and Culture," *UK Research and Innovation*, 2019, accessed July 5, 2019, https://gtr.ukri.org/projects?ref=AH/R004684/1.

[88] James Gallagher, "Aphantasia."

[89] Stefania De Vito and Paolo Bartolomeo, "Refusing to Imagine? On the Possibility of Psychogenic Aphantasia. A Commentary on Zeman Et al. (2015)," *Cortex* 74 (2016): 1-5 (PDF), doi:10.1016/j.cortex.2015.06.013.

[90] As cited in J. Cotard, "Perte De La Vision Mentale Dans La Mélancolie Anxieuse.," *Archives of Neurology* 6 (1884):209-295.

[91] Stefania De Vito et al., "Refusing to Imagine? On the Possibility," 2.

[92] As cited in J. Cotard, "Perte."

[93] As cited in A. Magalhães E Lemos, "Perte De La Vision Mentale Des Objets (formes Et Couleurs) Dans La Mélancolie Anxieuse.," *Annales Médico-psychologiques* 6 (1906): 6-31.

[94] As cited in J. Cotard, "Perte."

[95] As cited in Stefano Zago et al., "Is the Charcot and Bernard Case (1883) of Loss of Visual Imagery Really Based on Neurological Impairment?" *Cognitive Neuropsychiatry* 16, no. 6 (2011): 481-504, doi:10.1080/13546805.2011.556024.

[96] Stefania De Vito et al., "Refusing to Imagine? On the Possibility," 4.

[97] Hakwan Lau, "Is Consciousness a Battle between Your Beliefs and Perceptions? – Hakwan Lau: Aeon Ideas," *Aeon*, July 06, 2019, accessed July 06, 2019, https://aeon.co/ideas/is-consciousness-a-battle-between-your-beliefs-and-perceptions.

[98] V. S. Ramachandran and Sandra Blakeslee, *Phantoms in the Brain: Probing the Mysteries of the Human Mind* (New York: Harper Perennial, 2009).

3. NO INFINITY

[1] Steve Patterson, "Logic and Infinity: The Errors of Calculus," Steve Patterson, May 14, 2016, accessed July 06, 2019, http://steve-patterson.com/logic-and-infinity/.

[2] Esther F. Kutter et al., "Single Neurons in the Human Brain Encode Numbers," *Neuron* 100, no. 3 (2018): 753-761, doi:10.1016/j.neuron.2018.08.036.

[3] As cited in Ilka Diester and Andreas Nieder, "Semantic Associations between Signs and Numerical Categories in the Prefrontal Cortex," PLoS Biology 5, no. 11 (2007): 2684-2695, doi:10.1371/journal.pbio.0050294 and M. S. Livingstone et al., "Symbol Addition by Monkeys Provides Evidence for Normalized Quantity Coding," *Proceedings of the National Academy of Sciences* 111, no. 18 (2014): 6822-6827, doi:10.1073/pnas.1404208111.

[4] Esther F. Kutter et al., "Single Neurons," 757-758.

[5] As cited, respectively, in Elissa M. Aminoff, Kestutis Kveraga, and Moshe Bar, "The Role of the Parahippocampal Cortex in Cognition," *Trends in Cognitive Sciences* 17, no. 8 (2013): 379-390, doi:10.1016/j.tics.2013.06.009, Gabriel Kreiman, Christof Koch, and Itzhak Fried, "Category-specific Visual Responses of Single

Neurons in the Human Medial Temporal Lobe," Nature Neuroscience 3, no. 9 (2000): 946-953, doi:10.1038/78868., Ueli Rutishauser, Adam N. Mamelak, and Erin M. Schuman, "Single-Trial Learning of Novel Stimuli by Individual Neurons of the Human Hippocampus-Amygdala Complex," *Neuron* 49, no. 6 (2006): 805-813, doi:10.1016/j.neuron.2006.02.015., Joshua Jacobs et al., "Direct Recordings of Grid-like Neuronal Activity in Human Spatial Navigation," *Nature Neuroscience* 16, no. 9 (2013): 1188-1190, doi:10.1038/nn.3466., Roy Mukamel et al., "Single-Neuron Responses in Humans during Execution and Observation of Actions," *Current Biology* 20, no. 8 (2010): 750-756, doi:10.1016/j.cub.2010.02.045.

[6] Michael C. Frank et al., "Number as a Cognitive Technology: Evidence from Pirahã Language and Cognition," *Cognition* 108, no. 3 (2008): 820, doi:10.1016/j.cognition.2008.04.007.

[7] Caleb Everett and Andrew Carnegie Fellow, "'Anumeric' People: What Happens When a Language Has No Words for Numbers?" *The Conversation*, July 08, 2019, accessed July 18, 2019, https://theconversation.com/anumeric-people-what-happens-when-a-language-has-no-words-for-numbers-75828.

[8] Peter Schumer, "When Did Humans First Learn to Count?" *The Conversation*, June 07, 2019, accessed July 06, 2019, https://theconversation.com/when-did-humans-first-learn-to-count-97511.

[9] Peter Schumer, "When Did Humans First Learn to Count?" *The Conversation*, June 07, 2019, accessed July 06, 2019, https://theconversation.com/when-did-humans-first-learn-to-count-97511.

[10] G. Donald Allen, "The History of Infinity," Texas A&M University Department of Mathematics, 2000-2003, 1-4, accessed July 6, 2019, https://www.math.tamu.edu/~dallen/masters/infinity/infinity.pdf.

[11] Ibid, 7.

[12] Alasdair Wilkins and Alasdair Wilkins, "A Brief Introduction to Infinity," *Gizmodo*, May 02, 2013, accessed July 06, 2019, https://gizmodo.com/a-brief-introduction-to-infinity-5809689.

[13] Ibid.

[14] Field, Paul, and Eric W. Weisstein, "Zeno's Paradoxes," From Wolfram MathWorld, accessed July 06, 2019, http://mathworld.wolfram.com/ZenosParadoxes.html.

[15] Wesley C. Salmon, "SPACE, TIME, AND MOTION," Dartmouth University Mathematics Department, accessed July 06, 2019, https://math.dartmouth.edu/~matc/Readers/HowManyAngels/SpaceTimeMotion/STM.html.

[16] Steve Patterson, "Infinite Things Do Not Exist," Steve-patterson.com (blog), January 10, 2016, accessed July 6, 2019, http://steve-patterson.com/infinite-things-do-not-exist/.

[17] Ibid.

[18] Ibid.

[19] Charles Q. Choi, "Our Expanding Universe: Age, History & Other Facts," Space.com, June 17, 2017, accessed July 06, 2019, https://www.space.com/52-the-expanding-universe-from-the-big-bang-to-today.html.

[20] Tribune.com.pk, "Stephen Hawking Says 'nothing' Was around before Origin of Universe," *The Express Tribune*, March 05, 2018, accessed July 06, 2019, https://tribune.com.pk/story/1651558/3-stephen-hawking-says-nothing-around-origin-universe/.

[21] John Carl Villanueva, "Big Crunch," *Universe Today*, December 25, 2015, accessed July 06, 2019, https://www.universetoday.com/37018/big-crunch/.

[22] Nola Taylor Redd, "What Is the Shape of the Universe?" Space.com, January 16, 2014, accessed July 06, 2019, https://www.space.com/24309-shape-of-the-universe.html.

[23] S. W. Hawking and Thomas Hertog, "A Smooth Exit from Eternal Inflation?" *Journal of High Energy Physics* 2018, no. 4 (2018): 1-13, doi:10.1007/jhep04(2018)147.

4. NO PERSPECTIVE

[1] Tom Schneider, "The Unreasonable Effectiveness of Mathematics," *The Unreasonable Effectiveness of Mathematics*, May 24, 2001, accessed July 08, 2019, http://www.calvin.edu/~scofield/courses/m161/materials/readings/Hamming.unreasonable.html.

[2] Ibid.

[3] Ibid.

[4] Ibid.

[5] Ibid.

[6] Ibid.

[7] Lisa Zyga, "Is Mathematics an Effective Way to Describe the World?" Phys.org, September 03, 2013, accessed July 08, 2019, https://phys.org/news/2013-09-mathematics-effective-world.html.

[8] Panu Raatikainen, "Gödel's Incompleteness Theorems," *Stanford Encyclopedia of Philosophy*, January 20, 2015, accessed July 08, 2019, https://plato.stanford.edu/entries/goedel-incompleteness/.

[9] Eric W. Weisstein, "Euclid's Postulates," *Wolfram Mathworld*, June 13, 2019, accessed July 8, 2019, http://mathworld.wolfram.com/EuclidsPostulates.html.

[10] Ray Toal, "Gödel's Incompleteness Theorems," *Gödel's Incompleteness Theorems*, accessed July 08, 2019, https://cs.lmu.edu/~ray/notes/godeltheorems/.

[11] Tom Schneider, "The Unreasonable Effectiveness."

[12] Alan Bustany, "How Can a Point Have 0 Dimensions and Still Exist?" Online posting, September 7, 2015, Quora, accessed July 8, 2019, https://www.quora.com/How-can-a-point-have-0-dimensions-and-still-exist.

[13] Howard C. Cromwell et al., "Sensory Gating: A Translational Effort from Basic to Clinical Science," *Clinical EEG and Neuroscience* 39, no. 2 (2008): 1-2, accessed July 8, 2019, doi:10.1177/155005940803900209.

[14] Ibid, 2-4.

[15] Ibid, 2.

[16] Chia-Hsiung Cheng et al., "Sensory Gating, Inhibition Control and Gamma Oscillations in the Human Somatosensory Cortex," *Scientific Reports* 6, no. 1 (2016): 1-8, accessed July 8, 2019, doi:10.1038/srep20437.

[17] Ibid, 4-5.

[18] Ibid, 5.

[19] Ibid.

[20] Ibid.

[21] As cited in Hiroki Nakata et al., "Somato-motor Inhibitory Processing in Humans: A Study with MEG and ERP," *European Journal of Neuroscience* 22, no. 7 (2005): 1784-1792, doi:10.1111/ j.1460-9568.2005.04368.x., Hiroki Nakata et al., "Effects of ISI and Stimulus Probability on Event-related Go/nogo Potentials after Somatosensory Stimulation," *Experimental Brain Research* 162, no. 3 (2004): 293-299, doi:10.1007/s00221-004-2195-4., Hiroki Nakata et al., "Temporal Dynamics of Neural Activity in Motor Execution and Inhibition Processing," *European Journal of Neuroscience* 41, no. 11 (2015): 1448-1458, doi:10.1111/ejn.12889., Junichi Chikazoe et al., "Activation of Right Inferior Frontal Gyrus during Response Inhibition across Response Modalities," *Journal of Cognitive Neuroscience* 19, no. 1 (2007): 69-80, doi:10.1162/ jocn.2007.19.1.69., and Hayato Tabu et al., "Common Inhibitory Prefrontal Activation during Inhibition of Hand and Foot Responses," *NeuroImage* 59, no. 4 (2012): 3373-3378, doi:10.1016/j. neuroimage.2011.10.092.

[22] As cited in Bartos, M., Vida, I. & Jonas, P. Synaptic mechanisms of synchronized gamma oscillations in inhibitory interneuron networks. *Nat Rev Neurosci* 8, 45–56 (2007)., Brunel, N. & Wang, X. J. What determines the frequency of fast network oscillations with irregular neural discharges? I. Synaptic dynamics and excitation-inhibition balance. J *Neurophysiol* 90, 415–430 (2003).

[23] Declan N.c. Jones et al., "Developing New Drugs for Schizophrenia: From Animals to the Clinic," *Animal and Translational Models for CNS Drug Discovery*, 2008, 199-261, doi:10.1016/ b978-0-12-373861-5.00008-4.s

[24] L.a. Jones et al., "Cognitive Mechanisms Associated with Auditory Sensory Gating," Brain and Cognition 102 (2016): 33, accessed July 8, 2019, doi:10.1016/j.bandc.2015.12.005.

[25] Ibid, 37.

[26] Ibid.

[27] Ibid, 38.

[28] Ibid, 39.

[29] Ibid, 41.

[30] Ibid, 42.

[31] Ibid.

[32] Darya L. Zabelina, Ph.D., "Creativity and Sensory Gating," *Psychology Today*, January 23, 2015, accessed July 08, 2019, https://www.psychologytoday.com/us/blog/finding-butterfly/201501/creativity-and-sensory-gating.

[33] Li Wan, Ph.D. et al., "P50 Sensory Gating and Attentional Performance," *International Journal of Psychophysiology* 67, no. 2 (2008): 2, doi:10.1016/j.ijpsycho.2007.10.008.

[34] As cited in Michael I. Posner and Steven E. Petersen, "The Attention System of the Human Brain," *Annual Review of Neuroscience* 13, no. 1 (1990): 25-42, doi:10.1146/annurev.ne.13.030190.000325.

[35] Li Wan, Ph.D. et al., "P50 Sensory Gating," 7.

[36] Ibid, 7.

[37] Bob Michaël Fennis and Wolfgang Stroebe, T*he Psychology of Advertising* (London: Routledge, 2016).

[38] Ibid, 21-22.

[39] Ibid, 22.

[40] Ibid, 21-22.

[41] As cited in Anthony C. Greenwald, *Psychological Foundations of Attitudes* (New York U.a.: Academic Press, 1969), 147-170., Richard E. Petty, Timothy C. Brock, and Thomas M. Ostrom, *Cognitive Responses in Persuasion* (New York: Psychology Press, 2014).

[42] Ibid, 37-38.

[43] Ibid, 38-40.

[44] Ibid, 40.

[45] Michael, "The Psychology of Advertising," *Exploring Your Mind*, April 19, 2018, accessed July 09, 2019, https://exploringyourmind.com/psychology-of-advertising/.

[46] Bamber Gascoigne, "History of Measurement," *History of Measurement*, 2001, accessed July 09, 2019, http://www.historyworld.net/wrldhis/PlainTextHistories.asp?historyid=ac07.

[47] Karl M. Petruso, "Early Weights and Weighing in Egypt and the Indus Valley," *M Bulletin* (Museum of Fine Arts, Boston) 79:45, accessed July 8, 2019, Retrieved from http://www.jstor.org/stable/4171634.

[48] As cited in W. M. Flinders Petrie, Ancient Weights and Measures (London: Quaritch, 1926), 17-19.

[49] Natasha Frost and Natasha Frost, "A Brief History of the Kilogram, and Why Scientists Are Ready to Revise It," *Quartz*, November 12, 2018, , accessed July 09, 2019, https://qz.com/1458672/the-history-of-the-international-prototype-kilogram/.

[50] Philip Smith, B.A., "Libra," LacusCurtius • Roman Weights and Measures - Libra (Smith's Dictionary, 1875), May 8, 2018, , accessed July 09, 2019, http://penelope.uchicago.edu/Thayer/E/Roman/Texts/secondary/SMIGRA*/Libra.html.

[51] Ed Lowther, "A Short History of the Pound," *BBC News*, February 14, 2014, accessed July 09, 2019, https://www.bbc.com/news/uk-politics-26169070.

[52] "Cubit - How Many Scruples in a Dram? 8 Historical Measurements," *Merriam-Webster*, accessed July 09, 2019, https://www.merriam-webster.com/words-at-play/origins-of-units-of-measure/cubit.

[53] "Liter," *Merriam-Webster*, accessed July 09, 2019, https://www.merriam-webster.com/dictionary/liter.

[54] "Gallon," Dictionary.com, accessed July 09, 2019, https://www.dictionary.com/browse/gallon.

[55] Lauren McGuire, "Time after Time: What Is So Tricky about Time?" *Australian Primary Mathematics Classroom* 12, no. 2 (2007): 30-32, accessed July 8, 2019, https://eric.ed.gov/?id=EJ793979.

[56] Sidney Smith, "Babylonian Time Reckoning," *Iraq* 31, no. 1 (1969): 74-81, accessed July 8, 2019, doi:10.2307/4199869.

[57] "Claude Monet and Pierre-Auguste Renoir," *Claude Monet and Pierre-Auguste Renoir*, 2010, accessed July 09, 2019, https://www.claude-monet.com/monet-and-renoir.jsp.

[58] G.E. Moore, "The Nature of Reality and Objects of Perception," Proceedings of the Aristotelian Society, *New Series* 6 (1905): 68, accessed July 9, 2019, http://www.jstor.org/stable/4543729.

[59] "*Alice in Wonderland* (1951)," Transcripts Wiki, accessed July 10, 2019, https://transcripts.fandom.com/wiki/Alice_in_Wonderland_(1951).

5. NO NORMAL

[1] "The Newsroom/Bullies."

[2] "Normal," *Merriam-Webster*, accessed July 11, 2019, https://www.merriam-webster.com/dictionary/normal.

[3] Ibid.

[4] Aldous Huxley, *Brave New World Revisited* (New York: Harper Perennial, 1958), 51.

[5] Simon Worrall, "Why Race Is Not a Thing, According to Genetics," *National Geographic*, October 16, 2017, accessed July 11, 2019, https://news.nationalgeographic.com/2017/10/genetics-history-race-neanderthal-rutherford/.

[6] Ibid.

[7] Ibid.

[8] Gwendolyn Keita, "Discussing Discrimination," *American Psychological Association*, accessed July 11, 2019, https://www.apa.org/helpcenter/keita-qa.

[9] "Dual Pathways to a Better America: Preventing Discrimination and Promoting Diversity," *American Psychological Association*, 2012, accessed July 10, 2019, http://www.apa.org/pubs/info/reports/promoting-diversity.aspx.

[10] "The Odd Couple/My Strife in Court," in *The Odd Couple*, February 16, 1973.

[11] Beverly D. Flaxington, "Don't Assume I Know What You Mean," *Psychology Today*, October 5, 2012, accessed July 11, 2019, https://www.psychologytoday.com/us/blog/understand-other-people/201210/don-t-assume-i-know-what-you-mean.

[12] Ibid.

[13] David Tyson, "A Quote by David Tyson," *Goodreads*, accessed July 11, 2019, https://www.goodreads.com/quotes/121739-true-friendship-comes-when-silence-between-two-people-is-comfortable.

[14] "MBTI Basics," The Myers & Briggs Foundation - MBTI® Basics, accessed July 11, 2019, https://www.myersbriggs.org/my-mbti-personality-type/mbti-basics/home.htm?bhcp=1.

[15] Marcus Credé, Michael Bashshur, and Sarah Niehorster, "Reference Group Effects in the Measurement of Personality and Attitudes," *Journal of Personality Assessment* 92, no. 5 (2010): 390-399, doi:10.1080/00223891.2010.497393.

[16] Wu Youyou et al., "Birds of a Feather Do Flock Together," *Psychological Science* 28, no. 3 (2017): 276-284, doi:10.1177/0956797616678187.

[17] Ibid, 277.

[18] Ibid, 278.

[19] Ibid, 277-278.

[20] PsychScience, "Couples, Friends Show Similarity in Personality Traits after All," *EurekAlert!* February 11, 2017, accessed July 11, 2019, https://www.eurekalert.org/pub_releases/2017-02/afps-cfs021117.php.

[21] Ibid.

[22] Julie Beck, "How Friendships Change When You Become an Adult," *The Atlantic*, October 26, 2015, accessed July 11, 2019, https://www.theatlantic.com/health/archive/2015/10/how-friendships-change-over-time-in-adulthood/411466/.

[23] Ibid.

[24] Ibid.

[25] Ibid.

[26] Ibid.

[27] Oprah Winfrey, "A Quote by Oprah Winfrey," *Goodreads*, accessed July 11, 2019, https://www.goodreads.com/quotes/4602-everyone-wants-to-ride-with-you-in-the-limo-but.

[28] A. C. Little, B. C. Jones, and L. M. Debruine, "Facial Attractiveness: Evolutionary Based Research," *Philosophical Transactions of the Royal Society B: Biological Sciences* 366, no. 1571 (2011): 1638-1659, doi:10.1098/rstb.2010.0404.

[29] Ibid, 1639-1640.

[30] Ibid, 1640-1641.

[31] Ibid, 1642.

[32] As cited in Karl Grammer and Randy Thornhill, "Human (Homo Sapiens) Facial Attractiveness and Sexual Selection: The Role of Symmetry and Averageness.," *Journal of Comparative Psychology*

108, no. 3 (1994): 233-242, doi:10.1037//0735-7036.108.3.233.,
Michael R. Cunningham, "Measuring the Physical in Physical
Attractiveness: Quasi-experiments on the Sociobiology of Female
Facial Beauty.," *Journal of Personality and Social Psychology* 50,
no. 5 (1986): 925-935, doi:10.1037//0022-3514.50.5.925., Doug
Jones and Kim Hill, "Criteria of Facial Attractiveness in Five Populations," *Human Nature* 4, no. 3 (1993): 271-296, doi:10.1007/
bf02692202., D. I. Perrett et al., "Effects of Sexual Dimorphism
on Facial Attractiveness," *Nature* 394, no. 6696 (1998): 884-887,
doi:10.1038/29772.

[33] As cited in Anthony C. Little et al., "Womens Preferences for
Masculinity in Male Faces Are Highest during Reproductive Age
Range and Lower around Puberty and Post-menopause," *Psycho-
neuroendocrinology* 35, no. 6 (2010): 912-920, doi:10.1016/j.psyn-
euen.2009.12.006., Jovana Vukovic et al., "Circum-menopausal
Effects on Womens Judgements of Facial Attractiveness," *Biology
Letters* 5, no. 1 (2009): , doi:10.1098/rsbl.2008.0478.

[34] As cited in Daniel Brian Krupp, Lisa M. Debruine, and Benedict
C. Jones, "Apparent Health Encourages Reciprocity," *Evolution
and Human Behavior* 32, no. 3 (2011): 198-203, doi:10.1016/j.
evolhumbehav.2010.10.001.

[35] As cited in B.c Jones et al., "Facial Symmetry and Judgements
of Apparent Health," *Evolution and Human Behavior* 22, no. 6
(2001): 417-429, doi:10.1016/s1090-5138(01)00083-6., B. C.
Jones et al., "Menstrual Cycle, Pregnancy and Oral Contraceptive
Use Alter Attraction to Apparent Health in Faces," *Proceedings
of the Royal Society B: Biological Sciences* 272, no. 1561 (2005):
347-354, doi:10.1098/rspb.2004.2962.

[36] A.C. Little et al., "Facial Attractiveness," 1643.

[37] As cited in Manfred Milinski and Theo C. M. Bakker, "Female
Sticklebacks Use Male Coloration in Mate Choice and Hence
Avoid Parasitized Males," *Nature* 344, no. 6264 (1990): 330-333,
doi:10.1038/344330a0., Sarah R. Pryke and Simon C. Griffith,
"Red Dominates Black: Agonistic Signalling among Head Morphs
in the Colour Polymorphic Gouldian Finch," *Proceedings of the
Royal Society B: Biological Sciences* 273, no. 1589 (2006): 949-

957, doi:10.1098/rspb.2005.3362., Joanna M. Setchell and E. Jean Wickings, "Dominance, Status Signals and Coloration in Male Mandrills (Mandrillus Sphinx)," *Ethology* 111, no. 1 (2005): 25-50, doi:10.1111/j.1439-0310.2004.01054.x., Corri Waitt et al., "Evidence from Rhesus Macaques Suggests That Male Coloration Plays a Role in Female Primate Mate Choice," *Proceedings of the Royal Society of London. Series B: Biological Sciences* 270, no. Suppl_2 (2003): doi:10.1098/rsbl.2003.0065.; Innes C. Cuthill et al., "Colour Bands, Dominance, and Body Mass Regulation in Male Zebra Finches (Taeniopygia Guttata)," *Proceedings of the Royal Society of London. Series B: Biological Sciences* 264, no. 1384 (1997): 1093-1099, doi:10.1098/rspb.1997.0151.

[38] As cited in Sascha Schwarz and Marie Singer, "Romantic Red Revisited: Red Enhances Mens Attraction to Young, but Not Menopausal Women," J*ournal of Experimental Social Psychology* 49, no. 1 (2013): 161-164, doi:10.1016/j.jesp.2012.08.004.

[39] As cited in Ian D. Stephen et al., "Facial Skin Coloration Affects Perceived Health of Human Faces," *International Journal of Primatology* 30, no. 6 (2009): 845-857, doi:10.1007/s10764-009-9380-z.

[40] As cited in Russell A. Hill and Robert A. Barton, "Red Enhances Human Performance in Contests," *Nature* 435, no. 7040 (2005): 293, doi:10.1038/435293a., Anthony C. Little and Russell A. Hill, "Attribution to Red Suggests Special Role in Dominance Signalling," Journal of Evolutionary Psychology 5, no. 1 (2007): 161-168, doi:10.1556/jep.2007.1008., Andrew J. Elliot et al., "The Effect of Red on Avoidance Behavior in Achievement Contexts," *Personality and Social Psychology Bulletin* 35, no. 3 (2008): 365-375, doi:10.1177/0146167208328330.

[41] As cited in Stephen, Ian D. et al., 2009, 845-857.

[42] A.C. Little et al., "Facial Attractiveness," 1644.

[43] As cited in "Effects of Sexual Dimorphism on Facial Attractiveness," *Foundations in Social Neuroscience*, 2002, doi:10.7551/mitpress/3077.003.0065., Diane S. Berry and Sheila Brownlow, "Were the Physiognomists Right?" *Personality and Social Psychology Bulletin* 15, no. 2 (1989): 266-279,

doi:10.1177/0146167289152013., Caroline F. Keating, "Gender and the Physiognomy of Dominance and Attractiveness," *Social Psychology Quarterly* 48, no. 1 (1985): 61, doi:10.2307/3033782., Leslie Zebrowitz Mcarthur and Karen Apatow, "Impressions of Baby-Faced Adults," *Social Cognition* 2, no. 4 (1984): 315-342, doi:10.1521/soco.1984.2.4.315., Leslie Zebrowitz Mcarthur and Diane S. Berry, "Cross-Cultural Agreement in Perceptions of Babyfaced Adults," *Journal of Cross-Cultural Psychology* 18, no. 2 (1987): 165-192, doi:10.1177/0022002187018002003.

[44] A.C. Little et al., "Facial Attractiveness," 1644.

[45] As cited in Victor S. Johnston et al., "Male Facial Attractiveness: Evidence for Hormone-mediated Adaptive Design," *Evolution and Human Behavior* 22, no. 4 (2001): 251-267, doi:10.1016/s1090-5138(01)00066-6., B.c. Jones et al., "Commitment to Relationships and Preferences for Femininity and Apparent Health in Faces Are Strongest on Days of the Menstrual Cycle When Progesterone Level Is High," *Hormones and Behavior* 48, no. 3 (2005): 283-290, doi:10.1016/j.yhbeh.2005.03.010., I.s Penton-Voak and D.i Perrett, "Female Preference for Male Faces Changes Cyclically," *Evolution and Human Behavior* 21, no. 1 (2000): 39-48, doi:10.1016/s1090-5138(99)00033-1.

[46] A.C. Little et al.,"Facial Attractiveness," 1645.

[47] As cited in L. Welling et al., "Men Report Stronger Attraction to Femininity in Womens Faces When Their Testosterone Levels Are High," Hormones and Behavior 54, no. 5 (2008): 703-708, doi:10.1016/j.yhbeh.2008.07.012.

[48] As cited in Alan H. Bittles and James V. Neel, "The Costs of Human Inbreeding and Their Implications for Variations at the DNA Level," *Nature Genetics* 8, no. 2 (1994): 117-121, doi:10.1038/ng1094-117.

[49] As cited in Benedict C. Jones et al., "Integrating Gaze Direction and Expression in Preferences for Attractive Faces," *Psychological Science* 17, no. 7 (2006): 588-591, doi:10.1111/j.1467-9280.2006.01749.x., J. O'Doherty et al., "Beauty in a Smile: The Role of Medial Orbitofrontal Cortex in Facial Attractiveness," *Neuropsychologia* 41, no. 2 (2003): 147-155, doi:10.1016/s0028-3932(02)00145-8.

[50] A.C. Little et al., "Facial Attractiveness," 1650.

[51] As cited in Gillian Rhodes et al., "Orientation-Contingent Face Aftereffects and Implications for Face-Coding Mechanisms," *Current Biology* 14, no. 23 (2004): 2119-2123, doi:10.1016/j. cub.2004.11.053., Michael A. Webster and Otto H. Maclin, "Figural Aftereffects in the Perception of Faces," Psychonomic Bulletin & Review 6, no. 4 (1999): 647-653, doi:10.3758/bf03212974., Gillian Rhodes et al., "Fitting the Mind to the World," Psychological *Science* 14, no. 6 (2003): 558-566, doi:10.1046/j.0956-7976.2003. psci_1465.x.

[52] As cited in K. W. Eva and T. J. Wood, "Are All the Taken Men Good? An Indirect Examination of Mate-choice Copying in Humans," *Canadian Medical Association Journal* 175, no. 12 (2006): 1573-1574, doi:10.1503/cmaj.061367.

[53] As cited in Sarah E. Hill and David M. Buss, "The Mere Presence of Opposite-Sex Others on Judgments of Sexual and Romantic Desirability: Opposite Effects for Men and Women," *Personality and Social Psychology Bulletin* 34, no. 5 (2008): 635-647, doi:10.1177/0146167207313728.

[54] As cited in Anthony C. Little et al., "Social Influence in Human Face Preference: Men and Women Are Influenced More for Long-term than Short-term Attractiveness Decisions," E*volution and Human Behavior* 29, no. 2 (2008): 140-146, doi:10.1016/j.evolhumbehav.2007.11.007.

[55] "What Is the Americans with Disabilities Act (ADA)?" *ADA National Network*, July 09, 2019, accessed July 12, 2019, https:// adata.org/learn-about-ada.

[56] "Disability," *Merriam-Webster*, accessed July 12, 2019, https:// www.merriam-webster.com/dictionary/disability.

[57] Hilary Mitchell, "15 People Told Us Their Stories Of Disability Discrimination At Work," *BuzzFeed*, August 02, 2017, accessed July 12, 2019, https://www.buzzfeed.com/hilarywardle/disability-discrimination-in-the-workplace.

[58] Karla Culbertson, "Working Through My Insecurities About My Disability," *The Mighty*, July 12, 2019, accessed July 12, 2019, https://themighty.com/2018/01/working-through-insecurities-about-disability/.

[59] Ibid.

[60] Claudia Dreifus, "Life and the Cosmos, Word by Painstaking Word," *The New York Times*, May 09, 2011, accessed July 12, 2019, https://www.nytimes.com/2011/05/10/science/10hawking.html.

[61] Roger K. Blashfield et al., "The Cycle of Classification: DSM-I Through DSM-5," *Annual Review of Clinical Psychology* 10, no. 1 (2014): 25, doi:10.1146/annurev-clinpsy-032813-153639.

[62] American Psychiatric Association, "*Diagnostic and Statistical Manual of Mental Disorders (DSM-5®)*, Fifth Edition," Descriptive Text, , accessed July 12, 2019, https://www.appi.org/Diagnostic_and_Statistical_Manual_of_Mental_Disorders_DSM-5_Fifth_Edition.

[63] Roger K. Blashfield et al., "The Cycle," 25-51.

[64] "The State of Mental Health in America," *Mental Health America*, November 01, 2018, , accessed July 12, 2019, http://www.mentalhealthamerica.net/issues/state-mental-health-america.

[65] Albert "Skip" Rizzo, Ph.D., "Speaking of Psychology: Improving Lives through Virtual Reality Therapy," *American Psychological Association*, 2019, accessed July 12, 2019, https://www.apa.org/research/action/speaking-of-psychology/virtual-reality.aspx.

[66] Zaharia Mihai, "AI Applications in Psychology," *Expert Systems for Human, Materials and Automation*, 2011, doi:10.5772/16620.

[67] David Adam, "Mental Health: On the Spectrum," *Nature* 496, no. 7446 (2013): 416-418, doi:10.1038/496416a.

[68] "The New DSM-5: Schizophrenia Spectrum and Other Psychotic Disorders," Mental Help The New DSM5 Schizophrenia Spectrum and Other Psychotic Disorders Comments, accessed July 13, 2019, https://www.mentalhelp.net/schizophrenia/the-new-dsm-5/.

[69] Ibid.

[70] Nancy C. Andreasen, "The Relationship between Creativity and Mood Disorders," *Dialogues in Clinical Neuroscience* 10, no. 2 (January 2008): 251, https://www.ncbi.nlm.nih.gov/pmc/articles/PMC3181877/pdf/DialoguesClinNeurosci-10-251.pdf.

[71] Ibid, 252.

[72] Ibid, 253.

73 Ibid, 252-254.

74 Christa L. Taylor, "Creativity and Mood Disorder: A Systematic Review and Meta-Analysis," *Perspectives on Psychological Science* 12, no. 6 (2017): 1040-1076, doi:10.1177/1745691617699653.

75 Ibid, 1043.

76 Maria Popova, "The Angels and Demons of Genius: Robert Lowell on What It's Like to Be Bipolar," *Brain Pickings*, March 03, 2017, accessed July 13, 2019, https://www.brainpickings.org/2016/02/26/robert-lowell-bipolar/.

77 Ibid.

78 Christa L. Taylor, "Creativity," 1040-1076.

79 Ibid, 1043.

80 Ibid.

81 Howard Gardner, *Frames of Mind: The Theory of Multiple Intelligences* (New York: Basic Books, 2011).

82 As cited in Howard Gardner, Intelligence Reframed: Multiple Intelligences for the 21st Century (New York, NY: Basic Books, 1999).

83 Howard Gardner, F*rames of Mind*, 114-121.

84 Ibid, 168-171.

85 As cited in Howard Gardner, Intelligence Reframed.

86 Howard Gardner, *Frames of Mind*, 217-220.

87 Ibid, 77-80.

88 Ibid, 241.

89 Ibid, 179-186.

90 "Wechsler IQ Test," Wechsler IQ Test, 2017, accessed July 13, 2019, https://wechsleriqtest.com/.

91 Lynn Waterhouse, "Multiple Intelligences, the Mozart Effect, and Emotional Intelligence: A Critical Review," *Educational Psychologist* 41, no. 4 (2006): 210, doi:10.1207/s15326985ep4104_1.

92 As cited in J. Geake and P. Hansen, "Neural Correlates of Intelligence as Revealed by FMRI of Fluid Analogies," *NeuroImage* 26, no. 2 (2005): 555-564, doi:10.1016/j.neuroimage.2005.01.035., W. Johnson and T. Bouchard, "The Structure of Human Intelligence: It Is Verbal, Perceptual, and Image Rotation (VPR), Not

Fluid and Crystallized," *Intelligence* 33, no. 4 (2005): 393-416, doi:10.1016/j.intell.2004.12.002., Wendy Johnson et al., "Just One G: Consistent Results from Three Test Batteries," *Intelligence* 32, no. 1 (2004): 95-107, doi:10.1016/s0160-2896(03)00062-x., M. Mcrorie, "Synaptic Transmission Correlates of General Mental Ability," *Intelligence* 32, no. 3 (2004): 263-275, doi:10.1016/j. intell.2003.12.003.

[93] As cited in Arthur W. Toga and Paul M. Thompson, "Genetics Of Brain Structure And Intelligence," *Annual Review of Neuroscience* 28, no. 1 (2005): 1-23, doi:10.1146/annurev.neuro.28.061604.135655.

[94] As cited in J. Geake and P. Hansen, "Neural Correlates."

[95] As cited in G. Roth and U. Dicke, "Evolution of the Brain and Intelligence," *Trends in Cognitive Sciences* 9, no. 5 (2005): 250-257, doi:10.1016/j.tics.2005.03.005.

[96] As cited in Howard Gardner, "Audiences for the Theory of Multiple Intelligences," *Teachers College Record* 106, no. 1 (2004): 212-220, doi:10.1111/j.1467-9620.2004.00329.x.

[97] As cited in Howard Gardner, *Intelligence Reframed: Multiple Intelligences for the 21st Century* (New York, NY: Basic Books, 1999), 106.

[98] Lynn Waterhouse, "*Multiple Intelligences*," 211.

[99] Ibid.

[100] Ibid.

[101] As cited in Daniel Kahneman, "A Perspective on Judgment and Choice: Mapping Bounded Rationality.," *American Psychologist* 58, no. 9 (2003): 697-720, doi:10.1037/0003-066x.58.9.697.

[102] Lynn Waterhouse, "*Multiple Intelligences*," 212.

[103] Ibid, 212-213.

[104] Ibid, 212.

[105] Ibid.

[106] Ibid.

[107] As cited in Denise Dellarosa Cummins, "The Evolutionary Roots of Intelligence and Rationality," *Common Sense, Reasoning, and Rationality*, 2002, 132-147, doi:10.1093/0195147669.003.000 7., Gregory J. Velicer, "Evolution of Cooperation: Does Selfishness

Restraint Lie Within?" *Current Biology* 15, no. 5 (2005): 173-175, doi:10.1016/j.cub.2005.02.045.

[108] "Emotional Intelligence," Daniel Goleman, accessed July 13, 2019, http://www.danielgoleman.info/topics/emotional-intelligence/.

[109] John (Jack) Mayer, Ph.D., Peter Salovey, Ph.D., and David Caruso, Ph.D., "MSCEIT™ 1 — Mayer-Salovey-Caruso Emotional Intelligence Test," Introduction, 2010, accessed July 13, 2019, https://mikegosling.com/pdf/MSCEITDescription.pdf.

[110] Reuven Bar-On, Ph.D., "EQ-i BarOn Emotional Quotient Inventory," *Eqi-133-resource*, September 3, 2003, 1-14, accessed July 13, 2019, http://www.eitrainingcompany.com/wp-content/uploads/2009/04/eqi-133-resource.pdf.

[111] Elizabeth J. Austin et al., "Measurement of Trait Emotional Intelligence: Testing and Cross-validating a Modified Version of Schutte Et Al.s (1998) Measure," *Personality and Individual Differences* 36, no. 3 (2004): 555-562, doi:10.1016/s0191-8869(03)00114-4., Nicola S. Schutte et al., "Development and Validation of a Measure of Emotional Intelligence," Personality and Individual Differences 25, no. 2 (1998): 167-177, doi:10.1016/s0191-8869(98)00001-4.

[112] Andrew H. Kemp et al., "Toward An Integrated Profile Of Emotional Intelligence: Introducing A Brief Measure," Journal of *Integrative Neuroscience* 04, no. 01 (2005): 41-62, doi:10.1142/s0219635205000677.

[113] Reuven Bar-On, Ph.D.,"EQ-I," 2.

[114] Nicola S. Schutte et al, "Development and Validation," 175.

[115] Ibid, 176.

[116] Ibid.

[117] Andrew H. Kemp et al., "Toward An Integrated Profile," 49, 53.

[118] As cited in John D. Mayer, David R. Caruso, and Peter Salovey, "Emotional Intelligence Meets Traditional Standards for an Intelligence," *Intelligence* 27, no. 4 (1999): 267-298, doi:10.1016/s0160-2896(99)00016-1., D. Ruble, "The Role of Gender-related Processes in the Development of Sex Differences in Self-evaluation and Depression," *Journal of Affective Disorders* 29, no. 2-3 (1993): 97-128, doi:10.1016/0165-0327(93)90027-h.

[119] Andrew H. Kemp et al., *"Toward An Integrated Profile,"* 55.

[120] Ibid.

[121] Ibid, 56.

[122] Ibid, 50.

[123] Lynn Waterhouse, *"Multiple Intelligences,"* 212.

[124] Ibid, 218.

[125] As cited in Joel Paris, "Neurobiological Dimensional Models of Personality: A Review of the Models of Cloninger, Depue, and Siever," *Journal of Personality Disorders* 19, no. 2 (2005): 156-170, doi:10.1521/pedi.19.2.156.62629.

[126] Anna-Lena Schubert et al., "Faster, but Not Smarter: An Experimental Analysis of the Relationship between Mental Speed and Mental Abilities," *Intelligence* 71 (2018): 66-75, doi:10.1016/j.intell.2018.10.005.

[127] Ibid, 73.

6. NO DECISIONS

[1] Joel Kinnaman, "Joel Kinnaman Quotes," BrainyQuote.com, 2019, accessed July 13, 2019, https://www.brainyquote.com/citation/quotes/joel_kinnaman_695367.

[2] Ezequiel Morsella et al., "Homing in on Consciousness in the Nervous System: An Action-based Synthesis," *Behavioral and Brain Sciences* 39 (2015): 15, doi:10.1017/s0140525x15000643.

[3] Ibid, 1-2.

[4] Alexia Elejalde-Ruiz, "Going with Your Gut," *Chicago Tribune*, June 13, 2012, accessed July 13, 2019, https://www.chicagotribune.com/lifestyles/ct-xpm-2012-06-13-sc-health-0613-gut-feelings-20120613-story.html.

[5] *Alive*, dir. Frank Marshall, perf. Ethan Hawke, Vincent Spano, Josh Hamilton (USA|Canada: Film Andes S.A., Paramount Pictures, The Kennedy/Marshall Company, Touchstone Pictures, 2002), DVD.

[6] Adam Klosin et al., "Transgenerational Transmission of Environmental Information in C. Elegans," *Science* 356, no. 6335 (2017): 320-323, doi:10.1126/science.aah6412.

[7] Ibid, 320.

[8] Avaneesh Pandey, "Scientists Observe Epigenetic Memories Being Passed Down For 14 Generations In Roundworms," *International Business Times*, April 21, 2017, April 21, 2017, accessed July 13, 2019, https://www.ibtimes.com/scientists-observe-epigenetic-memories-being-passed-down-14-generations-roundworms-2528649.

[9] Akira O'Connor, "This Is Your Brain On...déjà Vu," *O'Connor Memory Judgements Lab*, August 16, 2016, accessed July 14, 2019, http://akiraoconnor.org/2016/08/16/this-is-your-brain-on-deja-vu/.

[10] Jessica Hamzelou, "Mystery of Déjà Vu Explained – It's How We Check Our Memories," *NewScientist*, August 16, 2016, August 16, 2016, accessed July 14, 2019, https://www.newscientist.com/article/2101089-mystery-of-deja-vu-explained-its-how-we-check-our-memories/.

[11] Ibid.

[12] Tarja Porkka-Heiskanen, "Adenosine in Sleep and Wakefulness," *Annals of Medicine* 31, no. 2 (July 8, 1999): abstract, accessed July 14, 2019, doi:10.3109/07853899908998788.

[13] "Why Do We Sleep, Anyway?" Why Do We Sleep, Anyway? | *Healthy Sleep*, accessed July 14, 2019, http://healthysleep.med.harvard.edu/healthy/matters/benefits-of-sleep/why-do-we-sleep.

[14] Ronald E. Dahl, "The Impact of Inadequate Sleep on Childrens Daytime Cognitive Function," *Seminars in Pediatric Neurology* 3, no. 1 (1996): 44, doi:10.1016/s1071-9091(96)80028-3.

[15] As cited in Ronald E. Dahl, William E. Pelham, and Michelle Wierson, "The Role of Sleep Disturbances in Attention Deficit Disorder Symptoms: A Case Study," *Journal of Pediatric Psychology* 16, no. 2 (1991): 229-239, doi:10.1093/jpepsy/16.2.229., Daniel Picchietti and Karla Dzienkowski, "Restless Legs Syndrome and Periodic Limb Movements Disorder in Children and Adolescents," *Attention Deficit Disorder*, 2006, 147-158, doi:10.3109/9781420004724-23., Ch. Guilleminault et al., "Children and Nocturnal Snoring: Evaluation of the Effects of Sleep Related Respiratory Resistive Load and Daytime Functioning,"

European Journal of Pediatrics 139, no. 3 (1982): 165-171, doi:10.1007/bf01377349.

[16] E. Filevich et al., "Metacognitive Mechanisms Underlying Lucid Dreaming," *Journal of Neuroscience* 35, no. 3 (2015): 1082, doi:10.1523/jneurosci.3342-14.2015.

[17] Ibid, 1086.

[18] As cited in Katerina Semendeferi et al., "Prefrontal Cortex in Humans and Apes: A Comparative Study of Area 10," American *Journal of Physical Anthropology* 114, no. 3 (2001): 224-241, doi:10.1002/1096-8644(200103)114:33.3.co;2-9.

[19] As cited in C. D. Frith, "The Role of Metacognition in Human Social Interactions," *Philosophical Transactions of the Royal Society B: Biological Sciences* 367, no. 1599 (2012): 2213-2223, doi:10.1098/rstb.2012.0123.

[20] As cited in Martin Dresler et al., "Neural Correlates of Dream Lucidity Obtained from Contrasting Lucid versus Non-Lucid REM Sleep: A Combined EEG/fMRI Case Study," *Sleep* 35, no. 7 (2012): 1017-1020, doi:10.5665/sleep.1974.

[21] Nancy Chick, "Metacognition," Vanderbilt University, May 07, 2018, accessed July 14, 2019, https://cft.vanderbilt.edu/guides-sub-pages/metacognition/.

[22] Rafael Polanía et al., "The Precision of Value-based Choices Depends Causally on Fronto-parietal Phase Coupling," Nature News, August 20, 2015, 1-10, accessed July 14, 2019, https://www.nature.com/articles/ncomms9090.

[23] Ibid, 3.

[24] Ibid.

[25] Ibid.

[26] Ibid, 7.

[27] Ibid.

[28] Ibid.

[29] Matt Killingsworth, "A Wandering Mind Is an Unhappy Mind," *PsycEXTRA Dataset*, 2011, 932, doi:10.1037/e634112013-170.

[30] Ibid.

[31] David Rock, "New Study Shows Humans Are on Autopilot Nearly Half the Time," *Psychology Today*, November 14, 2010, ac-

cessed July 14, 2019, https://www.psychologytoday.com/us/blog/your-brain-work/201011/new-study-shows-humans-are-autopilot-nearly-half-the-time.

[32] Norman A. S. Farb et al., "Attending to the Present: Mindfulness Meditation Reveals Distinct Neural Modes of Self-reference," *Social Cognitive and Affective Neuroscience* 2, no. 4 (2007): 314, doi:10.1093/scan/nsm030.

[33] Ibid, 316.

[34] David Rock, "The Neuroscience of Mindfulness," *Psychology Today*, October 11, 2009, accessed July 14, 2019, https://www.psychologytoday.com/us/blog/your-brain-work/200910/the-neuro-science-mindfulness.

[35] Norman A. S. Farb et al., *"Attending to the Present,"* 316.

[36] David Rock, "The Neuroscience of Mindfulness."

[37] Ibid.

7. NO IDENTITY

[1] Erik H. Erikson, *Identity and the Life Cycle* (New York: Norton, 1980).

[2] Jean Piaget and Eleanor Duckworth, *Genetic Epistemology*. Translated by Eleanor Duckworth (New York: Columbia University Press, 1970).

[3] Martha Lally and Suzanne Valentine-French, LIFESPAN DEVELOPMENT: *A Psychological Perspective* (Lake County, IL: Indepedent, 2017), 20, 2017, accessed July 15, 2019, http://dept.clcillinois.edu/psy/LifespanDevelopment.pdf.

[4] Ibid, 83.

[5] Ibid, 81-83.

[6] Ibid, 83.

[7] Ibid, 118-121.

[8] Ibid, 159-161.

[9] Ibid, 212-214.

[10] Ibid, 81.

[11] Jacques Haenen, Hubert Schrijnemakers, and Job Stufkens, "Sociocultural Theory and the Practice of Teaching Historical Con-

cepts," *Vygotskys Educational Theory in Cultural Context*, 2003, 246-266, doi:10.1017/cbo9780511840975.014.

[12] As cited in René Van Der. *Veer and Jaan Valsiner, The Vygotsky Reader* (Oxford: Blackwell, 1994), 359.

[13] Ibid.

[14] Jacques Haenen et al., "*Sociocultural Theory and the Practice*," 251-252.

[15] Ibid, 252-254.

[16] Ibid, 252.

[17] Ibid, 253.

[18] Ibid.

[19] Ibid.

[20] Rheta Devries, "Piagets Social Theory," *Educational Researcher* 26, no. 2 (1997): 4, doi:10.2307/1176032.

[21] Ibid.

[22] Ibid, 5.

[23] Ibid.

[24] Ibid.

[25] Ibid.

[26] Ibid, 6.

[27] Ibid.

[28] Ibid, 7-8.

[29] Ibid, 9.

[30] As cited in Jean Piaget, Leslie Smith, and Terrance Brown, *Sociological Studies* (London: Routledge, 1995), 196.

[31] As cited in Jean Piaget, Leslie Smith, and Terrance Brown, *Sociological Studies* (London: Routledge, 1995), 210.

[32] Rheta Devries, "*Piagets Social Theory*," 9.

[33] Ibid.

[34] Ibid, 11.

[35] As cited in Jean Piaget, Intelligence and Affectivity: Their Relationship during Child Development (Palo Alto, CA: Annual Reviews, 1981).

[36] Ibid.

[37] Rheta Devries, "*Piagets Social Theory*," 12.

[38] Erik H. Erikson, Identity and the Life Cycle.

[39] Ibid, 63.

[40] Ibid, 66, 71.

[41] Ibid, 66.

[42] Ibid.

[43] Ibid, 73-84.

[44] Ibid, 77.

[45] Ibid, 84-95.

[46] Ibid, 95-102.

[47] Ibid, 102-109.

[48] Ibid, 109-113.

[49] Ibid, 113-114.

[50] Ibid, 114-115.

[51] Gwendolyn T. Sorell and Marilyn J. Montgomery, "Feminist Perspectives on Erikson S Theory: Their Relevance for Contemporary Identity Development Research," *Identity* 1, no. 2 (2001): 97-128, doi:10.1207/s1532706xid0102_01.

[52] Ibid, 98.

[53] Ibid.

[54] Ibid, 99.

[55] Ibid.

[56] Ibid.

[57] Ibid.

[58] Ibid, 100, 110.

[59] Ibid, 101.

[60] As cited in James E. Côté and Anton L. Allahar, *Generation on Hold Coming of Age in the Late Twentieth Century* (New York: New York Univ. Press, 1996).

[61] Gwendolyn T. Sorell and Marilyn J. Montgomery, *"Feminist Perspectives,"* 102.

[62] As cited in Carol Gilligan, *In a Different Voice: Psychological Theory and Womens Development* (Cambridge, MA: Harvard University Press, 2016).

[63] As cited in Kenneth J. Gergen, "The Place of the Psyche in a Constructed World," *Theory & Psychology* 7, no. 6 (1997): 723-746, doi:10.1177/0959354397076001., Rom Harré and Grant Gillett, *The Discursive Mind* (Thousand Oaks, CA: SAGE, 1994).

[64] As cited in Judith V. Jordan, *Women's Growth in Connection: Writings from the Stone Center* (London: Guilford Press, 1991), 7.
[65] James E. Marcia, "Development and Validation of Ego-identity Status.," *Journal of Personality and Social Psychology* 3, no. 5 (1966): 551-558, doi:10.1037/h0023281., James E. Marcia, "Identity in Adolescence," Handbook of Adolescent Psychology, 1980, 159-187, https://www.researchgate.net/publication/233896997_Identity_in_adolescence.
[66] Dan P. McAdams et al., "Stories of Commitment," *Journal of Personality and Social Psychology* 72, no. 3 (1997): 678-694, doi:http://dx.doi.org/10.1037/0022-3514.72.3.678.
[67] Ibid, 678.
[68] As cited in Erik H. Erikson, *Gandhi's Truth: On the Origins of Militant Nonviolence* (NY: Norton).
[69] As cited in Dan P. Mcadams and Ed De St. Aubin, "A Theory of Generativity and Its Assessment through Self-report, Behavioral Acts, and Narrative Themes in Autobiography.," *Journal of Personality and Social Psychology* 62, no. 6 (1992): 1003-1015, doi:10.1037/0022-3514.62.6.1003.
[70] Ibid.
[71] Dan P. McAdams et al., *"Stories of Commitment,"* 683.
[72] Ibid, 678.
[73] Ibid, 683.
[74] Ibid.
[75] Ibid.
[76] Ibid.
[77] Ibid, 683-684.
[78] Ibid, 684.
[79] Ibid.
[80] Ibid.
[81] Ibid.
[82] Ibid, 684-685.
[83] Ibid, 687.
[84] Ibid, 688.
[85] Ibid.
[86] Ibid, 690.

[87] Ibid.

[88] Todd E. Feinberg, *From Axons to Identity: Neurological Explorations of the Nature of the Self* (New York: W.W. Norton, 2009), XI.

[89] Jill Bolte Taylor, "My Stroke of Insight" (speech), February 2008, accessed July 18, 2019, https://www.ted.com/talks/jill_bolte_taylor_s_powerful_stroke_of_insight.

[90] Ibid.

[91] Todd E. Feinberg, *From Axons to Identity*, 2-3.

[92] Ibid, 3-4.

[93] Ibid, 5-7.

[94] Ibid, 8-9.

[95] Ibid, 9.

[96] Ibid, 12.

[97] Ibid, 17-18.

[98] Ibid.

[99] Ibid, 25-26.

[100] Ibid, 26-27.

[101] Ibid, 27-28.

[102] Ibid, 32-33.

[103] Ibid, 105-106.

[104] Ibid, 41-42.

[105] Cheng, Chia-Hsiung et al., "Sensory Gating," 1.

[106] Todd E. Feinberg, *From Axons to Identity*, 43-44.

[107] Ibid, 44.

[108] Ibid, 45.

[109] Ibid, 47-48.

[110] As cited in John R. Searle, "Consciousness," *Annual Review of Neuroscience* 23, no. 1 (2000): 561, doi:10.1146/annurev.neuro.23.1.557.

[111] As cited in Todd E. Feinberg, "The Nested Hierarchy of Consciousness: A Neurobiological Solution to the Problem of Mental Unity," *Neurocase* 6, no. 2 (2000): 75-81, doi:10.1080/13554790008402762.

[112] As cited in Wilfrid Sellars, *Science, Perception and Reality* (London: Routledge & Kegan Paul, 1963)., P. Meehl, "*The Com-*

pleat Autocerebroscopist: A Thought Experiment on Professor Feigl's Mind/body Identity Thesis," in *Mind, Matter, and Method,* ed. PK Feyeraband and G. Maxwell (Minneapolis: University of Minnesota Press, 1966), 103-180., P. Teller, "Subjectivity and Knowing What It's Like.," in *Emergence or Reduction? Essays on the Prospects of Nonreductive Physicalism,* ed. A. Beckermann, H. Flohr, and J. Kim (Berlin and New York: Walter De Gruyer, 1992), 180-200.

[113] Todd E. Feinberg, *From Axons to Identity,* 190-191.

[114] As cited in T. E. Feinberg et al., "Two Alien Hand Syndromes," *Neurology* 42, no. 1 (1992): 19-24, doi:10.1212/wnl.42.1.19., K. Baynes and MS Gazzaniga, "Callosal Disconnection," in *Behavioral Neurology and Neuropsychology,* ed. TE Feinberg and M. Farah, 2nd ed. (NY: McGraw-Hill, 2003), 401-409., MS Gazzaniga, *The Social Brain* (NY: Basic Books, 1985)., E. Zaidel and M. Iacoboni, "The Callosal Syndromes," in *Clinical Neuropsychology,* ed. KM Heilman and E. Valenstein, 4th ed. (NY: Oxford University Press, 2003).

[115] Todd E. Feinberg, From Axons to Identity, 196-198.

[116] Ibid, 198.

[117] Ibid, 197-198.

[118] Ibid, 201.

[119] Ibid, 208.

[120] Virginia Woolf, *The Waves* (New York: Harcourt Brace Jovanovich, 1978), 161.

AUTHOR BIOGRAPHY

[1] Howard Lloyd Blumenfeld, *Students Reinvention of Straight-line Solutions to Systems of Linear Ordinary Differential Equations,* Master's thesis, San Diego State University, 2006.

[2] Chris Rasmussen and Howard Blumenfeld, "Reinventing Solutions to Systems of Linear Differential Equations: A Case of Emergent Models Involving Analytic Expressions," *The Journal of Mathematical Behavior* 26, no. 3 (2007): 195-210, doi:10.1016/j.jmathb.2007.09.004.

FIGURES

[1] S. Sheppard, S*miling Tree Stump*, Humorous, in Shutterstock, Inc. [US], accessed July 23, 2019, https://www.shutterstock.com/image-photo/smiling-tree-stump-1015960705?studio=1.

[2] Xpixel, *Photo Rorschach Inkblot Test Isolated on White Background* - Image, in Shutterstock, Inc. [US], accessed July 23, 2019, https://www.shutterstock.com/image-photo/photo-rorschach-inkblot-test-isolated-on-606320885?src=ieVaNND8GUJTBfxIqIg-D6Q-1-0&studio=1.

[3] Golunovystock, *Young Ballerinas in Motion*. Rhythmic Gymnastics. Teenage Sport, Healthy Teen Lifestyle. Pretty Girls with Flying Ribbons, Dance Class Background, Ballet Concept - Image, in Shutterstock, Inc. [US], accessed July 23, 2019, https://www.shutterstock.com/image-photo/young-ballerinas-motion-rhythmic-gymnastics-teenage-730314913?src=eAOiCILRy47tCRVWh-pEx-Q-1-4&studio=1.

[4] Peteri, Optical Illusion. *Young Beautiful Princess or Old Ugly Woman?* Vector Illustration. - Vector, in Shutterstock, Inc. [US], accessed July 23, 2019, https://www.shutterstock.com/image-vector/optical-illusion-young-beautiful-princess-old-67150864?src=VSsFhYUKa5mX4eFWS1pFPQ-1-1&studio=1.

[5] Pierre-Auguste Renoir, *La Grenouillere*, 1869, National Museum, Stockholm, Sweden, in Alamy, accessed July 24, 2019, https://www.alamy.com/.

[6] Claude Monet, *Bain à La Grenouillère*, 1869, Oil Painting, The Metropolitan Museum of Art, New York, in Shutterstock, Inc. [US], accessed July 24, 2019, https://www.shutterstock.com/image-illustration/la-grenouillere-by-claude-monet-1869-747216142?studio=1.

[7] Kiselev Andrey Valerevich, *Close-up Portrait of a Beautiful Young Woman and a Man*. Fashionable Couple Posing at Studio. - Image, in Shutterstock, Inc. [US], accessed July 24, 2019, https://www.shutterstock.com/image-photo/closeup-portrait-beautiful-young-woman-man-327972284?src=UG3gtOiJ21R_p-FfKU_yfQ-1-38&studio=1.

APPENDIX

[1] Silberbogel, Vector Diagram of Anatomy of Human Brain - Vector, in Shutterstock, Inc. [US], accessed July 24, 2019, https://www.shutterstock.com/image-vector/vector-diagram-anatomy-human-brain-366858926?studio=1.

[2] Tefi, *Synapse Detailed Anatomy*, Beautiful Colorful Illustration. Neuron Passes Signal. At the Right Side Closer Look at Ligand Gated Ion Channel. - Vector, in Shutterstock, Inc. [US], accessed July 24, 2019, https://www.shutterstock.com/image-vector/synapse-detailed-anatomy-beautiful-colorful-illustration-395465926?src=library&studio=1.

References

"10 of the Best Words in the World (that Don't Translate into English)." *The Guardian*. July 27, 2018. Accessed July 04, 2019. https://www.theguardian.com/world/2018/jul/27/10-of-the-best-words-in-the-world-that-dont-translate-into-english.

Abbott, Alison. "Fractal Secrets of Rorschach's Famed Ink Blots Revealed." *Nature News*. Accessed July 04, 2019. https://www.nature.com/news/fractal-secrets-of-rorschach-s-famed-ink-blots-revealed-1.21473?error=cookies_not_supported&code=d86a3f5b-b5b7-4bd7-a9cc-0207df1aec27.

Adam, David. "Mental Health: On the Spectrum." *Nature* 496, no. 7446 (2013): 416-18. doi:10.1038/496416a.

Alais, David, and John Cass. "Multisensory Perceptual Learning of Temporal Order: Audiovisual Learning Transfers to Vision but Not Audition." *PLoS ONE* 5, no. 6 (2010): 1-9. doi:10.1371/journal.pone.0011283.

"*Alice in Wonderland* (1951)." Transcripts Wiki. Accessed July 10, 2019. https://transcripts.fandom.com/wiki/Alice_in_Wonderland_(1951). This transcript is for the original 1951 movie.

Alive. Directed by Frank Marshall. Performed by Ethan Hawke, Vincent Spano, Josh Hamilton. USA|Canada: Film Andes S.A., Paramount Pictures, The Kennedy/Marshall Company, Touchstone Pictures, 2002. DVD.

Allen, G. Donald. *"The History of Infinity."* Texas A&M University Department of Mathematics. 2000-2003. Accessed July 6, 2019. https://www.math.tamu.edu/~dallen/masters/infinity/infinity.pdf.

American Psychiatric Association. *"Diagnostic and Statistical Manual of Mental Disorders (DSM-5®),* Fifth Edition." Descriptive Text. Accessed July 12, 2019. https://www.appi.org/Diagnostic_and_Statistical_Manual_of_Mental_Disorders_DSM-5_Fifth_Edition.

Americas Greatest Hits: History. Warner Bros., 1983, CD.

Aminoff, Elissa M., Kestutis Kveraga, and Moshe Bar. "The Role of the Parahippocampal Cortex in Cognition." *Trends in Cognitive Sciences* 17, no. 8 (2013): 379-90. doi:10.1016/j.tics.2013.06.009.

Andreasen, Nancy C. "The Relationship between Creativity and Mood Disorders." *Dialogues in Clinical Neuroscience* 10, no. 2 (January 2008): 251-55. https://www.ncbi.nlm.nih.gov/pmc/articles/PMC3181877/pdf/DialoguesClinNeurosci-10-251.pdf.

Aronson, H. "Influence of Lysergic Acid Diethylamide (LSD-25) on Subjective Time." *Archives of General Psychiatry* 1, no. 5 (1959): 469. doi:10.1001/archpsyc.1959.03590050037003.

Atmanspacher, Harald, Thomas Filk, and Hartmann Romer. "Quantum Zeno Features of Bistable Perception." *Biological Cybernetics* 90, no. 1 (2004): 33-40. doi:10.1007/s00422-003-0436-4.

Atmanspacher, Harald, and Thomas Filk. "Temporal Nonlocality in Bistable Perception." *Journal of Mathematical Psychology* 54 (2010): 314-21. doi:10.1063/1.4773119.

Austin, Elizabeth J., Donald H. Saklofske, Sandra H.s Huang, and Deanne Mckenney. "Measurement of Trait Emotional Intelligence: Testing and Cross-validating a Modified Version of Schutte Et Al.s

(1998) Measure." *Personality and Individual Differences* 36, no. 3 (2004): 555-62. doi:10.1016/s0191-8869(03)00114-4.

Bachmann, Talis, Endel Põder, and Iiris Luiga. "Illusory Reversal of Temporal Order: The Bias to Report a Dimmer Stimulus as the First." *Vision Research* 44, no. 3 (2004): 241-46. doi:10.1016/j.visres.2003.10.012.

Baltzell, George W. "Constitution of the United States - We the People." *Constitution for the United States - We the People*. Accessed July 04, 2019. https://constitutionus.com/.

Bar-On, Reuven, Ph.D. "EQ-i BarOn Emotional Quotient Inventory." Eqi-133-resource. September 3, 2003. Accessed July 13, 2019. http://www.eitrainingcompany.com/wp-content/uploads/2009/04/eqi-133-resource.pdf.

Baynes, K., and MS Gazzaniga. "Callosal Disconnection." *In Behavioral Neurology and Neuropsychology*, edited by TE Feinberg and M. Farah, 401-09. 2nd ed. NY: McGraw-Hill, 2003.

Beck, Julie. "How Friendships Change When You Become an Adult." *The Atlantic*. October 26, 2015. Accessed July 11, 2019. https://www.theatlantic.com/health/archive/2015/10/how-friendships-change-over-time-in-adulthood/411466/.

Berry, Diane S., and Sheila Brownlow. "Were the Physiognomists Right?" *Personality and Social Psychology Bulletin* 15, no. 2 (1989): 266-79. doi:10.1177/0146167289152013.

Bittles, Alan H., and James V. Neel. "The Costs of Human Inbreeding and Their Implications for Variations at the DNA Level." *Nature Genetics* 8, no. 2 (1994): 117-21. doi:10.1038/ng1094-117.

Blashfield, Roger K., Jared W. Keeley, Elizabeth H. Flanagan, and Shannon R. Miles. "The Cycle of Classification: DSM-I Through

DSM-5." *Annual Review of Clinical Psychology* 10, no. 1 (2014): 25-51. doi:10.1146/annurev-clinpsy-032813-153639.

Blumenfeld, Adam. Interview by author. January/February, 2019.

Blumenfeld, Howard Lloyd. *Students Reinvention of Straight-line Solutions to Systems of Linear Ordinary Differential Equations.* Master's thesis, San Diego State University, 2006.

Bustany, Alan. "How Can a Point Have 0 Dimensions and Still Exist ?" Online posting. September 7, 2015. *Quora.* Accessed July 8, 2019. https://www.quora.com/How-can-a-point-have-0-dimensions-and-still-exist.

Castelli, F. "Autism, Asperger Syndrome and Brain Mechanisms for the Attribution of Mental States to Animated Shapes." *Brain* 125, no. 8 (2002): 1839-849. doi:10.1093/brain/awf189.

Cheng, Chia-Hsiung, Pei-Ying S. Chan, David M. Niddam, Shang-Yueh Tsai, Shih-Chieh Hsu, and Chia-Yih Liu. "Sensory Gating, Inhibition Control and Gamma Oscillations in the Human Somatosensory Cortex." *Scientific Reports* 6, no. 1 (2016): 1-8. Accessed July 8, 2019. doi:10.1038/srep20437. PDF (pages 1-8) available at https://www.nature.com/articles/srep20437.pdf

Chick, Nancy. "*Metacognition.*" Vanderbilt University. May 07, 2018. Accessed July 14, 2019. https://cft.vanderbilt.edu/guides-sub-pages/metacognition/.

Chikazoe, Junichi, Seiki Konishi, Tomoki Asari, Koji Jimura, and Yasushi Miyashita. "Activation of Right Inferior Frontal Gyrus during Response Inhibition across Response Modalities." *Journal of Cognitive Neuroscience* 19, no. 1 (2007): 69-80. doi:10.1162/jocn.2007.19.1.69.

Choi, Charles Q. "Our Expanding Universe: Age, History & Other

Facts." *Space.com*. June 17, 2017. Accessed July 06, 2019. https://www.space.com/52-the-expanding-universe-from-the-big-bang-to-today.html.

"Claude Monet and Pierre-Auguste Renoir." *Claude Monet and Pierre-Auguste Renoir*. 2010. Accessed July 09, 2019. https://www.claude-monet.com/monet-and-renoir.jsp.

Cotard, J. "Perte De La Vision Mentale Dans La Mélancolie Anxieuse." *Archives of Neurology* 6 (1884): 209-95.

Côté, James E., and Anton L. Allahar. *Generation on Hold Coming of Age in the Late Twentieth Century*. New York: New York Univ. Press, 1996.

Credé, Marcus, Michael Bashshur, and Sarah Niehorster. "Reference Group Effects in the Measurement of Personality and Attitudes." *Journal of Personality Assessment* 92, no. 5 (2010): 390-99. doi:10.1080/00223891.2010.497393.

Cromwell, Howard C., Ryan P. Mears, Li Wan, and Nash N. Boutros. "Sensory Gating: A Translational Effort from Basic to Clinical Science." *Clinical EEG and Neuroscience 39*, no. 2 (2008): 69-72. Accessed July 8, 2019. doi:10.1177/155005940803900209. PDF version of the article is p. 1-8 and is available at https://www.ncbi.nlm.nih.gov/pmc/articles/PMC4127047/pdf/nihms505411.pdf

"Cubit - How Many Scruples in a Dram? 8 Historical Measurements." *Merriam-Webster*. Accessed July 09, 2019. https://www.merriam-webster.com/words-at-play/origins-of-units-of-measure/cubit.

Culbertson, Karla. "Working Through My Insecurities About My Disability." *The Mighty*. July 12, 2019. Accessed July 12, 2019. https://themighty.com/2018/01/working-through-insecurities-about-disability/.

Cummins, Denise Dellarosa. "The Evolutionary Roots of Intelligence and Rationality." *Common Sense, Reasoning, and Rationality*, 2002, 132-47. doi:10.1093/0195147669.003.0007.

Cunningham, Michael R. "Measuring the Physical in Physical Attractiveness: Quasi-experiments on the Sociobiology of Female Facial Beauty." *Journal of Personality and Social Psychology* 50, no. 5 (1986): 925-35. doi:10.1037//0022-3514.50.5.925.

Cuthill, Innes C., Sarah Hunt, Colette Cleary, and Corinna Clark. "Colour Bands, Dominance, and Body Mass Regulation in Male Zebra Finches (Taeniopygia Guttata)." *Proceedings of the Royal Society of London*. Series B: Biological Sciences 264, no. 1384 (1997): 1093-099. doi:10.1098/rspb.1997.0151.

Dahl, Ronald E., William E. Pelham, and Michelle Wierson. "The Role of Sleep Disturbances in Attention Deficit Disorder Symptoms: A Case Study." *Journal of Pediatric Psychology* 16, no. 2 (1991): 229-39. doi:10.1093/jpepsy/16.2.229.

Dahl, Ronald E. "The Impact of Inadequate Sleep on Childrens Daytime Cognitive Function." *Seminars in Pediatric Neurology* 3, no. 1 (1996): 44-50. doi:10.1016/s1071-9091(96)80028-3.

"The Newsroom/Bullies."

Dark. Produced by Baran Bo Odar, Jantje Friese, Quirin Berg, Max Wiedemann, and Justnya Müsch. Performed by Louis Hofmann, Andreas Pietschmann, Daan Lennard Liebrenz, Lisa Vicari, Ludger Bökelmann, Julika Jenkins, Mark Waschke. Dark. December 1, 2017. Accessed December 2017. https://www.netflix.com/title/80100172.

Day, Nicholas. "Humans at Birth Are Drawn to Faces, Regardless of Species." *Lehighvalleylive.com*. April 09, 2013. Accessed July 04, 2019. https://www.lehighvalleylive.com/entertainment-general/2013/04/humans_at_birth_are_drawn_to_f.html.

Devries, Rheta. "Piagets Social Theory." *Educational Researcher* 26, no. 2 (1997): 4-17. doi:10.2307/1176032.

Dicarlo, James J., Davide Zoccolan, and Nicole C. Rust. "How Does the Brain Solve Visual Object Recognition?" *Neuron* 73, no. 3 (2012): 415-34. doi:10.1016/j.neuron.2012.01.010.

Diester, Ilka, and Andreas Nieder. "Semantic Associations between Signs and Numerical Categories in the Prefrontal Cortex." *PLoS Biology 5*, no. 11 (2007): 2684-695. doi:10.1371/journal.pbio.0050294.

"Disability." *Merriam-Webster*. Accessed July 12, 2019. https://www.merriam-webster.com/dictionary/disability.

Dorata, Joanna. *Word Red Written in Red Crayon on Paper* - Image. In Shutterstock, Inc. [US]. Accessed July 24, 2019. https://www.shutterstock.com/image-photo/word-red-written-crayon-on-paper-299045213?studio=1.
Royalty-free stock photo ID: 299045213

Dreifus, Claudia. "Life and the Cosmos, Word by Painstaking Word." *The New York Times*. May 09, 2011. Accessed July 12, 2019. https://www.nytimes.com/2011/05/10/science/10hawking.html.

Dresler, Martin, Renate Wehrle, Victor I. Spoormaker, Stefan P. Koch, Florian Holsboer, Axel Steiger, Hellmuth Obrig, Philipp G. Sämann, and Michael Czisch. "Neural Correlates of Dream Lucidity Obtained from Contrasting Lucid versus Non-Lucid REM Sleep: A Combined EEG/fMRI Case Study." *Sleep* 35, no. 7 (2012): 1017-020. doi:10.5665/sleep.1974.

"Dual Pathways to a Better America: Preventing Discrimination and Promoting Diversity." *American Psychological Association*. 2012. Accessed July 10, 2019. http://www.apa.org/pubs/info/reports/promoting-diversity.aspx.

"Effects of Sexual Dimorphism on Facial Attractiveness." *Foundations in Social Neuroscience*, 2002. doi:10.7551/mitpress/3077.003.0065.

Elejalde-Ruiz, Alexia. "Going with Your Gut." *Chicago Tribune*, June 13, 2012. Accessed July 13, 2019. https://www.chicagotribune.com/lifestyles/ct-xpm-2012-06-13-sc-health-0613-gut-feelings-20120613-story.html.

Eliot, T. S. *Four Quartets*. San Diego, CA: Harcourt Brace Jovanovich, 1988.

Elliot, Andrew J., Markus A. Maier, Martin J. Binser, Ron Friedman, and Reinhard Pekrun. "The Effect of Red on Avoidance Behavior in Achievement Contexts." *Personality and Social Psychology Bulletin* 35, no. 3 (2008): 365-75. doi:10.1177/0146167208328330.

"Emotional Intelligence." Daniel Goleman. Accessed July 13, 2019. http://www.danielgoleman.info/topics/emotional-intelligence/.

Ephratt, Michal. "The Functions of Silence." *Journal of Pragmatics* 40, no. 11 (2008): 1909-938. doi:10.1016/j.pragma.2008.03.009.

Erikson, Erik H. Gandhi's *Truth: On the Origins of Militant Nonviolence*. NY: Norton.

Erikson, Erik H. *Identity and the Life Cycle*. New York: Norton, 1980. Originally published in 1959.
Eva, K. W., and T. J. Wood. "Are All the Taken Men Good? An Indirect Examination of Mate-choice Copying in Humans." *Canadian Medical Association Journal* 175, no. 12 (2006): 1573-574. doi:10.1503/cmaj.061367.

Everett, Caleb, and Andrew Carnegie Fellow. "'Anumeric' People: What Happens When a Language Has No Words for Numbers?" *The Conversation*. July 08, 2019. Accessed July 18, 2019. https://theconversation.com/anumeric-people-what-happens-when-a-language-has-no-words-for-numbers-75828.

Farb, Norman A. S., Zindel V. Segal, Helen Mayberg, Jim Bean, Deborah Mckeon, Zainab Fatima, and Adam K. Anderson. "Attending to the Present: Mindfulness Meditation Reveals Distinct Neural Modes of Self-reference." *Social Cognitive and Affective Neuroscience* 2, no. 4 (2007): 313-22. doi:10.1093/scan/nsm030.

Feinberg, T. E., R. J. Schindler, N. G. Flanagan, and L. D. Haber. "Two Alien Hand Syndromes." *Neurology* 42, no. 1 (1992): 19-24. doi:10.1212/wnl.42.1.19.

Feinberg, Todd E. "The Nested Hierarchy of Consciousness: A Neurobiological Solution to the Problem of Mental Unity." *Neurocase* 6, no. 2 (2000): 75-81. doi:10.1080/13554790008402762.

Feinberg, Todd E. *From Axons to Identity: Neurological Explorations of the Nature of the Self.* New York: W.W. Norton, 2009.

Fennis, Bob Michaël, and Wolfgang Stroebe. *The Psychology of Advertising*. London: Routledge, 2016.

Field, Paul, and Eric W. Weisstein. "Zeno's Paradoxes." From Wolfram MathWorld. Accessed July 06, 2019. http://mathworld.wolfram.com/ZenosParadoxes.html.

Filevich, E., M. Dresler, T. R. Brick, and S. Kuhn. "Metacognitive Mechanisms Underlying Lucid Dreaming." *Journal of Neuroscience* 35, no. 3 (2015): 1082-088. doi:10.1523/jneurosci.3342-14.2015.

Flaxington, Beverly D. "Don't Assume I Know What You Mean." *Psychology Today*. October 5, 2012. Accessed July 11, 2019. https://www.psychologytoday.com/us/blog/understand-other-people/201210/don-t-assume-i-know-what-you-mean.

Fontes, Rhailana, Jéssica Ribeiro, Daya S. Gupta, Dionis Machado, Fernando Lopes-Júnior, Francisco Magalhães, Victor Hugo Bastos, Kaline Rocha, Victor Marinho, Gildário Lima, Bruna Velasques, Pedro Ribeiro, Marco Orsini, Bruno Pessoa, Marco Antonio Araujo Leite, and Silmar Teixeira. "Time Perception Mechanisms at Central Nervous System." *Neurology International* 8, no. 1 (2016): 14-22. doi:10.4081/ni.2016.5939.

Framingham, Jane. "Rorschach Inkblot Test." *Psych Central*. October 13, 2018. Accessed July 04, 2019. https://psychcentral.com/lib/rorschach-inkblot-test/.

Frank, Michael C., Daniel L. Everett, Evelina Fedorenko, and Edward Gibson. "Number as a Cognitive Technology: Evidence from Pirahã Language and Cognition." *Cognition* 108, no. 3 (2008): 819-24. doi:10.1016/j.cognition.2008.04.007.

Frith, C. D. "The Role of Metacognition in Human Social Interactions." *Philosophical Transactions of the Royal Society B: Biological Sciences* 367, no. 1599 (2012): 2213-223. doi:10.1098/rstb.2012.0123.

Frost, Natasha, and Natasha Frost. "A Brief History of the Kilogram, and Why Scientists Are Ready to Revise It." *Quartz*. November 12, 2018. Accessed July 09, 2019. https://qz.com/1458672/the-history-of-the-international-prototype-kilogram/.
Gallagher, James. "Aphantasia: A Life without Mental Images." *BBC News*. August 26, 2015. Accessed July 06, 2019. https://www.bbc.com/news/health-34039054.

"Gallon." Dictionary.com. Accessed July 09, 2019. https://www.dictionary.com/browse/gallon.

Gardner, Howard. *Intelligence Reframed: Multiple Intelligences for the 21st Century*. New York, NY: Basic Books, 1999.

Gardner, Howard. "Audiences for the Theory of Multiple Intelligences." *Teachers College Record* 106, no. 1 (2004): 212-20. doi:10.1111/j.1467-9620.2004.00329.x.

Gardner, Howard. *Frames of Mind: The Theory of Multiple Intelligences*. New York: Basic Books, 2011.

Gascoigne, Bamber. "History of Measurement." *History of Measurement*. 2001. Accessed July 09, 2019. http://www.historyworld.net/wrldhis/PlainTextHistories.asp?historyid=ac07.

Gazzaniga, MS. *The Social Brain*. NY: Basic Books, 1985.

Geake, J., and P. Hansen. "Neural Correlates of Intelligence as Revealed by FMRI of Fluid Analogies." *NeuroImage* 26, no. 2 (2005): 555-64. doi:10.1016/j.neuroimage.2005.01.035.

Gergen, Kenneth J. "The Place of the Psyche in a Constructed World." Theory & *Psychology* 7, no. 6 (1997): 723-46. doi:10.1177/0959354397076001.

Gil, Sandrine, and Sylvie Droit-Volet. "Time Perception, Depression and Sadness." *Behavioural Processes* 80, no. 2 (2009): 169-76. doi:10.1016/j.beproc.2008.11.012.

Gilligan, Carol. *In a Different Voice: Psychological Theory and Womens Development*. Cambridge, MA: Harvard University Press, 2016.

Grammer, Karl, and Randy Thornhill. "Human (Homo Sapiens) Facial Attractiveness and Sexual Selection: The Role of Symmetry and Averageness." *Journal of Comparative Psychology* 108, no. 3 (1994): 233-42. doi:10.1037//0735-7036.108.3.233.

Greenwald, Anthony C. P*sychological Foundations of Attitudes*. New York U.a.: Academic Press, 1969. The researchers only used material from pp. 147-170.

Griffin, Andrew. "You Might Not Be Able to Imagine Things, and Not Know It." *The Independent*. April 25, 2016. Accessed July 06, 2019. https://www.independent.co.uk/news/science/aphantasia-software-engineer-blake-ross-writes-mind-blowing-post-about-be-ing-unable-to-imagine-a7000216.html.

Grondin, Simon. "Timing and Time Perception: A Review of Recent Behavioral and Neuroscience Findings and Theoretical Directions." Attention, Perception, & *Psychophysics* 72, no. 3 (2010): 561-82. doi:10.3758/app.72.3.561.

Guilleminault, Ch., R. Winkle, R. Korobkin, and B. Simmons. "Children and Nocturnal Snoring: Evaluation of the Effects of Sleep Related Respiratory Resistive Load and Daytime Functioning." *European Journal of Pediatrics* 139, no. 3 (1982): 165-71. doi:10.1007/bf01377349.

Haenen, Jacques, Hubert Schrijnemakers, and Job Stufkens. "Sociocultural Theory and the Practice of Teaching Historical Concepts." *Vygotskys Educational Theory in Cultural Context*, 2003, 246-66. doi:10.1017/cbo9780511840975.014.

Hamzelou, Jessica. "Mystery of Déjà Vu Explained – It's How We Check Our Memories." *NewScientist*, August 16, 2016. August 16, 2016. Accessed July 14, 2019. https://www.newscientist.com/article/2101089-mystery-of-deja-vu-explained-its-how-we-check-our-memories/.

Harré, Rom, and Grant Gillett. *The Discursive Mind.* Thousand Oaks, CA: SAGE, 1994.

Hawking, S. W., and Thomas Hertog. "A Smooth Exit from Eternal Inflation?" *Journal of High Energy Physics* 2018, no. 4 (2018): 1-13. doi:10.1007/jhep04(2018)147.

Heberlein, A. S., and R. Adolphs. "Impaired Spontaneous Anthropomorphizing despite Intact Perception and Social Knowledge." *Proceedings of the National Academy of Sciences* 101, no. 19 (2004): 7487-491. doi:10.1073/pnas.0308220101.

Herzog, Michael H., Thomas Kammer, and Frank Scharnowski. "Time Slices: What Is the Duration of a Percept?" *PLOS Biology* 14, no. 4 (2016). doi:10.1371/journal.pbio.1002433.

Hill, Russell A., and Robert A. Barton. "Red Enhances Human Performance in Contests." *Nature* 435, no. 7040 (2005): 293. doi:10.1038/435293a.

Hill, Sarah E., and David M. Buss. "The Mere Presence of Opposite-Sex Others on Judgments of Sexual and Romantic Desirability: Opposite Effects for Men and Women." *Personality and Social Psychology Bulletin* 34, no. 5 (2008): 635-47. doi:10.1177/0146167207313728.

Hume, David. *The Natural History of Religion.* Boston: MobileReference.com, 2010.

Husserl, Edmund. "Vorlesungen Zur Phänomenologie Des Inneren Zeitbewußtseins." 2000. doi:10.1515/9783110916072.

Huxley, Aldous. *Brave New World Revisited.* New York: Harper Perennial, 1958.

Jacobs, Joshua, Christoph T. Weidemann, Jonathan F. Miller, Alec Solway, John F. Burke, Xue-Xin Wei, Nanthia Suthana, Michael R. Sperling, Ashwini D. Sharan, Itzhak Fried, and Michael J. Kahana. "Direct Recordings of Grid-like Neuronal Activity in Human Spatial Navigation." *Nature Neuroscience* 16, no. 9 (2013): 1188-190. doi:10.1038/nn.3466.

Jobs, Steve. YouTube. November 19, 2011. Accessed August 21, 2019. https://www.youtube.com/watch?v=UvEiSa6_EPA&fbclid=IwAR0Foxr7266U-jtzA1sD2ya8JlgHiM0QdE0qPCk6obli0g-SOGCi_fMgNl0E.

Johnson, W., and T. Bouchard. "The Structure of Human Intelligence: It Is Verbal, Perceptual, and Image Rotation (VPR), Not Fluid and Crystallized." *Intelligence* 33, no. 4 (2005): 393-416. doi:10.1016/j.intell.2004.12.002.

Johnson, Wendy, Thomas J. Bouchard, Robert F. Krueger, Matt Mcgue, and Irving I. Gottesman. "Just One G: Consistent Results from Three Test Batteries." *Intelligence* 32, no. 1 (2004): 95-107. doi:10.1016/s0160-2896(03)00062-x.

Johnston, Victor S., Rebecca Hagel, Melissa Franklin, Bernhard Fink, and Karl Grammer. "Male Facial Attractiveness: Evidence for Hormone-mediated Adaptive Design." *Evolution and Human Behavior* 22, no. 4 (2001): 251-67. doi:10.1016/s1090-5138(01)00066-6.

Jones, B. C., D. I. Perrett, A. C. Little, L. Boothroyd, R. E. Cornwell, D. R. Feinberg, B. P. Tiddeman, S. Whiten, R. M. Pitman, S. G. Hillier, D. M. Burt, M. R. Stirrat, M. J. Law Smith, and F. R. Moore. "Menstrual Cycle, Pregnancy and Oral Contraceptive Use Alter Attraction to Apparent Health in Faces." *Proceedings of the Royal Society B: Biological Sciences* 272, no. 1561 (2005): 347-54. doi:10.1098/rspb.2004.2962.

Jones, B.c, A.c Little, I.s Penton-Voak, B.p Tiddeman, D.m Burt, and D.i Perrett. "Facial Symmetry and Judgements of Apparent Health." *Evolution and Human Behavior* 22, no. 6 (2001): 417-29. doi:10.1016/s1090-5138(01)00083-6.

Jones, B.c., A.c. Little, L. Boothroyd, L.m. Debruine, D.r. Feinberg, M.j. Law Smith, R.e. Cornwell, F.r. Moore, and D.i. Perrett. "Commitment to Relationships and Preferences for Femininity and Apparent Health in Faces Are Strongest on Days of the Menstrual Cycle When Progesterone Level Is High." *Hormones and Behavior* 48, no. 3 (2005): 283-90. doi:10.1016/j.yhbeh.2005.03.010.

Jones, Benedict C., Lisa M. Debruine, Anthony C. Little, Claire A. Conway, and David R. Feinberg. "Integrating Gaze Direction and Expression in Preferences for Attractive Faces." *Psychological Science* 17, no. 7 (2006): 588-91. doi:10.1111/j.1467-9280.2006.01749.x.

Jones, Declan N.c., Jane E. Gartlon, Arpi Minassian, William Perry, and Mark A. Geyer. "Developing New Drugs for Schizophrenia: From Animals to the Clinic." *Animal and Translational Models for CNS Drug Discovery*, 2008, 199-261. doi:10.1016/b978-0-12-373861-5.00008-4.

Jones, Doug, and Kim Hill. "Criteria of Facial Attractiveness in Five Populations." *Human Nature* 4, no. 3 (1993): 271-96. doi:10.1007/bf02692202.

Jones, L.a., P.j. Hills, K.m. Dick, S.p. Jones, and P. Bright. "Cognitive Mechanisms Associated with Auditory Sensory Gating." *Brain and Cognition* 102 (2016): 33-45. Accessed July 8, 2019. doi:10.1016/j.bandc.2015.12.005.

Jordan, Judith V. *Womens Growth in Connection: Writings from the Stone Center*. London: Guilford Press, 1991.

Jörg, Ton. "Thinking in Complexity about Learning and Education: A Programmatic View." Complicity: *An International Journal of Complexity and Education* 6, no. 1 (2009): 1-22. doi:10.29173/cmplct8800.

Kahneman, Daniel. "A Perspective on Judgment and Choice: Mapping Bounded Rationality." *American Psychologist* 58, no. 9 (2003): 697-720. doi:10.1037/0003-066x.58.9.697.

Keating, Caroline F. "Gender and the Physiognomy of Dominance and Attractiveness." *Social Psychology Quarterly* 48, no. 1 (1985): 61. doi:10.2307/3033782.

Keita, Gwendolyn. "Discussing Discrimination." *American Psychological Association*. Accessed July 11, 2019. https://www.apa.org/helpcenter/keita-qa.

Kemp, Andrew H., Nicholas J. Cooper, Gerard Hermens, Evian Gordon, Richard Bryant, and Leanne M. Williams. "Toward An Integrated Profile Of Emotional Intelligence: Introducing A Brief Measure." *Journal of Integrative Neuroscience* 04, no. 01 (2005): 41-61. doi:10.1142/s0219635205000677.

Killingsworth, Matt. "A Wandering Mind Is an Unhappy Mind." PsycEXTRA Dataset, 2011, 932. doi:10.1037/e634112013-170.

Kinnaman, Joel. "Joel Kinnaman Quotes." BrainyQuote.com. 2019. Accessed July 13, 2019. https://www.brainyquote.com/citation/quotes/joel_kinnaman_695367.

Klosin, Adam, Eduard Casas, Cristina Hidalgo-Carcedo, Tanya Vavouri, and Ben Lehner. "Transgenerational Transmission of Environmental Information in C. Elegans." *Science* 356, no. 6335 (2017): 320-23. doi:10.1126/science.aah6412.

Kornmeier, Jürgen, and Michael Bach. "Ambiguous Figures – What Happens in the Brain When Perception Changes But Not the Stimulus." *Frontiers in Human Neuroscience* 6 (March 22, 2012): 1-23. doi:10.3389/fnhum.2012.00051.

Kraemer, David J. M., C. Neil Macrae, Adam E. Green, and William M. Kelley. "Sound of Silence Activates Auditory Cortex." *Nature* 434, no. 7030 (2005): 158. doi:10.1038/434158a.

Kreiman, Gabriel, Christof Koch, and Itzhak Fried. "Category-specific Visual Responses of Single Neurons in the Human Medial Temporal Lobe." *Nature Neuroscience* 3, no. 9 (2000): 946-53. doi:10.1038/78868.

Krupp, Daniel Brian, Lisa M. Debruine, and Benedict C. Jones. "Apparent Health Encourages Reciprocity." *Evolution and Human Behavior* 32, no. 3 (2011): 198-203. doi:10.1016/j.evolhumbehav.2010.10.001.

Kutter, Esther F., Jan Bostroem, Christian E. Elger, Florian Mormann, and Andreas Nieder. "Single Neurons in the Human Brain Encode Numbers." *Neuron* 100, no. 3 (2018): 753-61. doi:10.1016/j.neuron.2018.08.036.

Kuz, Sinem, Henning Petruck, Miriam Heisterüber, Harshal Patel, Beate Schumann, Christopher M. Schlick, and Ferdinand Binkofski. "Mirror Neuronsand Human-robot Interaction in Assembly Cells." *Procedia Manufacturing* 3 (2015): 402-08. doi:10.1016/j.promfg.2015.07.187.

Lally, Martha, and Suzanne Valentine-French. LIFESPAN DEVELOPMENT: A Psychological Perspective. Lake County, IL: Indepedent, 2017. 2017. Accessed July 15, 2019. http://dept.clcillinois.edu/psy/LifespanDevelopment.pdf.

Lau, Hakwan. "Is Consciousness a Battle between Your Beliefs and Perceptions? – Hakwan Lau: Aeon Ideas." *Aeon*. July 06, 2019. Accessed July 06, 2019. https://aeon.co/ideas/is-consciousness-a-battle-between-your-beliefs-and-perceptions.

"Liter." *Merriam-Webster*. Accessed July 09, 2019. https://www.merriam-webster.com/dictionary/liter.

Little, A. C., B. C. Jones, and L. M. Debruine. "Facial Attractiveness: Evolutionary Based Research." *Philosophical Transactions of the Royal Society B: Biological Sciences* 366, no. 1571 (2011): 1638-659. doi:10.1098/rstb.2010.0404.

Little, Anthony C., and Russell A. Hill. "Attribution to Red Suggests Special Role in Dominance Signalling." *Journal of Evolutionary Psychology* 5, no. 1 (2007): 161-68. doi:10.1556/jep.2007.1008.

Little, Anthony C., Robert P. Burriss, Benedict C. Jones, Lisa M. Debruine, and Christine A. Caldwell. "Social Influence in Human Face Preference: Men and Women Are Influenced More for Long-term than Short-term Attractiveness Decisions." *Evolution and Human Behavior* 29, no. 2 (2008): 140-46. doi:10.1016/j.evolhumbehav.2007.11.007.

Little, Anthony C., Tamsin K. Saxton, S. Craig Roberts, Benedict C. Jones, Lisa M. Debruine, Jovana Vukovic, David I. Perrett, David R. Feinberg, and Todd Chenore. "Womens Preferences for Masculinity in Male Faces Are Highest during Reproductive Age Range and Lower around Puberty and Post-menopause." *Psychoneuroendocrinology* 35, no. 6 (2010): 912-20. doi:10.1016/j.psyneuen.2009.12.006.

Livingstone, M. S., W. W. Pettine, K. Srihasam, B. Moore, I. A. Morocz, and D. Lee. "Symbol Addition by Monkeys Provides Evidence for Normalized Quantity Coding." *Proceedings of the*

*National Academy of Science*s 111, no. 18 (2014): 6822-827. doi:10.1073/pnas.1404208111.

Lowther, Ed. "A Short History of the Pound." *BBC News*. February 14, 2014. Accessed July 09, 2019. https://www.bbc.com/news/uk-politics-26169070.

Magalhães E Lemos, A. "Perte De La Vision Mentale Des Objets (formes Et Couleurs) Dans La Mélancolie Anxieuse." *Annales Médico-psychologiques* 6 (1906): 6-31.

Majaj, N. J., H. Hong, E. A. Solomon, and J. J. Dicarlo. "Simple Learned Weighted Sums of Inferior Temporal Neuronal Firing Rates Accurately Predict Human Core Object Recognition Performance." *Journal of Neuroscience* 35, no. 39 (2015): 13402-3418. doi:10.1523/jneurosci.5181-14.2015.

Marcia, James E. "Development and Validation of Ego-identity Status." *Journal of Personality and Social Psychology* 3, no. 5 (1966): 551-58. doi:10.1037/h0023281.

Marcia, James E. "Identity in Adolescence." *Handbook of Adolescent Psychology*, 1980, 159-87. https://www.researchgate.net/publication/233896997_Identity_in_adolescence.
In J. Adelson (Ed.)

Margulis, Elizabeth Hellmuth. "Silences in Music Are Musical Not Silent: An Exploratory Study of Context Effects on the Experience of Musical Pauses." *Music Perception: An Interdisciplinary Journal* 24, no. 5 (2007): 485-506. doi:10.1525/mp.2007.24.5.485.

Martinez-Conde, Susana. "The Fascinating Science Behind Why We See 'Faces' In Objects." *Mental Floss*. May 01, 2018. Accessed July 04, 2019. http://mentalfloss.com/article/538524/science-behind-pareidolia.

Masten, Luke. Short-Term Memory and Working Memory - Types of Memory - The Human Memory. 2019. Accessed July 05, 2019. http://www.human-memory.net/types_short.html.

Masten, Luke. Long-Term Memory - Types of Memory - The Human Memory. 2019. Accessed July 05, 2019. http://www.human-memory.net/types_long.html.

Mayer, John D., David R. Caruso, and Peter Salovey. "Emotional Intelligence Meets Traditional Standards for an Intelligence." *Intelligence 27*, no. 4 (1999): 267-98. doi:10.1016/s0160-2896(99)00016-1.

Mayer, John (Jack), Ph.D., Peter Salovey, Ph.D., and David Caruso, Ph.D. "MSCEIT™ 1 — Mayer-Salovey-Caruso Emotional Intelligence Test." Introduction. 2010. Accessed July 13, 2019. https://mikegosling.com/pdf/MSCEITDescription.pdf.

"MBTI Basics." The Myers & Briggs Foundation - MBTI® Basics. Accessed July 11, 2019. https://www.myersbriggs.org/my-mbti-personality-type/mbti-basics/home.htm?bhcp=1.

Mcadams, Dan P., and Ed De St. Aubin. "A Theory of Generativity and Its Assessment through Self-report, Behavioral Acts, and Narrative Themes in Autobiography." *Journal of Personality and Social Psychology* 62, no. 6 (1992): 1003-015. doi:10.1037/0022-3514.62.6.1003.

McAdams, Dan P., Ann Diamond, Ed De St. Aubin, and Mansfield Elizabeth. "Stories of Commitment." *Journal of Personality and Social Psychology* 72, no. 3 (1997): 678-94. doi:http://dx.doi.org/10.1037/0022-3514.72.3.678.

Mcarthur, Leslie Zebrowitz, and Karen Apatow. "Impressions of Baby-Faced Adults." *Social Cognition* 2, no. 4 (1984): 315-42. doi:10.1521/soco.1984.2.4.315.

Mcarthur, Leslie Zebrowitz, and Diane S. Berry. "Cross-Cultural Agreement in Perceptions of Babyfaced Adults." *Journal of Cross-Cultural Psychology* 18, no. 2 (1987): 165-92. doi:10.1177/0 022002187018002003.

McGuire, Lauren. "Time after Time: What Is So Tricky about Time?" *Australian Primary Mathematics Classroom* 12, no. 2 (2007): 30-32. Accessed July 8, 2019. https://eric.ed.gov /?id=EJ793979.

Mcrorie, M. "Synaptic Transmission Correlates of General Mental Ability." *Intelligence* 32, no. 3 (2004): 263-75. doi:10.1016/j. intell.2003.12.003.

Meehl, P. "The Compleat Autocerebroscopist: A Thought Experiment on Professor Feigl's Mind/body Identity Thesis." *In Mind, Matter, and Method*, edited by PK Feyeraband and G. Maxwell, 103-80. Minneapolis: University of Minnesota Press, 1966.

Michael. "The Psychology of Advertising." Exploring Your Mind. April 19, 2018. Accessed July 09, 2019. https://exploringyourmind. com/psychology-of-advertising/.

Mihai, Zaharia. "AI Applications in Psychology." *Expert Systems for Human, Materials and Automation*, 2011, 1-18. doi:10.5772/16620.

Milinski, Manfred, and Theo C. M. Bakker. "Female Sticklebacks Use Male Coloration in Mate Choice and Hence Avoid Parasitized Males." *Nature* 344, no. 6264 (1990): 330-33. doi:10.1038/344330a0.

Mitchell, Hilary. "15 People Told Us Their Stories Of Disability Discrimination At Work." *BuzzFeed*. August 02, 2017. Accessed July 12, 2019. https://www.buzzfeed.com/hilarywardle/disability-discrimination-in-the-workplace.

Monet, Claude. *Bain à La Grenouillère*. 1869. Oil Painting, The Metropolitan Museum of Art, New York. In Shutterstock, Inc. [US]. Accessed July 24, 2019. https://www.shutterstock.com/image-illustration/la-grenouillere-by-claude-monet-1869-747216142?studio=1. Royalty-free stock illustration ID: 747216142 La Grenouillere, by Claude Monet, 1869, French impressionist painting, oil on canvas. On right is the fashionable middle class restaurant built on a barge, joined by planks to a small island known as - Illustration

Moore, G.E. "The Nature of Reality and Objects of Perception." Proceedings of the Aristotelian Society, *New Series* 6 (1905): 68-127. Accessed July 9, 2019. http://www.jstor.org/stable/4543729.

Morsella, Ezequiel, Christine A. Godwin, Tiffany K. Jantz, Stephen C. Krieger, and Adam Gazzaley. "Homing in on Consciousness in the Nervous System: An Action-based Synthesis." *Behavioral and Brain Sciences* 39 (2015): 1-70. doi:10.1017/s0140525x15000643.

Mukamel, Roy, Arne D. Ekstrom, Jonas Kaplan, Marco Iacoboni, and Itzhak Fried. "Single-Neuron Responses in Humans during Execution and Observation of Actions." *Current Biology* 20, no. 8 (2010): 750-56. doi:10.1016/j.cub.2010.02.045.

Nakata, Hiroki, Koji Inui, Toshiaki Wasaka, Yohei Tamura, Tetsuo Kida, and Ryusuke Kakigi. "Effects of ISI and Stimulus Probability on Event-related Go/nogo Potentials after Somatosensory Stimulation." *Experimental Brain Research* 162, no. 3 (2004): 293-99. doi:10.1007/s00221-004-2195-4.

Nakata, Hiroki, Koji Inui, Toshiaki Wasaka, Kosuke Akatsuka, and Ryusuke Kakigi. "Somato-motor Inhibitory Processing in Humans: A Study with MEG and ERP." *European Journal of Neuroscience* 22, no. 7 (2005): 1784-792. doi:10.1111/j.1460-9568.2005.04368.x.

Nakata, Hiroki, Kiwako Sakamoto, Yukiko Honda, and Ryusuke Kakigi. "Temporal Dynamics of Neural Activity in Motor Execution and Inhibition Processing." *European Journal of Neuroscience* 41, no. 11 (2015): 1448-458. doi:10.1111/ejn.12889.

Nguyen, Clinton. "Science Made This Chamber Silent, Your Mind Is What Makes It Terrifying." *Vice.* October 29, 2015. Accessed July 04, 2019. https://www.vice.com/en_us/article/78kzez/science-made-this-chamber-silent-your-mind-is-what-makes-it-terrifying.

Nichols, D. E. "Psychedelics." *Pharmacological Reviews* 68, no. 2 (2016): 264-355. doi:10.1124/pr.115.011478.

"Normal." *Merriam-Webster*. Accessed July 11, 2019. https://www.merriam-webster.com/dictionary/normal.

Nosachev, GN. "Perception and Experience of Time with Depression in Manic-depressive Psychosis and Attack-like Schizophrenia by Patients." Z Nevropatol Psikh. 91 (1991): 114-17.

Nyberg, L., A. S. N. Kim, R. Habib, B. Levine, and E. Tulving. "Consciousness of Subjective Time in the Brain." *Proceedings of the National Academy of Sciences* 107, no. 51 (2010): 22356-2359. doi:10.1073/pnas.1016823108.

O'Connor, Akira. "This Is Your Brain On...déjà Vu." O'Connor Memory Judgements Lab. August 16, 2016. Accessed July 14, 2019. http://akiraoconnor.org/2016/08/16/this-is-your-brain-on-deja-vu/.

Oelze, Patricia. "The Use Of The Rorschach Inkblot Test In Psychology." Betterhelp. February 24, 2018. Accessed July 04, 2019. https://www.betterhelp.com/advice/psychologists/the-use-of-the-rorschach-inkblot-test-in-psychology/.

Peteri. Optical Illusion. *Young Beautiful Princess or Old Ugly Woman?* Vector Illustration. - Vector. In Shutterstock, Inc. [US]. Accessed July 23, 2019. https://www.shutterstock.com/image-vector/optical-illusion-young-beautiful-princess-old-67150864?src=VSsFhYUKa5mX4eFWS1pFPQ-1-1&studio=1. Royalty-free stock vector images ID: 67150864

Osborn, Corinne O'Keefe. "Retrograde Amnesia: Causes, Symptoms, and Treatment." *Healthline.* Accessed July 05, 2019. https://www.healthline.com/health/retrograde-amnesia. Medically reviewed by Timothy J. Legg, Ph.D., CRNP on October 16, 2017

Oyanadel, Cristián, and Gualberto Buela-Casal. "Percepción Del Tiempo Y Salud: La Influencia Del Perfil Temporal Equilibrado(BTP) Y El Perfil Temporal Negativo (NTP) En La Salud Física Y Mental." *Revista Argentina De Clinica Psicologica* XXVI (2017): 99-107. doi:10.24205/03276716.2017.1034.

O'Doherty, J., J. Winston, H. Critchley, D. Perrett, D.m Burt, and R.j Dolan. "Beauty in a Smile: The Role of Medial Orbitofrontal Cortex in Facial Attractiveness." *Neuropsychologia* 41, no. 2 (2003): 147-55. doi:10.1016/s0028-3932(02)00145-8.

Pandey, Avaneesh. "Scientists Observe Epigenetic Memories Being Passed Down For 14 Generations In Roundworms." *International Business Times*, April 21, 2017. April 21, 2017. Accessed July 13, 2019. https://www.ibtimes.com/scientists-observe-epigenetic-memories-being-passed-down-14-generations-roundworms-2528649.

Paris, Joel. "Neurobiological Dimensional Models of Personality: A Review of the Models of Cloninger, Depue, and Siever." *Journal of Personality Disorders* 19, no. 2 (2005): 156-70. doi:10.1521/pedi.19.2.156.62629.

Patterson, Steve. "Logic and Infinity: The Errors of Calculus." Steve Patterson. May 14, 2016. Accessed July 06, 2019. http://steve-patterson.com/logic-and-infinity/.

Patterson, Steve. "Infinite Things Do Not Exist." Steve-patterson.com (blog), January 10, 2016. Accessed July 6, 2019. http://steve-patterson.com/infinite-things-do-not-exist/.

Penton-Voak, I.s, and D.i Perrett. "Female Preference for Male Faces Changes Cyclically." *Evolution and Human Behavior* 21, no. 1 (2000): 39-48. doi:10.1016/s1090-5138(99)00033-1.

Perrett, D. I., K. J. Lee, I. Penton-Voak, D. Rowland, S. Yoshikawa, D. M. Burt, S. P. Henzi, D. L. Castles, and S. Akamatsu. "Effects of Sexual Dimorphism on Facial Attractiveness." *Nature* 394, no. 6696 (1998): 884-87. doi:10.1038/29772.

Petrie, W. M. Flinders. *Ancient Weights and Measures*. London: Quaritch, 1926.

Petruso, Karl M. "Early Weights and Weighing in Egypt and the Indus Valley." *M Bulletin* (Museum of Fine Arts, Boston) 79:44-51. Accessed July 8, 2019. Retrieved from http://www.jstor.org/stable/4171634.

Petty, Richard E., Timothy C. Brock, and Thomas M. Ostrom. *Cognitive Responses in Persuasion*. New York: Psychology Press, 2014.

Xpixel. Photo *Rorschach Inkblot Test Isolated on White Background* - Image. In Shutterstock, Inc. [US]. Accessed July 23, 2019. https://www.shutterstock.com/image-photo/photo-rorschach-inkblot-test-isolated-on-606320885?src=ieV-aNND8GUJTBfxIqIgD6Q-1-0&studio=1.
Royalty-free stock photo ID: 606320885

Piaget, Jean, and Eleanor Duckworth. *Genetic Epistemology.* Translated by Eleanor Duckworth. New York: Columbia University Press, 1970.

Piaget, Jean. *Intelligence and Affectivity: Their Relationship during Child Development.* Palo Alto, CA: Annual Reviews, 1981. Originally published in 1954.

Piaget, Jean, Leslie Smith, and Terrance Brown. *Sociological Studies.* London: Routledge, 1995. Originally published in 1928.

Picchietti, Daniel, and Karla Dzienkowski. "Restless Legs Syndrome and Periodic Limb Movements Disorder in Children and Adolescents." *Attention Deficit Disorder*, 2006, 147-58. doi:10.3109/9781420004724-23.

Polanía, Rafael, Marius Moisa, Alexander Opitz, Marcus Grueschow, and Christian C. Ruff. "The Precision of Value-based Choices Depends Causally on Fronto-parietal Phase Coupling." *Nature News.* August 20, 2015. Accessed July 14, 2019. https://www.nature.com/articles/ncomms9090.

Popova, Maria. "The Angels and Demons of Genius: Robert Lowell on What It's Like to Be Bipolar." *Brain Pickings.* March 03, 2017. Accessed July 13, 2019. https://www.brainpickings.org/2016/02/26/robert-lowell-bipolar/.

Porkka-Heiskanen, Tarja. "Adenosine in Sleep and Wakefulness." *Annals of Medicine* 31, no. 2 (July 8, 1999): 125-29. Accessed July 14, 2019. doi:10.3109/07853899908998788. Abstract

Posner, Michael I., and Steven E. Petersen. "The Attention System of the Human Brain." *Annual Review of Neuroscience* 13, no. 1 (1990): 25-42. doi:10.1146/annurev.ne.13.030190.000325.

Pryke, Sarah R., and Simon C. Griffith. "Red Dominates Black: Agonistic Signalling among Head Morphs in the Colour Polymorphic Gouldian Finch." *Proceedings of the Royal Society B: Biological Sciences* 273, no. 1589 (2006): 949-57. doi:10.1098/rspb.2005.3362.

PsychScience. "Couples, Friends Show Similarity in Personality Traits after All." *EurekAlert!* February 11, 2017. Accessed July 11, 2019. https://www.eurekalert.org/pub_releases/2017-02/afps-cfs021117.php.

Raatikainen, Panu. "Gödel's Incompleteness Theorems." *Stanford Encyclopedia of Philosophy*. January 20, 2015. Accessed July 08, 2019. https://plato.stanford.edu/entries/goedel-incompleteness/.

Ramachandran, V. S., and Sandra Blakeslee. *Phantoms in the Brain: Probing the Mysteries of the Human Mind*. New York: Harper Perennial, 2009.

"The Odd Couple/My Strife in Court." *In The Odd Couple*. February 16, 1973.

Rasmussen, Chris, and Howard Blumenfeld. "Reinventing Solutions to Systems of Linear Differential Equations: A Case of Emergent Models Involving Analytic Expressions." *The Journal of Mathematical Behavior* 26, no. 3 (2007): 195-210. doi:10.1016/j.jmathb.2007.09.004.

Redd, Nola Taylor. "What Is the Shape of the Universe?" Space.com. January 16, 2014. Accessed July 06, 2019. https://www.space.com/24309-shape-of-the-universe.html.

Renoir, Pierre-Auguste. *La Grenouillere*. 1869. National Museum, Stockholm, Sweden. In Alamy. Accessed July 24, 2019. https://www.alamy.com/. Purchased royalty-free rights on alamy.comImage ID: W3Y4E1 - RM

Rhodes, Gillian, Linda Jeffery, Tamara L. Watson, Colin W.g. Clifford, and Ken Nakayama. "Fitting the Mind to the World." *Psychological Science* 14, no. 6 (2003): 558-66. doi:10.1046/j.0956-7976.2003.psci_1465.x.

Rhodes, Gillian, Linda Jeffery, Tamara L. Watson, Emma Jaquet, Chris Winkler, and Colin W.g. Clifford. "Orientation-Contingent Face Aftereffects and Implications for Face-Coding Mechanisms." *Current Biology* 14, no. 23 (2004): 2119-123. doi:10.1016/j. cub.2004.11.053.

Rizzo, Albert "Skip", Ph.D. "Speaking of Psychology: Improving Lives through Virtual Reality Therapy." *American Psychological Association*. 2019. Accessed July 12, 2019. https://www.apa.org/research/action/speaking-of-psychology/virtual-reality.aspx.

Rock, David. "The Neuroscience of Mindfulness." *Psychology Today*. October 11, 2009. Accessed July 14, 2019. https://www.psychologytoday.com/us/blog/your-brain-work/200910/the-neuroscience-mindfulness.

Rock, David. "New Study Shows Humans Are on Autopilot Nearly Half the Time." *Psychology Today*. November 14, 2010. Accessed July 14, 2019. https://www.psychologytoday.com/us/blog/your-brain-work/201011/new-study-shows-humans-are-autopilot-nearly-half-the-time.

Roth, G., and U. Dicke. "Evolution of the Brain and Intelligence." *Trends in Cognitive Sciences* 9, no. 5 (2005): 250-57. doi:10.1016/j.tics.2005.03.005.

Ruble, D. "The Role of Gender-related Processes in the Development of Sex Differences in Self-evaluation and Depression." *Journal of Affective Disorders* 29, no. 2-3 (1993): 97-128. doi:10.1016/0165-0327(93)90027-h.

Ruby, Perrine M. "Experimental Research on Dreaming: State of the Art and Neuropsychoanalytic Perspectives." *Frontiers in Psychology* 2 (2011). doi:10.3389/fpsyg.2011.00286.

Rutishauser, Ueli, Adam N. Mamelak, and Erin M. Schuman. "Single-Trial Learning of Novel Stimuli by Individual Neurons of the Human Hippocampus-Amygdala Complex." *Neuron* 49, no. 6 (2006): 805-13. doi:10.1016/j.neuron.2006.02.015.

Sacks, Oliver. *The Man Who Mistook His Wife for a Hat and Other Clinical Tales*. Washington: Produced in Braille for the Library of Congress, National Library Service for the Blind and Physically Handicapped by Clovernook Home and School for the Blind, 1987.

Salmon, Wesley C. "*SPACE, TIME, AND MOTION.*" Dartmouth University Mathematics Department. Accessed July 06, 2019. https://math.dartmouth.edu/~matc/Readers/HowManyAngels/SpaceTimeMotion/STM.html. Much of the material in this chapter has been adapted from my Introduction in Wesley C. Salmon, ed., Zeno's Paradoxes, copyright " 1970, The Bobbs-Merrill Co., Inc. By permission of the publisher.

Sard, Melanie. "Reflected Words: Meaning and Silence in Language and Translation." DigitalCommons@Macalester College. 2005. Accessed July 04, 2019. http://digitalcommons.macalester.edu/philo/vol15/iss1/3.

Scharnowski, F., J. Ruter, J. Jolij, F. Hermens, T. Kammer, and M. H. Herzog. "Long-lasting Modulation of Feature Integration by Transcranial Magnetic Stimulation." *Journal of Vision* 9, no. 6 (2009): 1-10. doi:10.1167/9.6.1.

Schlegel, A., P. J. Kohler, S. V. Fogelson, P. Alexander, D. Konuthula, and P. U. Tse. "Network Structure and Dynamics of the Mental Workspace." *Proceedings of the National Academy of Sciences* 110, no. 40 (2013): 16277-6282. doi:10.1073/pnas.1311149110.

Schneider, Tom. "The Unreasonable Effectiveness of Mathematics." The Unreasonable Effectiveness of Mathematics. May 24, 2001. Accessed July 08, 2019. http://www.calvin.edu/~scofield/courses/m161/materials/readings/Hamming.unreasonable.html. Reprinted From: *The American Mathematical Monthly* Volume 87 Number 2 February 1980 (with permission)

Schubert, Anna-Lena, Dirk Hagemann, Gidon T. Frischkorn, and Sabine C. Herpertz. "Faster, but Not Smarter: An Experimental Analysis of the Relationship between Mental Speed and Mental Abilities." *Intelligence* 71 (2018): 66-75. doi:10.1016/j.intell.2018.10.005.

Schumer, Peter. "When Did Humans First Learn to Count?" *The Conversation*. June 07, 2019. Accessed July 06, 2019. https://theconversation.com/when-did-humans-first-learn-to-count-97511.

Schutte, Nicola S., John M. Malouff, Lena E. Hall, Donald J. Haggerty, Joan T. Cooper, Charles J. Golden, and Liane Dornheim. "Development and Validation of a Measure of Emotional Intelligence." *Personality and Individual Differences* 25, no. 2 (1998): 167-77. doi:10.1016/s0191-8869(98)00001-4.

Schwarz, Sascha, and Marie Singer. "Romantic Red Revisited: Red Enhances Mens Attraction to Young, but Not Menopausal Women." *Journal of Experimental Social Psychology* 49, no. 1 (2013): 161-64. doi:10.1016/j.jesp.2012.08.004.

Searle, John R. "Consciousness." *Annual Review of Neuroscience* 23, no. 1 (2000): 557-78. doi:10.1146/annurev.neuro.23.1.557.

Searls, Damion. "Can We Trust the Rorschach Test? | Damion Searls." *The Guardian*. February 21, 2017. Accessed July 03, 2019. https://www.theguardian.com/science/2017/feb/21/rorschach-test-inkblots-history.

Sellars, Wilfrid. *Science, Perception and Reality*. London: Routledge & Kegan Paul, 1963.

Semendeferi, Katerina, Este Armstrong, Axel Schleicher, Karl Zilles, and Gary W. Van Hoesen. "Prefrontal Cortex in Humans and Apes: A Comparative Study of Area 10." *American Journal of Physical Anthropology* 114, no. 3 (2001): 224-41. doi:10.1002/1096-8644(200103)114:33.3.co;2-9.

"Sensory Deprivation Tank: Effects and Health Benefits." *Healthline*. 2018. Accessed July 04, 2019. https://www.healthline.com/health/sensory-deprivation-tank.

Setchell, Joanna M., and E. Jean Wickings. "Dominance, Status Signals and Coloration in Male Mandrills (Mandrillus Sphinx)." *Ethology* 111, no. 1 (2005): 25-50. doi:10.1111/j.1439-0310.2004.01054.x.

Shahabifar, Ali, and Ataollah Movahedinia. "Comparing Time Perception among Morphine-Derived Drugs Addicts and Controls." *Addict Health* 8, no. 1 (January 5, 2016): 32-40.

Sheppard, S. *Smiling Tree Stump*. Humorous. In Shutterstock, Inc. [US]. Accessed July 23, 2019. https://www.shutterstock.com/image-photo/smiling-tree-stump-1015960705?studio=1. Royalty-free stock photo ID: 1015960705

Silver, Rae, and William J. Schwartz. "The Suprachiasmatic Nucleus Is a Functionally Heterogeneous Timekeeping Organ." *Methods in Enzymology Circadian Rhythms*, 2005, 451-65. doi:10.1016/s0076-6879(05)93022-x.

Simon, Paul, Art Garfunkel, Paul Simon, and Franz Xaver Gruber, writers. *The Essential Simon & Garfunkel*. CD.

Smith, Philip, B.A. "Libra." LacusCurtius • Roman Weights and Measures - Libra (Smith's Dictionary, 1875). May 8, 2018. Accessed July 09, 2019. http://penelope.uchicago.edu/Thayer/E/Roman/Texts/secondary/SMIGRA*/Libra.html.

Smith, Sidney. "Babylonian Time Reckoning." *Iraq* 31, no. 1 (1969): 74-81. Accessed July 8, 2019. doi:10.2307/4199869.

Sorell, Gwendolyn T., and Marilyn J. Montgomery. "Feminist Perspectives on Erikson S Theory: Their Relevance for Contemporary Identity Development Research." *Identity* 1, no. 2 (2001): 97-128. doi:10.1207/s1532706xid0102_01.

Stephen, Ian D., Miriam J. Law Smith, Michael R. Stirrat, and David I. Perrett. "Facial Skin Coloration Affects Perceived Health of Human Faces." *International Journal of Primatology* 30, no. 6 (2009): 845-57. doi:10.1007/s10764-009-9380-z.

Su, Yi-Huang, and Elvira Salazar-López. "Visual Timing of Structured Dance Movements Resembles Auditory Rhythm Perception." *Neural Plasticity* 2016 (2016): 1-17. doi:10.1155/2016/1678390.

Tefi. Synapse Detailed Anatomy, Beautiful Colorful Illustration. Neuron Passes Signal. At the Right Side Closer Look at Ligand Gated Ion Channel. - Vector. In Shutterstock, Inc. [US]. Accessed July 24, 2019. https://www.shutterstock.com/image-vector/synapse-detailed-anatomy-beautiful-colorful-illustration-395465926?src=library&studio=1.
Royalty-free stock vector images ID: 395465926

Tabu, Hayato, Tatsuya Mima, Toshihiko Aso, Ryosuke Takahashi, and Hidenao Fukuyama. "Common Inhibitory Prefrontal Activation during Inhibition of Hand and Foot Responses." *NeuroImage* 59, no. 4 (2012): 3373-378. doi:10.1016/j.neuroimage.2011.10.092.

Taylor, Christa L. "Creativity and Mood Disorder: A Systematic Review and Meta-Analysis." *Perspectives on Psychological Science* 12, no. 6 (2017): 1040-076. doi:10.1177/1745691617699653.

Taylor, Jill Bolte. "My Stroke of Insight." Speech. February 2008. Accessed July 18, 2019. https://www.ted.com/talks/jill_bolte_taylor_s_powerful_stroke_of_insight.
Taylor, R. P., T. P. Martin, R. D. Montgomery, J. H. Smith, A. P. Micolich, C. Boydston, B. C. Scannell, M. S. Fairbanks, and B. Spehar. "Seeing Shapes in Seemingly Random Spatial Patterns: Fractal Analysis of Rorschach Inkblots." *Plos One* 12, no. 2 (2017). doi:10.1371/journal.pone.0171289.

Teller, P. "Subjectivity and Knowing What It's Like." *In Emergence or Reduction? Essays on the Prospects of Nonreductive Physicalism*, edited by A. Beckermann, H. Flohr, and J. Kim, 180-200. Berlin and New York: Walter De Gruyer, 1992.

"The New DSM-5: Schizophrenia Spectrum and Other Psychotic Disorders." Mental Help The New DSM5 Schizophrenia Spectrum and Other Psychotic Disorders Comments. Accessed July 13, 2019. https://www.mentalhelp.net/schizophrenia/the-new-dsm-5/.

"The State of Mental Health in America." *Mental Health America.* November 01, 2018. Accessed July 12, 2019. http://www.mentalhealthamerica.net/issues/state-mental-health-america.

Bashutskyy. *Three Cool Beer Bottles, Isolated on White.* - Image. In Shutterstock, Inc. [US]. Accessed July 24, 2019. https://www.shutterstock.com/image-photo/three-cool-beer-bottle-iisolated-on-100736191?studio=1.
Royalty-free stock photo ID: 100736191

Toal, Ray. "Gödel's Incompleteness Theorems." Gödel's Incompleteness Theorems. Accessed July 08, 2019. https://cs.lmu.edu/~ray/notes/godeltheorems/.

Toga, Arthur W., and Paul M. Thompson. "Genetics Of Brain Structure And Intelligence." *Annual Review of Neuroscience* 28, no. 1 (2005): 1-23. doi:10.1146/annurev.neuro.28.061604.135655. "Traffic Jam in Empty Space." *ScienceDaily*. January 18, 2017. Accessed July 04, 2019. https://www.sciencedaily.com/releases/2017/01/170118132244.htm.

Tribune.com.pk. "Stephen Hawking Says 'nothing' Was around before Origin of Universe." *The Express Tribune*. March 05, 2018. Accessed July 06, 2019. https://tribune.com.pk/story/1651558/3-stephen-hawking-says-nothing-around-origin-universe/.

Tyson, David. "A Quote by David Tyson." *Goodreads*. Accessed July 11, 2019. https://www.goodreads.com/quotes/121739-true-friendship-comes-when-silence-between-two-people-is-comfortable.

Valerevich, Kiselev Andrey. *Close-up Portrait of a Beautiful Young Woman and a Man. Fashionable Couple Posing at Studio.* - Image. In Shutterstock, Inc. [US]. Accessed July 24, 2019. https://www.shutterstock.com/image-photo/closeup-portrait-beautiful-young-woman-man-327972284?src=UG3gtOiJ21R_p-FfKU_yfQ-1-38&studio=1. Royalty-free stock photo ID: 327972284

Silberbogel. V*ector Diagram of Anatomy of Human Brain* - Vector. In Shutterstock, Inc. [US]. Accessed July 24, 2019. https://www.shutterstock.com/image-vector/vector-diagram-anatomy-human-brain-366858926?studio=1. Royalty-free stock vector images ID: 366858926

Veer, René Van Der., and Jaan Valsiner. *The Vygotsky Reader*. Oxford: Blackwell, 1994.

Velicer, Gregory J. "Evolution of Cooperation: Does Selfishness Restraint Lie Within?" *Current Biology* 15, no. 5 (2005): 173-75. doi:10.1016/j.cub.2005.02.045.

Villanueva, John Carl. "Big Crunch." *Universe Today*. December 25, 2015. Accessed July 06, 2019. https://www.universetoday.com/37018/big-crunch/.

Vito, Stefania De, and Paolo Bartolomeo. "Refusing to Imagine? On the Possibility of Psychogenic Aphantasia. A Commentary on Zeman Et al. (2015)." *Cortex* 74 (2016): 334-35. doi:10.1016/j.cortex.2015.06.013. (Pages 1-5 in PDF version)

Vukovic, Jovana, Benedict C. Jones, Lisa M. Debruine, Anthony C. Little, David R. Feinberg, and Lisa L.m Welling. "Circum-menopausal Effects on Womens Judgements of Facial Attractiveness." *Biology Letters* 5, no. 1 (2009): 62-64. doi:10.1098/rsbl.2008.0478.

Waitt, Corri, Anthony C. Little, Sarah Wolfensohn, Paul Honess, Anthony P. Brown, Hannah M. Buchanan-Smith, and David I. Perrett. "Evidence from Rhesus Macaques Suggests That Male Coloration Plays a Role in Female Primate Mate Choice." *Proceedings of the Royal Society of London. Series B: Biological Sciences* 270, no. Suppl_2 (2003). doi:10.1098/rsbl.2003.0065.

Wan, Li, Ph.D., Bruce H. Friedman, Ph.D., Nash N. Boutros, M.D., and Helen J. Crawford, Ph.D. "P50 Sensory Gating and Attentional Performance." *International Journal of Psychophysiology* 67, no. 2 (2008): 91-100. doi:10.1016/j.ijpsycho.2007.10.008. PDF of the article is numbered pp. 1-22 and is available here: https://www.ncbi.nlm.nih.gov/pmc/articles/PMC2292346/pdf/nihms40883.pdf

Waterhouse, Lynn. "Multiple Intelligences, the Mozart Effect, and Emotional Intelligence: A Critical Review." *Educational Psychologist* 41, no. 4 (2006): 207-25. doi:10.1207/s15326985ep4104_1.
Waytz, Adam, John Cacioppo, and Nicholas Epley. "Who Sees Human?" *Perspectives on Psychological Science* 5, no. 3 (2010): 219-32. doi:10.1177/1745691610369336.

Webster, Michael A., and Otto H. Maclin. "Figural Aftereffects in the Perception of Faces." *Psychonomic Bulletin & Review* 6, no. 4 (1999): 647-53. doi:10.3758/bf03212974.

"Wechsler IQ Test." Wechsler IQ Test. 2017. Accessed July 13, 2019. https://wechsleriqtest.com/.

Weisstein, Eric W. "Euclid's Postulates." *Wolfram Mathworld*. June 13, 2019. Accessed July 8, 2019. http://mathworld.wolfram.com/EuclidsPostulates.html.

Welling, L., B. Jones, L. Debruine, F. Smith, D. Feinberg, A. Little, and E. Aldujaili. "Men Report Stronger Attraction to Femininity in Womens Faces When Their Testosterone Levels Are High." *Hormones and Behavior* 54, no. 5 (2008): 703-08. doi:10.1016/j.yhbeh.2008.07.012.

"What Are Your Miranda Rights?" Miranda Warning. Accessed July 04, 2019. http://www.mirandawarning.org/whatareyourmirandarights.html.

"What Is the Americans with Disabilities Act (ADA)?" *ADA National Network*. July 09, 2019. Accessed July 12, 2019. https://adata.org/learn-about-ada.

"Why Do We Sleep, Anyway?" Why Do We Sleep, Anyway? | *Healthy Sleep*. Accessed July 14, 2019. http://healthysleep.med.harvard.edu/healthy/matters/benefits-of-sleep/why-do-we-sleep. This content was last reviewed on December 18, 2007

Wilkins, Alasdair, and Alasdair Wilkins. "A Brief Introduction to Infinity." *Gizmodo*. May 02, 2013. Accessed July 06, 2019. https://gizmodo.com/a-brief-introduction-to-infinity-5809689.
Williamson, Victoria. "The Music of Silence." *Music Psychology*. April 2, 2011. Accessed July 04, 2019. http://musicpsychology.co.uk/the-music-of-silence/.

Winfrey, Oprah. "A Quote by Oprah Winfrey." *Goodreads*. Accessed July 11, 2019. https://www.goodreads.com/quotes/4602-everyone-wants-to-ride-with-you-in-the-limo-but.
Could not locate the primary source for this quotation.
Wittmann, Marc. "Moments in Time." *Frontiers in Integrative Neuroscience* 5 (October 18, 2011): 1-9. doi:10.3389/fnint.2011.00066.

Woolf, Virginia. *The Waves*. New York: Harcourt Brace Jovanovich, 1978.

Worrall, Simon. "Why Race Is Not a Thing, According to Genetics." *National Geographic*. October 16, 2017. Accessed July 11, 2019. https://news.nationalgeographic.com/2017/10/genetics-history-race-neanderthal-rutherford/.

Yanakieva, Steliana, Naya Polychroni, Neiloufar Family, Luke T. J. Williams, David P. Luke, and Devin B. Terhune. "The Effects of Microdose LSD on Time Perception: A Randomised, Double-blind, Placebo-controlled Trial." *Psychopharmacology* 236, no. 4 (2018): 1159-170. doi:10.1007/s00213-018-5119-x.

Yarovitskii, VB, and VA Baturin. "Reproduction of the Minute Time Interval in Depression in Patients with Schizophrenia and Manicdepressive Psychosis." *Z Nevropatol Psikh* 91 (1991): 112-14.

Golunovystock. *Young Ballerinas in Motion. Rhythmic Gymnastics. Teenage Sport, Healthy Teen Lifestyle. Pretty Girls with Flying Ribbons, Dance Class Background, Ballet Concept* - Image. In Shutterstock, Inc. [US]. Accessed July 23, 2019. https://www.shutterstock.com/image-photo/young-ballerinas-motion-rhythmic-gymnastics-teenage-730314913?src=eAOiCILRy47tCRVWhpEx-Q-1-4&studio=1. Royalty-free stock photo ID: 730314913

Youyou, Wu, David Stillwell, H. Andrew Schwartz, and Michal

Kosinski. "Birds of a Feather Do Flock Together." *Psychological Science* 28, no. 3 (2017): 276-84. doi:10.1177/0956797616678187.

Zabelina, Darya L., Ph.D. "Creativity and Sensory Gating." *Psychology Today*. January 23, 2015. Accessed July 08, 2019. https://www.psychologytoday.com/us/blog/finding-butterfly/201501/creativity-and-sensory-gating.

Zago, Stefano, Nicola Allegri, Marta Cristoffanini, Roberta Ferrucci, Mauro Porta, and Alberto Priori. "Is the Charcot and Bernard Case (1883) of Loss of Visual Imagery Really Based on Neurological Impairment?" *Cognitive Neuropsychiatry* 16, no. 6 (2011): 481-504. doi:10.1080/13546805.2011.556024.

Zaidel, E., and M. Iacoboni. "The Callosal Syndromes." *In Clinical Neuropsychology*, edited by KM Heilman and E. Valenstein, 347-403. 4th ed. NY: Oxford University Press, 2003.

Zeman, Adam, Michaela Dewar, and Sergio Della Sala. "Lives without Imagery – Congenital Aphantasia." *Cortex* 73 (2015): 1-18. doi:10.1016/j.cortex.2015.05.019.

Zeman, Adam. "Extreme Imagination in Mind, Brain and Culture." UK Research and Innovation. 2019. Accessed July 5, 2019. https://gtr.ukri.org/projects?ref=AH/R004684/1. Ongoing research by Adam Zeman as of the date accessed.

Zimbardo, PG, and JN Boyd. "Putting Time in Perspective: A Valid, Reliable Individual-differences Metric." *Journal of Personal & Social Psychology* 77 (1999): 1271-288.

Zimbardo, Philip G., Richard M. Sword, and Rosemary K. M. Sword. *The Time Cure: Overcoming PTSD with the New Psychology of Time Perspective Therapy*. San Francisco: Jossey-Bass, 2012.

Zyga, Lisa. "Is Mathematics an Effective Way to Describe the World?" Phys.org. September 03, 2013. Accessed July 08, 2019. https://phys.org/news/2013-09-mathematics-effective-world.html.

List of Abbreviations

ADA: American Disabilities Act.
ADHD: attention deficit hyperactivity disorder.
AI: Artificial Intelligence.
ANT: attention-level network test.
AP: attentional performance.
BHS: Beck Hopelessness Scale.
BMI: Body Mass Index.
BTP: balanced time perspective.
DID: Dissociative Identity Disorder.
DMS: Delusional misidentification syndromes.
DNA: Deoxyribonucleic Acid.
DSM: Diagnostic and Statistical Manual of Mental Disorders.
E: Extroverted.
E10: empty 10-second time interval.
E60: empty 60-second time interval.
EEG: electroencephalogram.
EI: Emotional intelligence.
EIQ: Emotional intelligence quotient.
EQ-I: Emotional Quotient Inventory.
ERP: event-related potential.
F: Feeling.
F: future.
fMRI: Functional magnetic resonance imaging.
g: General intelligence model for intelligence.
GABA: gamma-aminobutryic acid.
GBS: Generative Behavioral Checklist.
HRQL: Health-related quality of life measurement.
I: Introverted.

IDAQ: Individual Differences in Anthropomorphism Question-naire.

IPIP: International Personality Item Pool.

IQ: Intelligence Quotient.

ISI: interstimulus-interval.

IT: inferior temporal cortex.

IT: Integrative Therapy.

J: Judging.

LaWS of RAD IT: Learned weighted sums of randomly selected average neuronal responses spatially distributed over monkey inferior temporal cortex.

LGS: Loyola Generativity Scale.

LSD: lysergic acid diethylamide.

MBTI: Myers Briggs Type Indicator.

MEG: magnetoencephalography.

MI: Multiple Intelligences.

MIPS: Multiple Information Processing Systems.

MNS: mirror neuron system.

mPFC: medial prefrontal cortex.

MRI: Magnetic Resonance Imaging.

MSCEIT: Mayer-Salovey-Caruso-Emotional Intelligence Test.

NHTC: Neural Hierarchy Theory of Consciousness.

NTP: negative time profile.

OCD: obsessive-compulsive disorder.

OSPAN: operation span.

P: Perceiving.

P50 ERP: event-related potential, occurring 50 ms following the presentation of a stimulus.

Per: photo inducible period genes which oscillate with a circadian rhythm.

PF: present fatalistic.

PH: present hedonistic.

PN: past negative.

PP: past positive.

PTSD: post-traumatic stress disorder.

REM: rapid eye movement.

RHT: retinohypothalmic tract.
RISK: group for individuals who are neither BTP nor NTP.
S: Sensing.
S1 and S2: two identical stimuli in the sensory gating experiment.
SAT: Scholastic Aptitude Test.
SCN: superchiasmatic nucleus.
SG: sensory gating.
SI: contralateral primary somatosensory cortex.
SMI: severe mental illness.
SSEIT: Schutte self-report EI test.
SSS: Stanford Sleepiness Scale.
T: Thinking.
TE: time estimation.
TMS: Transcranial Magnetic Stimulation..
TOJ: temporal order judgment.
TP: time perspective.
VAS: visual analogue scale.
VR: Virtual Reality.
ZPD: Zone of Proximal Development.
ZTPI: Zimbardo Time Perspective Inventory

Index

"

"clock" genes · 24-25
"face patch" neural networks · 4
"g" · 153-54

A

abbreviated · 72, 153, 191
abstract reasoning · 168, 187
academic concepts · 188-89
accommodation · 141, 188
Acoustic silences · 14
Active friendships · 130
Active listening · 121
ADA · 139
Adapted cognition theory · 155
ADHD · 95, 98, 144, 177
advantage · 9, 35, 122, 164, 201, 210-11, 214
Advertisements · 99-103
affect-based · 100
agreeableness · 125, 158
AI · 63, 145
Aldous Huxley · 116
alerting phase · 96
algebra · 81
alien hand syndrome · 227
Alzheimer's disease · 221-22

ambiguous figure · 36, 56
amygdala · 5, 87
Androcentric theories · 208
anechoic chamber · 21-22
aneurysm · 223
anosognosia · 219
ANT · 96, 98
anterior cingulate gyrus · 90, 96, 183
Anterograde amnesia · 39
anthropomorphism · 4-6
anxiety · 21, 25, 62-63, 140, 163, 166, 171, 173, 178-79, 181, 183, 211, 214
AP ·96-98, 218
Aphantasia · 59-63
archetypes · 137
argument-based · 100
artificial intelligence · 143-44
asomatognosia · 220
Asperger's syndrome · 141
assimilation · 188
atoms of thought · 32
attentional performance · 96
attention-level network test · 96
Attractiveness · x, 102, 133-38
auditory cortex · 16, 38, 93, 97, 229
auditory cortices · 32
Auditory imagery · 16-17
Auditory perception · 14
autism disorder · 141
autonomous morality · 193, 94
autonomy vs. shame/doubt · 200
averageness · 134, 236
avoidant behavior · 178

B

Babylonian water-clock · 106
basal ganglia · 26, 87, 161
beat-based mechanism · 31, 35
Beqa · 104
BHS · 48
Big Bang · 76-7
bipolar depression · 95
bipolar disorder · 46, 48, 145-46, 149-49
black hole · 75, 77
bodily self · 219
Bodily-kinesthetic intelligence · 152
bradycardia · 25
Brain Resource Inventory for Emotional Intelligence Test ·
    157,159
brain stimulation · 88, 179-80
BRIEF · 159-60
Broca's area · 161
BTP · 47, 49-50

C

cadential arrival · 16
Calculus · 74, 79
Cantor set · 72
Capgras syndrome · 221
cardinality · 71-72
Central Intelligences Agency · 154
centroparietal region · 97
cerebellum · 26, 28, 229
Cheating · 156
childhood attachments · 211
chronesthesia · 27, 29
Chronostasis · 29
circadian rhythm · 23-25

Clarity · 212, 217
coding schemes · 210-11, 213
cognitive response model · 101
cognitive science · 143
color phi phenomenon · 51
Coloration · 135, 138
commitment story · 210, 216
concrete operational stage · 186-87, 198
conscientiousness · 125, 158, 16-61
consciousness · i, x, 28-29, 33, 50-51, 55-56, 63-64, 166, 193, 216, 225-26, 228-31
contamination sequences · 212-13
Continuity · 32, 63, 65, 212, 216, 232
continuum hypothesis · 72
contralateral primary somatosensory cortex · 88
co-operation · 192-95, 197-98
corpus callosum · 227
Cotard delusion · 62
COUNT · 28
Counting · i, 28, 61-61, 67-71, 191-91
creativity · x, 61, 93-95, 147-150, 171
critical feminist standpoint · 206
Cryptochrome · 27
cubit · 104
cutaneous rabbit effect · 52

D

dance movements · 34-35
daydreaming · 182, 224, 251
decision-making · x, 40, 97, 102, 124, 155, 166, 168-69, 171, 173, 175-76, 178, 180
default "narrative" network · 181
default network · 181-83
déjà vu ·xi, 174-75, 225
delay estimation test · 42-43

deliberative intelligence · 155
delusional misidentification syndromes · 221
dementia · 9, 225, 225
Denisovans · 11
depression · 46, 48, 63-63, 90, 95, 140, 142, 145-46, 148-49, 159, 178, 181-81, 201, 204
Depth · 53, 86, 148, 212
detailed personal ideoloy ·
DID · 210
different systems/different channels · 210, 225, 261
digital watch · 55
digits · 68-69
direct experience network · 181, 183
direct speech act · 20
disabilities · 139-40, 162
disability · 118, 139-41, 223
discrimination · 2, 8, 42-43, 114, 117-18, 120, 139-40, 161
discriminator · 64-65
Dissociation · 224-25
dissociative episode · 224
Dissociative identity disorder · 225
diversity · x, 117, 133-34, 163, 208, 228
DMS · 221-22
Dopamine · 44, 46, 87
Dormant friendships · 131
dram · 105
drugs · 42-43, 149
DSM · 141, 144-145
DSM 5 · 141, 144-145
DSM-IV-TR · 48, 225
dual-process theories of cognition · 102
duration-based mechanism · 34

E

early blessing · 210
EEG · 36, 86-91, 94-97, 159-60
EI · 157-61
Einstein · 82
emotional intelligence · 157-59, 161
emotive · 19, 214
emptiness · i, 13, 22
enactment · 19
episodic memory · 28-29
EQ-I · 157-58
equilibrated social exchange · 196
equilibration · 188, 196
Erikson · 185, 199-201, 203-05
ERP · 91, 93-95, 125
ERP P50 · 90
error-checking · 169, 175
ethnocentric foundationalism · 205
Euclid · 83
event-related potentials · 90
everyday concepts · 189
Existential intelligence · 151
experienced moment · 33-34, 36-37, 41, 50
extraversion · 103, 125-26, 158, 160

F

F ·47-49, 124
Facebook ·60, 125-265
faces · i, 3, 8-9, 36, 44, 60, 131, 134-37, 236
facial shapes · 135
Facial symmetry · 134
false memory · 175
family blessing · 211
Faraday cage · 91

Feature fusion ·51-52
Feinberg · 220
feminist · xi, 206-08
fertility · 134, 136, 138
Figure 1
pareidiola · 8-9, 233
Figure 2
Rorschach Inkblot · 233
Figure 3
rhythmic visual movements · 234, 236
Figure 4
old woman/young woman figure · 70, 107, 235
Figure 5
La Grenouillere by Renoir · 107-09, 235
Figure 6
La Grenouillere by Monet · 107-09, 134, 236,
Figure 7
beautiful female and male image · 236
Figure 8
anatomy and functional areas of the human brain · 237
Figure 9
diagram of communication between neurons · 238
fMRI · 7, 16, 28, 58, 90, 154, 175
formal mental operations · 187
formal operational stage · 186-87
free will · x, 165, 168-69, 171
Fregoli syndrome · 221
friendships · 122-23, 127-30, 201-03
frontal and superior parietal lobes · 29, 58, 96
frontal cortex · 26, 28, 58, 181
frontal lobe · 28, 96, 153-54, 160
frontal regions · 175, 228
frontocentral region · 97
frontopolar cortex · 177
fugue · 225
functional moment · 31, 33, 37

functional moments · 31, 33, 37, 41
fusiform gyrus · 9
FUTURE · 28-29

G

Galileo · 79-80
gallëta · 105
Galperin · xi, 190-91
GAN · 63-65
Gardner · 150, 153-54, 157
GBC · 210
general intelligence · 153-54, 160-62
general intelligence model for intelligence · 153
general knowledge · 162
generalist genes · 155
Generative Behavioral Checklist · 210
generativity · 209-10, 212, 214-16
generativity vs. stagnation · 204
generator · 63-64
genetic epistemology · 186
Genetic kinship · 136
Genetic memories · xi, 173-74
Genetics · 117, 142, 155, 173
Georg Cantor · 91
glutamate · 24
Gödel · x, 83-84
Goleman · 157
Go-Nogo · 89
grouping of coordinated actions · 197
gut feeling · 167-68, 176

H

hard problem of consciousness · xi, 226
Hawking-Hertog theory · 77
helpers versus enemies · 211
heteronomous morality · 192, 194
heteronomy · 198
high schizotypy · 97-98
highly generative adults · 209, 214-15
hippocampus · 26, 28-29, 39, 87, 175, 181
Holocaust · 116, 173
Homo Sapiens · 117
HRQL · 48
hyperphantasia · 61, 63

I

IDAQ · 5-6
identity vs. identity diffusion · 202
impression · 6, 29-30, 54, 99
impressionism · 107-08
indecisive · 179-80
indecisiveness · xi, 179-80
individual differences in fluid intelligence · 92
industry vs. inferiority · 201
inferior temporal cortex · 1-2
infinity · 67, 71-72, 74-75, 78
initiative vs. guilt · 201
inner monologue · 223
insula · 167, 183
integrity vs. despair and disgust ·204
intentionality · 5, 226, 229, 230
intimacy and distantiation vs. self-absorption · 203
intraparietal sulcus · 28
intrapersonal intelligence · 152
intrusive thoughts · 179

intuitive intelligence · 155
IPIP · 125
IQ · 92, 153-54, 157, 160
irrational number · 81

J

Jill Bolte Taylor · 217

K

kilogram · 105
Korsakoff syndrome · 39

L

La Grenouillere · 107-09, 235
language · 7, 17-18, 20, 32-33, 38, 40, 52, 60, 79, 103-04, 132-33,
        152, 155-56, 161, 186-87, 190, 196, 214, 217-18, 220, 230
laser intelligence · 154
latent inhibition task · 91-93
LaWS of RAD IT · 4
left frontal cortex · 28
left frontal lobe · 28
left hemiplegia · 219
left lateral parietal cortex · 28
left-hemisphere neocortex · 161
Less generative adults · 209, 214-15
LGS · 209
libra · 105
life story · 209-13, 215
linguistic intelligence · 152
litre · 105
little scientist · 192
Logical-mathematical intelligence · 151

long-term memories · 38-40, 216
long-term memory · 37-38, 40-41, 59, 65, 155
low schizotypy · 97
lower generative · 214
Loyola Generativity Scale · 83, 209
LSD · 44-45
lucid dreaming · 177

M

machine learning · 143-45
Mahatma Gandhi · 209
Martin Luther · 146
materialized level · 190
mathematics · x, 60, 69, 71-75, 79-85, 103-04, 340-41
mating · 133, 135, 137-38
MBTI · 123-24
measurement · x, 23, 45, 48, 81, 87, 103-06, 111-12
medial frontal cortex · 58, 181
medial prefrontal cortex · 28, 87
MEG · 89-89
Memory consolidation · 38
Mental health ·x, 37, 47-48, 91, 131, 141-42, 144-50, 163, 174
mental imagery · 41, 57-63, 191
mental level · 191
mental presence · 37, 39-41
mental representations · 59, 189, 195, 197
mental searchlight · 154
mental unity · 226, 230
metacognition · 167, 176-78
metric system · 104-05
metronome · 33-34, 36
MI · 150, 153-57, 159-60
microaggressions · 118-21
midbrain · 87
mindfulness · xi, 49, 181, 183

Mind-wandering · 181-81
MIPS · 154-55
Miranda rights · 20
mirror neuron system · 7, 155, 160
MNS · 7-8
Monet · 107, 109, 235
Monsieur X · 61-62
mood disorders · 146-50, 159
Moral steadfastness · 212
mPFC · 87
MSCEIT · 157-58
Multiple Information Processing Systems · 153-54
Multiple Intelligences · 150, 154, 156
music · ix, 14-17, 31, 33-34, 102-03, 131, 151, 155, 161, 185
Musical intelligence · 151
mutual respect · 193, 195-98
MyPersonality · 125

N

naive realism · 205
narrative approaches · 209
narrative delusions · 224
narrative self · 216, 223
Naturalist intelligence · 150
Neanderthals · 117
neural networks · 1-2, 4, 25-26, 38-39, 53-54, 59, 61-65, 137, 154-56, 229-31
neurology · 143
neuroticism · 125, 158, 160-61
nicotine · 95-95, 98, 152
nowness · 30, 37
NTP · 47, 49-50,

O

object permanence · 186, 195
object recognition · x, 1-4, 98, 112
object representation · 86, 186
occipital lobes · 2, 7
OCD · 178
ontological subjectivity · 226
openness · 125-26, 158, 160-61
openness to experience · 125-26, 158
optic nerves · 24, 53
Optical illusions · 12
orienting phase · 96
OSPAN · 92
oxytocin · 160

P

pacemaker-switch-accumulator mechanism · 26
paleo-genetics · 117
parahippocampal cortex · 68
parallel postulate · 83
paralysis · 219
pareidolia · 8-9, 233
parietal cortex · 7, 26, 28-29, 38, 90, 179
Passive frame theory · 166-67
PAST · 28-29
pauses · 14-15, 17, 37
Per · 24-25
perception of time · 23, 26, 44
perceptual level · 190
perceptual narrowing · 8
perceptual reality monitoring · 4
pervasive developmental disorder into autism spectrum disorder ·
        141
pet rock · 220

PF · 47-49
PH · 47-48
phantom limb pain · 64-65
phatic function · 20
Piaget · xi, 185-86, 188-89, 191-98, 208, 216
Pirahá · 68
PN · 46-49
Poetic silence · 20
Points · 30, 52, 54, 72, 84-85,109, 117, 210
post-modern ·207-08
potention ·30
pound ·105
PP ·46-48
prefrontal cortex · 28, 38, 50, 87, 90, 93, 95, 169, 179, 181
preoperational stage · 186
PRESENT · 28
Procedural silence · 19
processing speed ·161-62
prosocial goals for the future · 213
protagonist · 2019
psilocybin · 44
psychogenic amnesia · 225
psychosocial constructivism · 216
PTSD · 47, 143-44
Pythagoras · 81

Q

qualia · 226, 228-29

R

Real-time · 76-77
reciprocity · 195-98
redemption · 212-13
redemptive affective sequences · 210

reference group effect · 126
referential silence · 18
reflective listening · 12
regulations · 194, 198
relational self · 221
relationship management · 157
REM · 50, 176-77
REMEMBER · 28-29
Renoir · 107-08, 235
REST · 28
retention · 30
Retinal ganglion cells · 24
Retrograde amnesia · 39
RHT · 24
Rhythm · 33-36, 170
Richard Hamming · 79-81, 84
right cerebellum · 28
right or a concession · 20
RISK · 47-49-50
Rorschach · 9-12, 233
Rorschach test · 9, 11-12
roundworm · 173

S

Salem Witch trials · 143
same system/different channels · 54
same system/same channel ·53
scalars · 82
schema · 188, 198
schemas · 188, 198
schizophrenia · 46, 48-49, 91, 95, 97, 14, 145
SCN · 23-26
Searle · 226
self · ix, xi, 27, 70, 199, 207-08, 213, 216-19, 221, 223, 225-27,
    230-31

self-awareness · 157, 167, 178, 230
self-management · 157
sensorimotor stage · 28-30, 186
Sensory deprivation tanks · 21-22
sensory gating · 86, 90, 96-97
serotonin · 44
SG · 86-91, 93-98
SG ratio · 88, 91, 93-94
short-term memory 38-40, 65, 216
SI · 88-90
silence · ix, 13-22, 37, 122
Simon effect · 92
singularity · 75-78
sleep · 44, 50, 90, 143, 176-77, 200
sleep deprivation · 176
SMI · 46-50, 63
smokers · 96-97, 162
Smoking · 42, 87, 95, 97-98
sociability · 151
social awareness · 9, 157
social cheating detection · 156
sociomoral theory of child development · 192
Somatoparaphrenia · 220
Spatial intelligence · 152
specious present · 30
spectrum diagnoses · 145
spherical geometry · 83
split-brain patients · 227
SSEIT · 157-59
SSS · 48
Standpoint epistemology · x, 206
Stephen Hawking · 76-77, 141
Sternberg memory scanning test · 162
stroke · 26, 217-220, 222
Stroop effect · 91-92
Stroop task · 91-92

subjective time · 27-29, 42, 46
substance abuse · 142
suffering of others · 210, 212, 215
sundial · 105
Symmetry · 133, 136

T

tachycardia · 25
temporal · 29, 31-37, 39-40, 44-45, 51, 53-56, 58, 61, 63, 68, 105, 222
temporal cortex · 1-2, 58
temporal lobes · 2, 61
temporoparietal region · 219
thalamus · 28-29, 39
the Devil's hand · 220
The Psychology of Advertising · 98-99
the suffering of others · 210, 215
theorems · 73, 80-84
therapies · 142-143, 180
Thomas Hertog · 77
thought experiments · 73, 82
time discrimination · 42-43
time estimation · 42, 46, 48-50
time perception · ix, 26, 42, 44, 46, 50, 57, 63
time reproduction · 42-43
time slices · 51, 57
Timeless · 24
TMS · 2, 51-52
TOJ · 54
tonic pitch · 16
TP · 46-47
TPT · 47
Transcendental numbers · 81
Transdermal nicotine · 152
trust vs. mistrust · 199

U

Unconscious feature integration · 54, 56
unconsciousness · 50, 55, 57
universal-ism · 205
universe · x, 75-78
University of Iowa Writers' Workshop · 147
US Standard system · 104

V

vagus nerve ·167
Value-based indecisiveness · 180
VAS · 45
vasopressin · 160
vasotocin · 160
Vectors · 82
ventral visual stream · 2-3
verbal level · 190
Vernier · 52
Vincent Van Gogh · 146
Virginia Woolf · 232
virtual action ·196
virtual reality therapy · 144
visual cortex · 2, 32, 37, 57, 67, 90
Vygotsky · xi, 185, 188-89, 192, 208, 216

W

warmth · 19, 103, 135, 137, 161, 230
Wernicke's area · 161
white hole · 77
white matter · 162
Women Writers' Conference · 147
Working memory · 37-38, 40, 50, 92, 153-55

Z

Zeno's Dichotomy Paradox · 73
Zeno's Paradoxes · 73
zone of proximal development · 189
ZPD · 189
ZTPI · 48

Social Media and Contact Information

For media or speaking inquiries, please contact Howard Blumenfeld by email at thementalarchitect7@gmail.com or by visiting his website at http://www.thementalarchitect.com.

To receive the latest news and updates from Howard, please visit his Facebook page at https://www.facebook.com/thementalarchitect/, his Instagram account @the_mental_architect, or his Goodreads account at https://www.goodreads.com/the_mental_architect.

Acknowledgments

Growing up with a clinical psychologist, Arnold Blumenfeld, for a father, psychology naturally became a personal passion. Writing about pertinent and novel issues in psychology fascinated me, and I aimed to do so in a way that would be accessible to anyone interested in the mysteries of the mind. There are many individuals to whom I am thankful for helping me write this book, and without them, this journey would never have been possible.

I want to thank my wife Victoria (Torie) for providing me with the confidence and inspiration for writing this book. The idea to write it came to me after we watched Season 1 of the German sci-fi thriller Dark Season 1 on Netflix. The way the show portrayed time travel, connecting the past to the future, and making certain events timeless in an apparent paradox, was fascinating. Following the completion of the first series of the show, Torie and I had numerous late-night conversations about time perception, reality, and other philosophical topics, leading to my desire to write a book. She provided me with her diary and told me to write down all of our ideas in there to help organize the book into chapters, and so we spent time roughly outlining what would soon become Mental Architecture.

Torie was supportive of me throughout the entire process and encouraged me to write, keep writing, and never give up. Whenever I came across a fascinating journal article, news story, or something else that warranted my attention, I shared it with her, and she provided feedback. She also read through every last page of my less-than-stellar first draft and helped me craft the final draft into this book. She was truly there for me every step of the way, and I cannot overemphasize how important it is to have someone there for you who believes in you and reminds you of your talent and potential.

My son Adam was also instrumental in helping me complete the book. Within the past few years, he learned how to play electric guitar, program in various programming languages, and speed-solve a Rubik's cube. Watching him excel at these things was inspirational for me. Adam is a precocious child with a knack for picking information up quickly, and he was fascinated by the topics in my book. He read a few of the early drafts of the first few chapters and thoroughly enjoyed them. I am very proud of him and all that he has accomplished so far in life.

I would also like to personally thank all of my friends, family, and colleagues who graciously and enthusiastically supported me during this time. Your kind and encouraging words mean a lot to me, and I would not be where I am as a writer if it were not for you.

Author Biography

A California native, Howard spent the formative years of his life growing up in the Santa Clarita Valley, a sprawling suburb in Los Angeles county. His love of mathematics, psychology, and literature made him an excellent candidate for Revelle College at the University of California, San Diego, where he earned a Bachelor's Degree in Pure Mathematics with two minor degrees in Psychology and Literature/Writing. He went on to earn his Master's Degree in Mathematics with an emphasis in Community College Teaching, from San Diego State University.

While he was an undergraduate, he worked with the late Dr. J. Christian Gillin, an internationally renowned sleep specialist and psychiatrist at UCSD and the Veterans Affairs San Diego Healthcare system. Dr. Gillin was instrumental in the advancement of sleep medicine and the understanding of how sleep deprivation affects cognitive reasoning abilities, and an invaluable mentor. Howard was similarly inspired by Dr. Stuart Anstis, who taught him about the nature of sensation and perception, and Dr. John Polich, who offered his valuable insights into the connections between mathematics and psychology. Howard also worked for three years at the UCSD Science & Engineering library, where he furthered his interest in the physical and biological sciences.

At SDSU, Howard worked with Dr. Chris Rasmussen in the field of mathematics education, a discipline that combined behavioral psychology with mathematics. He published a Master's thesis about straight-line solutions to ordinary differential equations and a peer-reviewed journal article on emergent mathematics involving systems of linear differential equations. He began his teaching career in mathematics working part-time for various community colleges in San Diego County before obtaining his first full-time position at San Diego Miramar College. He secured his next full-time position at Las Positas College (LPC) in Livermore, CA, where he still resides. For the past three years, he served as the Professional Development Committee chair in addition to teaching a full load of classes.

While at LPC, Howard befriended Dr. Ernie Jones, Emeritus professor of psychology, who was passionate about his field of study. Ernie brought some great minds and personalities to LPC, including Dr. Temple Grandin, Dr. William Dement, and the original "Rainman" Kim Peek, and Howard had the opportunity to meet and talk with some of them. Ernie and Howard spoke regularly about hot topics in psychology, and Ernie encouraged him to follow his passion and write about novel and exciting psychology ideas.

Howard also gave numerous presentations, both locally and at conferences, on a wide range of topics including community building, the use of social media and technology in the classroom, and mathematics teaching techniques. He is also a founding member of two professional development groups at Las Positas College, "Working Together" and "The Teaching Institute," centered around forming meaningful communities, of practice among faculty and staff. He is the recipient of numerous professional awards and recognition, including the 2014 John and Suanne Roueche National Award for Innovation and Leadership in Higher Education.

Howard and his family currently reside in Oakley, CA. In his spare time, he enjoys weightlifting, cooking, baking, traveling, and spending time with his family. Howard also loves reading about the latest developments in the social and physical sciences and is interested in learning more about age-old philosophical questions such as the origin of the universe, the nature of time, and how the brain works. He is also a proud uncle to his sister Alexis' new baby girl Mackenzie Rain Botton.